CONTEMPORARY'S

GED

TEST 3: SCIENCE

PREPARATION FOR THE HIGH SCHOOL
EQUIVALENCY EXAMINATION

Reviewer
Connie Eichhorn, GED Instructor
Omaha Public Schools
Omaha, Nebraska

CONTEMPORARY BOOKS

a division of NTC/CONTEMPORARY PUBLISHING GROUP
Lincolnwood, Illinois USA

Photo credits: p. 16 © Jeff Smith/The Image Bank; p. 32 © Kay Chernush/The Image Bank; p. 42 © Lou Jones/The Image Bank; p. 62 © Jay Freis/The Image Bank; p. 80 © Guido A. Rossi/The Image Bank; p. 112 © Steve Dunwell/The Image Bank; p. 148 © National Aeronautics and Space Administration; p. 174 © UPI/Bettmann; p. 212 © Erik Leigh/The Image Bank

ISBN: 0-8092-9466-4

Published by McGraw-Hill/Contemporary,
4255 West Touhy Avenue,
Lincolnwood (Chicago), Illinois 60712-1975 U.S.A.
© 2001, 1994 Robert Mitchell

123456789 VH 16 15 14 13 12 11 10 98765432

Contents

To the Student

If you're studying to pass the GED Tests, you're in good company. In 1992, the most recent year for which figures are available, over 790,000 people took the tests. Of this number, nearly 480,000 actually received their certificates. Why do so many people choose to take the GED Tests? Some do so to get a job or to get a better one than they already have. Others take the tests so that they can go on to college or vocational school. Still others pursue their GED diplomas to feel better about themselves or to set good examples for their children.

Americans and Canadians alike, from all walks of life, have passed their GED Tests and obtained diplomas. Some well-known graduates include country music singers Waylon Jennings and John Michael Montgomery, comedian Bill Cosby, Olympic gold medalist Mary Lou Retton, former New Jersey Governor James J. Florio, Wendy's Old-Fashioned Hamburgers founder Dave Thomas, Delaware State Senator Ruth Ann Minner, U.S. Senator Ben Nighthorse Campbell of Colorado, motion picture actor Kelly McGillis, Famous Amos Chocolate Chip Cookies creator Wally Amos, *Parade* magazine editor Walter Anderson, NBA referee Tommy Nuñez, and Triple Crown winner jockey Ron Turcotte.

This book has been designed to help you, too, succeed on the test. It will provide you with instruction in the skills you need to pass, background information on key science concepts, and plenty of practice with the kinds of test items you will find on the real test.

WHAT DOES GED STAND FOR?

GED stands for the Tests of General Educational Development. The GED Test is a national examination developed by the GED Testing Service of the American Council on Education. The credential received for passing the test is widely recognized by colleges, training schools, and employers as equivalent to a high school diploma.

While the GED Test measures skills and knowledge normally acquired in four years of high school, much that you have learned informally or through other types of training can help you pass the test.

The GED Test is available in English, French, and Spanish and on audiocassette, in Braille, and in large print.

WHAT SHOULD I KNOW TO PASS THE TEST?

The test consists of five examinations in the areas of writing skills, social studies, science, literature and the arts, and mathematics. The chart on the next page outlines the main content areas, the breakdown of questions, and the time allowed per test.

v

THE GED TESTS			
Test	*Minutes*	*Questions*	*Percentage*
1: Writing Skills Part 1: Conventions of English	75	55	Sentence Structure 35% Usage 35% Mechanics 30%
Part 2: The Essay	45	1 topic	
2: Social Studies	85	64	History 25% Economics 20% Political Science 20% Geography 15%* Behavioral Sciences 20%*
3: Science	95	66	Life Sciences 50% Physical Sciences 50%
4: Literature and the Arts	65	45	Popular Literature 50% Classical Literature 25% Commentary 25%
5: Mathematics	90	56	Arithmetic 50% Algebra 30% Geometry 20%

*In Canada, 20% of the test is based on Geography and 15% on Behavioral Sciences.

On all five tests, you are expected to demonstrate the ability to think about many issues. You also are tested on knowledge and skills you have acquired from life experiences, television, radio, books and newspapers, consumer products, and advertising. In addition to the above information, keep these facts in mind:

1. Three of the five tests—Literature and the Arts, Science, and Social Studies— require that you answer questions based on reading passages or interpreting cartoons, diagrams, maps, charts, and graphs in these content areas. Developing strong reading and thinking skills is the key to succeeding on these tests.

2. The Writing Skills Test requires you to be able to detect and correct errors in sentence structure, grammar, punctuation, and spelling. You also will have to write a composition of approximately 200 words on a topic familiar to most adults.

3. The Mathematics Test consists mainly of word problems to be solved. Therefore, you must be able to combine your ability to perform computations with problem-solving skills.

WHO MAY TAKE THE TESTS?

In the United States, Canada, and many territories, people who have not graduated from high school and who meet specific eligibility requirements (age, residency, etc.) may take the tests. Since eligibility requirements vary, it would be useful to contact your local GED testing center or the director of adult education in your state, province, or territory for specific information.

WHAT IS A PASSING SCORE ON THE GED TEST?

Again, this varies from area to area. To find out what you need to pass the test, contact your local GED testing center. However, you must keep two scores in mind. One score represents the minimum score you must get on each test. For example, if your state requires minimum scores of 40, you must get at least 40 points on every test. Additionally, you must meet the requirements of a minimum average score on all five tests. For example, if your state requires a minimum average score of 45, you must get a total of 225 points to pass. The two scores together, the minimum score and the minimum average score, determine whether you pass or fail the GED Test.

To understand this better, look at the scores of three people who took the test in a state that requires a minimum score of 40 and a minimum average score of 45 (225 total). Ann and Willie did not pass, but Ramon did. See if you can tell why.

	Ann	Willie	Ramon
Test 1	44	42	43
Test 2	43	43	48
Test 3	38	42	47
Test 4	50	40	52
Test 5	50	40	49
	225	207	239

Ann made the total of 225 points but fell below the minimum score on Test 3. Willie passed each test but failed to get the 225 points needed; just passing the individual tests was not enough. Ramon passed all the tests and exceeded the minimum score. Generally, to receive a GED credential, you must correctly answer half or a little more than half of the questions on each test.

MAY I RETAKE THE TEST?

You are allowed to retake some or all of the tests. Again, the regulations governing the number of times that you may retake the tests and the time you must wait before retaking them are set by your state, province, or territory. Some states require you to take a review class or to study on your own for a certain amount of time before taking the test again.

HOW CAN I BEST PREPARE FOR THE TEST?

Many libraries, community colleges, adult education centers, churches, and other institutions offer GED preparation classes. Some television stations broadcast classes to prepare people for the test. If you cannot find a GED preparation class locally, contact the director of adult education in your state, province, or territory or call the GED Hotline (800-62-MY-GED). This hotline will give you telephone numbers and addresses of adult education and testing centers in your area. The hotline is staffed 24 hours a day, seven days a week.

WHAT'S ON THE SCIENCE TEST?

The GED Science Test consists of 66 multiple-choice questions. About two-thirds of the questions will be based on reading passages of up to 250 words each. About one-third will be based on diagrams, charts, or graphs. These questions require you to know some of the basic science concepts that will be covered in this book. You will not have to recall an isolated fact as on some tests. Rather, you will read a passage or look at an illustration and answer questions based on it. To answer successfully, you will need to:

1. understand basic science concepts

2. interpret illustrations and reading passages

3. show that you can
  - understand what you read
  - apply information to a new situation
  - analyze relationships between ideas
  - make judgments about the material presented

Actually, you already do all of these different kinds of thinking in daily life. In this book, we will help you apply these skills to science materials.

The GED Science Test is broken down into these content areas:

Life Sciences	50%
• Biology	
Physical Sciences	50%
• Earth Science	
• Chemistry	
• Physics	

These subject areas are covered in chapters 5–9 of this book. However, keep in mind that a given question may draw from a number of these subjects. For example, a question on air pollution may draw from material covered in both biology and chemistry.

Also remember that you are being tested on your ability to think about certain ideas and concepts. You will be asked to do more than just find an answer that was given in a passage.

These are the thinking skills that will be tested and their percentages of the test:

Understanding Ideas	20%
Applying Ideas	30%
Analyzing Ideas	30%
Evaluating Ideas	20%

Chapters 1–4 of this book provide practice with these thinking skills. Bear in mind that by strengthening your thinking skills in general, you will be able to perform better on any type of test.

TEST-TAKING TIPS FOR SUCCESS

1. **Prepare physically.** Get plenty of rest and eat a well-balanced meal before the test so that you will have energy and will be able to think clearly. Last-minute cramming will probably not help as much as a relaxed and rested mind.

2. **Arrive early.** Be at the testing center at least 15 to 20 minutes before the starting time. Make sure you have time to find the room and to get situated. Keep in mind that many testing centers refuse to admit latecomers.

3. **Think positively.** Tell yourself you will do well. If you have studied and prepared for the test, you should succeed.

4. **Relax during the test.** Take half a minute several times during the test to stretch and breathe deeply, especially if you are feeling anxious or confused.

5. **Read the test directions carefully.** Be sure you understand how to answer the questions. If you have any questions about the test or about filling in the answer form, ask before the test begins.

6. **Know the time limit for each test.** The Science Test has a time limit of 95 minutes.

Some testing centers allow extra time, while others do not. You may be able to find out the policy of your testing center before you take the test, but always work according to the official time limit. If you have extra time, go back and check your answers.

7. **Have a strategy for answering questions.** You should read through the reading passages, or look over the materials, once and then answer the questions that follow. Read each question two or three times to make sure you understand it. It is best to refer back to the passage or illustration in order to confirm your answer choice. Don't try to depend on your memory of what you have just read or seen. Some people like to guide their reading by skimming the questions before reading a passage. Use the method that works best for you.

8. **Don't spend a lot of time on difficult questions.** If you're not sure of an answer, go on to the next question. Answer easier questions first and then go back to the harder questions. However, when you skip a question, be sure that you have skipped the same number on your answer sheet. Although skipping difficult questions is a good strategy for making the most of your time, it is very easy to get confused and throw off your whole answer key.

   Lightly mark the margin of your answer sheet next to the numbers of the questions you did not answer so that you know what to go back to. To prevent confusion when your test is graded, be sure to erase these marks completely after you answer the questions.

9. **Answer every question on the test.** If you're not sure of an answer, take an educated guess. When you leave a question unanswered, you will always lose points, but you can possibly gain points if you make a correct guess.

   If you must guess, try to eliminate one or more answers that you are sure are not correct. Then choose from the remaining answers. Remember, you greatly increase your chances if you can eliminate one or two answers before guessing. Of course, guessing should be used only when all else has failed.

10. **Clearly fill in the circle for each answer choice.** If you erase something, erase it completely. Be sure that you give only one answer per question; otherwise, no answer will count.

11. **Practice test taking.** Use the exercises, reviews, and especially the Post-Test and Practice Test in this book to better understand your test-taking habits and weaknesses. Use them to practice different strategies such as skimming questions first or skipping hard questions until the end. Knowing your own personal test-taking style is important to your success on the GED Test.

HOW TO USE THIS BOOK

If you are a student about to prepare for the GED Tests, you are to be admired. You have decided to resume an education that had been cut short. It is never easy to get back on track after you have been derailed, but, while it may not be easy, it will not be impossible. It will require determination and a lot of hard work.

This book will guide you through the types of questions you can expect to find on the Science Test. To answer some questions successfully, you may need to be aware of a few basic scientific ideas that you have heard or read about previously. Many of these are related to scientific issues that affect society as a whole. If you read newspapers, magazines, or books or if you watch scientific shows on television, you are already on the road to success. If you do not read very much or pay attention to science news, now is the time to start. Not only will you increase your science knowledge but you will also set a pattern for lifelong learning.

Before beginning this book, you should take the Pre-Test. This will give you a preview of what the Science Test includes, but, more important, it will help you identify which areas you need to concentrate on most. Use the chart at the end of the Pre-Test to pinpoint the types of questions you answered incorrectly and to determine what skills you need special work in. You may decide to concentrate on specific areas or to work through the entire book. We strongly suggest that you *do* work through the whole book to best prepare yourself for the actual test.

This book has a number of features designed to help make the task of test preparation easier as well as effective and enjoyable:

- A preliminary "warm-up" section of four chapters isolates the four thinking skills—*comprehension, application, analysis,* and *evaluation*—and provides you with plenty of practice in applying these skills; this section includes a broad sampling of passages and graphics from the subject areas covered on the Science Test; these sections are indicated by the symbol at the left.

- Skill builders (in the reading chapters only) reinforce science reading skills and concepts; these are indicated by the symbol at the left.

- Content chapters cover the essential science concepts you need to know; these are indicated by the symbol at the left.

- Questions from the four levels of thinking skills are presented in a format similar to the GED test

- High-interest reading passages deal with science issues currently affecting society

- A variety of exercise types maintain interest—matching, fill-in-the-blank, true/false, multiple-choice, and short essay questions.

- Writing activities based on thought-provoking issues provide an opportunity to practice critical thinking and writing skills for the essay portion of the GED Writing Skills Test; these are indicated by the symbol at the left.

- Over 400 practice questions strengthen science reading and thinking skills.

- An answer key (coded by skill level) for each section explains the correct answers for the exercises; if you make a mistake, you can learn from it by reading the explanation that follows the answer and then reviewing the question to analyze the error.

After you have worked through the five subject areas—Plant and Animal Biology, Science, Chemistry, and Physics—you should take the Post-Test. The Post-Test is a simulated GED Test that presents questions in the format, at the level of difficulty, and in the percentages found on the actual test. The Post-Test will help you determine whether you are ready for the GED Science Test and, if not, what areas of the book you need to review. The Post-Test evaluation chart at the end will be especially helpful for making this decision.

We realize that practice makes perfect. Therefore, we've added a Practice Test as a final indicator of your readiness for the real GED Test. This test is just like the Post-Test in terms of its format, level of difficulty, and percentages found on the real test. After you have completed the Practice Test, you will be able to finally determine whether you are ready to take the GED Test and, if not, what areas you need to review. As with the Post-Test, an evaluation chart is included to help you judge your performance.

Contemporary Books publishes a wide range of materials to help you prepare for the tests. These books are designed for home study or classroom use. Our GED preparation books are available through schools and bookstores and directly from the publisher. For the visually impaired, a large-print version is available. For further information, call Library Reproduction Service (LRS) at (800) 255-5002.

Finally, we'd like to hear from you. If our materials have helped you to pass the test or if you feel that we can do a better job preparing you, write to us at the address on the back of the book to let us know. We hope you enjoy studying for the GED Test with our materials and wish you the greatest success.

The Editors

Science Pre-Test

Directions: Before beginning to work on this book, take the Pre-Test. The purpose of this test is to help you determine which skills you need to develop in order to pass the Science Test.

The Science Pre-Test consists of 33 multiple-choice questions. All of the questions are based on charts, graphs, diagrams, and reading passages.

Answer each question as carefully as possible, choosing the best of five answer choices and blackening in the grid. If you find a question too difficult, do not waste time on it. Work ahead and come back to it later when you can think it through carefully.

When you have completed the test, check your work with the answers and explanations at the end of the section.

Use the Evaluation Chart on page 13 to determine which areas you need to review the most. For the best possible preparation for the Science Test, however, we advise you to work through this entire book.

PRE-TEST ANSWER GRID

1 ① ② ③ ④ ⑤	10 ① ② ③ ④ ⑤	19 ① ② ③ ④ ⑤	28 ① ② ③ ④ ⑤
2 ① ② ③ ④ ⑤	11 ① ② ③ ④ ⑤	20 ① ② ③ ④ ⑤	29 ① ② ③ ④ ⑤
3 ① ② ③ ④ ⑤	12 ① ② ③ ④ ⑤	21 ① ② ③ ④ ⑤	30 ① ② ③ ④ ⑤
4 ① ② ③ ④ ⑤	13 ① ② ③ ④ ⑤	22 ① ② ③ ④ ⑤	31 ① ② ③ ④ ⑤
5 ① ② ③ ④ ⑤	14 ① ② ③ ④ ⑤	23 ① ② ③ ④ ⑤	32 ① ② ③ ④ ⑤
6 ① ② ③ ④ ⑤	15 ① ② ③ ④ ⑤	24 ① ② ③ ④ ⑤	33 ① ② ③ ④ ⑤
7 ① ② ③ ④ ⑤	16 ① ② ③ ④ ⑤	25 ① ② ③ ④ ⑤	
8 ① ② ③ ④ ⑤	17 ① ② ③ ④ ⑤	26 ① ② ③ ④ ⑤	
9 ① ② ③ ④ ⑤	18 ① ② ③ ④ ⑤	27 ① ② ③ ④ ⑤	

Questions 1 and 2 refer to the following information.

Commercially prepared food that is sold in the United States often contains one or more types of food additives. Preservatives are chemicals that are placed in food to retard spoilage by bacteria. Artificial coloring is placed in food to change its color, while artificial flavoring and sweeteners are added to improve taste.

In recent years, medical researchers have discovered that certain kinds of food additives, when they are eaten in very large amounts, can cause cancer in laboratory animals. However, scientists have not been able to prove that small amounts of these additives are harmful to people. Yet, even without medical evidence of danger to consumers, some companies now sell foods that contain no preservatives, artificial coloring, or artificial flavoring.

1. Which of the following is *not* mentioned in the passage as a reason that additives are placed in food?

   (1) to retard spoilage
   (2) to improve its taste
   (3) to lower its cost
   (4) to change its color
   (5) to slow down the growth of bacteria

2. What assumption is made by food companies that sell food that is advertised as being 100 percent natural (containing no artificial additives)?

   (1) Food additives do not cause cancer.
   (2) Out of concern for their health, many customers will buy only food that is 100 percent natural.
   (3) Many customers feed their pets scraps of food, and 100 percent natural food will be safer for these pets.
   (4) Food that is 100 percent natural contains fewer calories than food in which additives have been placed.
   (5) Food that is 100 percent natural has a better appearance than food in which additives have been placed.

Question 3 is based on the following information.

3. Saccharin, a chemical substance 500 times sweeter than ordinary sugar, is used in the United States as a sugar substitute in many foods and beverages. In 1978, following the discovery that saccharin increases the incidence of bladder cancer in rats, the U.S. Food and Drug Administration began requiring that all products containing saccharin carry a warning label.

Which of the following studies could provide the most convincing evidence supporting the hypothesis that saccharin increases the risk of bladder cancer in humans?

   (1) a study of the eating habits of a group of people in the United States who do not have bladder cancer
   (2) a study of the eating habits of a group of bladder-cancer patients in a country where saccharin is not used
   (3) a study of the effects of saccharin on the health of rabbits and monkeys
   (4) a study of the eating habits of a group of bladder-cancer patients in the United States
   (5) a study of the exercise and sleeping habits of a group of bladder-cancer patients in the United States

Questions 4 and 5 refer to the graph below.

AVERAGE LIFE EXPECTANCY
(Years)

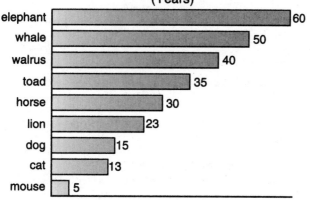

4. A general rule for animals is that the larger an animal is, the longer its life expectancy will be. As you can see from the bar graph above, an exception to this rule is the

   (1) walrus
   (2) toad
   (3) horse
   (4) dog
   (5) mouse

5. How many years longer is the average life expectancy of a whale than the average life expectancy of a dog?

   (1) 13 years
   (2) 24 years
   (3) 35 years
   (4) 50 years
   (5) 63 years

Questions 6 and 7 are based on the following passage.

   Sharks, the most feared of the large fish, are almost always predators that feed on other marine animals, from small fish such as sea bass and salmon to marine mammals such as elephant seals and whales. Shaped like a torpedo, a shark moves swiftly through the water and captures and rips its prey with rows of razor-sharp teeth. To aid in its endless search for food, a shark is equipped with a keen sense of smell, particularly for blood, and it can detect uneven vibrations in the water caused by an injured animal's swimming.

6. The torpedo-like shape of a shark gives the shark the survival advantage of

   (1) strength
   (2) speed
   (3) flexibility
   (4) keen vision
   (5) tough skin

7. One type of shark, the great white shark, is known for its tendency to attack swimmers and even small fishing boats. Suppose that you want to know whether the great white shark is in danger of becoming extinct. It would be most useful to know the estimated number of

   (1) teeth in the mouth of a great white shark
   (2) swimmers killed by great white sharks each year
   (3) types of sharks that are already extinct
   (4) great white sharks alive today compared to their numbers 20 years ago
   (5) diseases that affect great white sharks

Question 8 refers to the following chart.

CALORIE NEEDS PER DAY	
Very active man	4,500
Inactive man	3,000
Very active woman	3,000
Inactive woman	2,500
Teenage boy	3,200
Teenage girl	2,800
Children 1–6	1,200–1,600

8. Which of the following statements is best supported by information presented in the chart above?

   (1) Teenagers need more calories each day than young children because teenagers get more daily exercise.
   (2) On the average, men are physically larger than women.
   (3) Adults need more calories each day than children or teenagers.
   (4) It is more difficult for a man to lose weight than it is for a woman.
   (5) The daily calorie need of an adult increases as activity level increases.

9. At room temperature, hydrogen gas mixes freely with oxygen gas. Without a source of heat, the gases do not chemically react or change in any way. However, a flame or an electric spark will cause this quiet mixture of gases to explode violently.

   What is the best rule for storing hydrogen and oxygen gas cylinders (containers of gas)?

   (1) A danger sign should be placed next to oxygen gas cylinders.
   (2) Hydrogen gas cylinders should be stored at least six feet away from oxygen gas cylinders.
   (3) Smoking should be permitted around hydrogen gas cylinders only when no oxygen gas cylinders are nearby.
   (4) Hydrogen gas cylinders should be stored in a separate room, and preferably in a separate building, from where oxygen gas cylinders are stored.
   (5) Hydrogen gas cylinders should be stored with oxygen gas cylinders in a room that has steel-reinforced concrete walls.

Questions 10 and 11 refer to the illustration below.

10. Which phrase below is the best title for the above illustration?

    (1) Cliffs Overlooking an Ocean
    (2) The Movement of Sand Along a Beach
    (3) Cliff Erosion Caused by Tides
    (4) Growth and Decay of Sand Dunes
    (5) Changing Tide Levels on a Beach

11. One result of the action of the high-tide waves on the cliff illustrated above is

    (1) a decrease in the height of the cliff
    (2) a decrease in the amount of beach
    (3) an increase in the height of the cliff
    (4) an increase in the amount of beach
    (5) an increase in the height of the high tide

Questions 12 and 13 refer to the following passage.

You may have heard a weather reporter talk about a temperature inversion and the dangers of air pollution that accompany it. To understand what a temperature inversion is, you must first know that when weather conditions are normal, air temperature decreases with increasing altitude. In other words, the higher up you go, the colder it is. During an inversion, the opposite is true: the air gets warmer as altitude increases.

A temperature inversion occurs when a layer of warm air passes over a layer of cooler air next to the ground. The layer of cooler air, which may be several hundred feet thick, traps air pollutants and holds them close to the ground. The layer of warm air above prevents the pollutants from dispersing at a higher altitude as they normally would. This situation is especially dangerous in and around large cities where pollution from automobile exhausts and industrial smoke can be at a health-threatening level even when atmospheric conditions are normal.

12. A city that is experiencing a temperature inversion is most likely to be bothered by

    (1) snow
    (2) hot weather
    (3) air pollution
    (4) water pollution
    (5) congested traffic

13. During a temperature inversion in and around a heavily polluted large city, what is the best advice that the mayor can give to the city's residents?

    (1) Don't drive your car unless absolutely necessary.
    (2) Wear warm clothes when you leave the house.
    (3) Stay home from work until the inversion is over.
    (4) Leave the city for a few days.
    (5) Write letters to the weather bureau and complain.

Questions 14–16 refer to the following information.

An important principle in biology is that each living thing is adapted (physically suited) to survive best in the conditions present in its home environment. As illustrated below, one adaptation shown by birds is foot structure.

FOOT STRUCTURE VARIATIONS OF COMMON BIRDS

Wading (Heron) Grasping (Hawk) Perching (Warbler) Swimming (Duck) Running (Rhea)

14. Which of the five birds represented is most suited to use its feet to pick up and carry small land animals?

    (1) heron
    (2) hawk
    (3) warbler
    (4) duck
    (5) rhea

15. Which two drawings above would be of most interest to someone studying birds that get their food from rivers and lakes?

    (1) A and C
    (2) A and D
    (3) B and E
    (4) C and E
    (5) D and E

16. The drawings above would have the *least* relevance to a person interested in

    (1) the walking abilities of birds
    (2) the dietary habits of birds
    (3) illustrations of wildlife
    (4) the climbing ability of birds
    (5) the soaring ability of birds

Questions 17–20 refer to the following passage.

Chemists working in medical research have developed quite a number of pain-relieving drugs. They have also recently discovered that the human body produces its own pain relievers. Evidence shows that these natural painkillers, chemicals called *endorphins*, are produced by the body in response to the stress of tiring exercise. Chemists believe that endorphins are probably responsible for "runner's high," a feeling of calm and absence of pain experienced by athletes during long periods of strenuous running. What's more, although medical evidence is not conclusive, some chemists point out that the short-term depression many people feel when they must give up exercising on a regular basis may be a form of natural drug withdrawal!

After reading the above paragraph, three students made the following statements.

A. Even though endorphins are natural body chemicals, endorphin withdrawal is a serious drug problem.

B. Endorphins are types of chemicals produced by the body in response to strenuous exercise.

C. The reason I'm moody today is that I'm experiencing endorphin withdrawal from all the exercise I got last week.

17. Which of the statements is a correct restatement of information given in the passage?

(1) A only
(2) B only
(3) C only
(4) A and B only
(5) B and C only

18. Which of the statements is a hypothesis (a possible explanation of an observed fact or condition)?

(1) A only
(2) B only
(3) C only
(4) A and B only
(5) B and C only

19. Which of the following is the most reasonable prediction that can be made based on the information given in the passage?

(1) Further research will show that there is no such thing as endorphin withdrawal.
(2) The adverse side effects of all pain-relieving drugs will someday be eliminated.
(3) Learning to control a person's endorphin level may someday give doctors a new method of relieving pain.
(4) Chemists will someday discover that endorphins are present only in the bodies of people who are drug abusers.
(5) Further research will show that taking aspirin also causes the body to produce endorphins.

20. Considering what is now known about endorphins, for what symptom would synthetic endorphins most likely be recommended if they someday become a safe medicinal drug?

(1) chest pain due to a cold
(2) a headache due to a hangover
(3) an upset stomach
(4) a broken bone
(5) overall body soreness due to hard physical labor

Questions 21–23 refer to the following passage.

A storm cloud is much like a giant electricity generator. When the cloud forms, electric charges within the cloud separate. A positive charge accumulates near the top of the cloud, and a negative charge accumulates near the bottom. As the cloud passes overhead, the negatively charged lower part of the cloud causes a large positive charge to appear on the ground below. Because a positive charge is strongly attracted to a negative charge, this ground charge follows the cloud like a shadow. Both the negative charge in the cloud and the positive charge on the ground increase as the storm cloud grows.

Before lightning strikes the earth, the air between the cloud and the ground acts as an insulator and does not allow electricity to pass through it. However, when the electrical force pulling the cloud's negative charge toward the earth's positive charge becomes strong enough, it overcomes the resistance of the air. When this happens, lightning occurs: the negative charge rushes down from the cloud to meet the positive ground charge.

When lightning strikes the earth, it takes the path of least resistance. This path is most often just the shortest distance from the cloud to anything touching the ground. That's why lightning frequently strikes the highest point of an area—usually a tall tree, a high tower, or a skyscraper. People have also been struck, often when walking in an open area such as a field or when boating on a lake. In fact, the National Center for Health Statistics reports that about 125 Americans are killed by lightning each year, and more than 500 are injured.

Although lightning can't be prevented, there are ways to protect tall buildings from its destructive power. The most common way is with a lightning rod, a sharply pointed rod that runs from the highest point of the building down into the ground. The lightning rod is made of material like copper that conducts electricity rather than resisting it. If lightning strikes the rod, the electricity safely flows to the ground without damaging the building or harming the people inside.

21. For what reason is a lightning rod placed on a tall building?

(1) to help prevent lightning storms from occurring in the sky over the building
(2) to prevent lightning from striking near the building
(3) to protect the building from lightning by providing a high-resistance, safe electrical path to ground
(4) to protect the building from lightning by providing a low-resistance, safe electrical path to ground
(5) to prevent cloud-to-earth lightning bolts and cause cloud-to-cloud bolts instead

22. When lightning strikes an object like a tree, the object is heated as electricity passes through it.

Which of the following could be caused by lightning?

(1) a heat wave
(2) positive electrical charges accumulating on the ground
(3) negative electrical charges accumulating in a cloud
(4) a forest fire in a hot, dry area
(5) the separation of electrical charges within a cloud

23. Imagine that you're unexpectedly caught in a violent lightning storm while hiking in the countryside, thirteen miles away from your car. Of the options listed below, what is the safest course of action?

(1) Hike back to your car as quickly as possible.
(2) Go to the lowest point of an open area and lie down, preferably in a ditch or depression.
(3) Climb up a tree in order to get out of contact with the ground.
(4) Go to the highest point of an open area and wait for the storm to pass.
(5) Seek shelter next to the highest tree you can find.

Questions 24–27 refer to the following information.

Behavior is an organism's response to a stimulus. (A stimulus is anything that causes a living thing to act or to react in any way.) Below are five types of behavior demonstrated by vertebrate animals (animals with backbones). Three are types of inborn behavior, and two are types of learned behavior.

Inborn behavior:

reflex—an automatic response (usually a simple act that is done quickly) to an unexpected stimulus

instinct—an unlearned pattern of complex activity that an animal naturally undertakes as part of its life cycle

self-preservation—a reaction shown by an animal for the purpose of escaping life-threatening danger or for protecting itself from harm

Learned behavior:

conditioned response—a learned activity that an animal displays in response to a stimulus but not as a result of a decision-making process

intelligent behavior—a complex activity involving judgment and decision making that an animal chooses to undertake

24. Each time Jenny claps her hands, her dog Scruffy rolls over and barks. Scruffy is demonstrating behavior best classified as

    (1) reflex
    (2) instinct
    (3) self-preservation
    (4) conditioned response
    (5) intelligent behavior

25. When the cat came out the front door, the mouse on the steps ran for its life and ducked into its home in the woodpile. The mouse's running can best be called an act of

    (1) reflex
    (2) instinct
    (3) self-preservation
    (4) conditioned response
    (5) intelligent behavior

26. After six years of smoking more than one pack a day, Arne finally decided it was time to quit, and he gave up cigarettes. Arne's decision is an example of

    (1) reflex
    (2) instinct
    (3) self-preservation
    (4) conditioned response
    (5) intelligent behavior

27. During mating, the Adelie penguin of Antarctica builds a nest out of pebbles and the bones of its ancestors. This nest-building behavior is an example of

    (1) reflex
    (2) instinct
    (3) self-preservation
    (4) conditioned response
    (5) intelligent behavior

28. Heat and light are forms of energy that almost always occur together. Usually, a consumer product is designed primarily to provide either heat or light energy, not both. For example, after you strike a match, both heat and light are given off, but the main purpose of a match is to make something start burning. You would use a match to light a darkened room only if there were no other source of light available.

    For which two products below would heat be considered the *least* useful form of energy produced?

    A. a cigarette lighter
    B. a desk lamp
    C. an electric oven
    D. a candle

    (1) A and C
    (2) A and D
    (3) B and C
    (4) B and D
    (5) C and D

Questions 29–31 refer to the illustration below.

**LUNAR ECLIPSE
(ECLIPSE OF THE MOON)**

29. You can infer from the illustration that the word *orbit* refers to the

(1) size of the moon
(2) reflected light off the moon
(3) temperature of the moon
(4) path of the moon
(5) rotation speed of the moon

30. According to the illustration above, an eclipse of the moon occurs

(1) only once a month
(2) only once a year
(3) only when Earth is directly between the sun and the moon
(4) only when the moon is directly between Earth and sun
(5) only when the weather is clear on Earth and no clouds block the sunlight

31. Knowing that moonlight is reflected sunlight, what can you conclude happens during an eclipse of the moon?

(1) For a few minutes, the moon turns dark and seems to disappear from the sky.
(2) For a few minutes, the bright daytime sun turns dark and seems to disappear from the sky.
(3) The moon, which otherwise is only partly visible as a crescent, slowly becomes a full moon for a few minutes.
(4) The moon, which otherwise is not visible at all during that evening, slowly appears overhead as a full moon.
(5) The otherwise bright daytime sun becomes much dimmer, similar to when it's hidden behind a cloud layer.

Questions 32 and 33 refer to the following information.

The volume of an odd-shaped object such as a small ceramic statue can be measured by the immersion method, the steps of which are given below.

STEP 1. Get a measuring cup or a similar container that has a volume scale along its side. Fill the container partly full of water and record its volume.

volume scale

STEP 2. Place the statue in the water and notice that the water level rises in the container.

STEP 3. Record the new volume level reached by the surface of the water. This volume is the combined volume of the water and the statue.

STEP 4. Subtract the volume measured in step 1 from the volume measured in step 3. The difference between these two volumes is equal to the volume of the statue.

32. Which of the following must be assumed if the volume of the statue is to be measured accurately using the immersion method?

(1) The volume of the statue is less than the volume of water in the container.
(2) The volume of the statue is greater than the volume of water in the container.
(3) The weight of the statue is equal to the weight of the water in the container.
(4) As step 2 is carried out, the water level does not rise above the top of the statue.
(5) As step 3 is carried out, the statue is totally covered by water.

33. Which of the following would lead to the greatest source of error when using the immersion method to measure the volume of clay actually used in making the statue?

(1) the use of a liquid other than water for the volume measurements
(2) the unknown fact that the statue is hollow inside
(3) a change in water temperature during the time the volume measurements were made
(4) the spillage of water while the statue was being removed from the container
(5) the unknown fact that a mistake had been made in an earlier measurement of the statue's weight

ANSWERS BEGIN ON PAGE 11.

Pre-Test Answer Key

1. **(3)** Cost is the only factor listed that is not mentioned in the passage.

2. **(2)** Food companies correctly assume that there is a growing number of health-conscious people in the U.S. who do not want additives in their food. These companies produce 100 percent natural food to appeal to this market.

3. **(4)** The best evidence can be obtained by studying the eating habits of bladder-cancer patients because they have the disease in question. Choice (2) is not a good choice because these patients have not consumed saccharin.

4. **(2)** The toad is the exception because it has a longer life expectancy than the cat, dog, lion, or horse, all of which are likely to be larger.

5. **(3)** The difference in life expectancy is 50 years minus 15 years equals 35 years.

6. **(2)** According to the passage, the torpedo-like shape of a shark is related to the shark's ability to move swiftly.

7. **(4)** Long-term population change determines whether an animal is in danger of becoming extinct (choice 4). Choices (1), (2), and (3) are not relevant. Choice (5) is wrong; all the sharks might be killed by one disease, or they might be killed by hunters rather than diseases.

8. **(5)** Although choices (1) and (2) may also be true, only choice (5) is supported directly by information from the chart.

9. **(4)** Because of the explosive nature of these two gases, the best rule is to store them as far away from each other as is reasonably possible. It would be unwise to take any risk of having them explode.

10. **(3)** The drawing shows how wave action erodes a cliff, slowly moving the edge of the cliff farther inland and creating more beach in the process.

11. **(4)** As the cliff is undercut and worn away, the width of the beach increases. Neither the height of the cliff nor the height of the high tide is affected by wave action.

12. **(3)** During a temperature inversion, the air temperature is cooler but not necessarily cold, eliminating choice (1). As the passage states, air pollution is the main concern.

13. **(1)** Since some of the air pollution comes from automobile exhausts, city residents should be advised to leave their cars at home. Choices (3) and (4) are too drastic, and choice (5) wouldn't help.

14. **(2)** Of the foot structures shown, the grasping ability of the hawk is the most suitable to picking up and carrying small animals.

15. **(2)** The birds most apt to get their food from rivers and lakes are birds adapted for wading or swimming.

16. **(5)** Of the listed choices, (5) refers to the person whose interest is least likely to involve foot shape, structure, or function.

17. **(2)** Statement A is an opinion. Only statement B accurately restates the information in the passage.

18. **(3)** Only statement C offers an explanation for a condition (moodiness).

19. **(3)** Choice (3) is a reasonable prediction based on the currently known effects of endorphins. Choices (2), (4), and (5) are not supported by information given in the passage. Choice (1) disagrees with evidence about endorphins that's already available.

20. **(5)** The discomfort of overall body soreness is similar to the discomfort felt in strenuous exercise, the cause of natural endorphin release.

21. **(4)** Lightning can't be controlled, but, as the passage states, buildings can be made safe through the use of a lightning rod, a low-resistance electrical path to the ground.

22. **(4)** When a bolt of lightning heats a tree in a hot, dry area, the result can be a forest fire. Choices (2), (3), and (5) are all causes of lightning, not effects.

23. **(2)** During a lightning storm you do not want to be in a tree, next to a tree, or near a high point in an open area. Choice (2) is the safest of the listed places.

24. **(4)** A dog is taught tricks over a long period of time. Rolling over on command is a learned, practiced behavior: a conditioned response.

25. **(3)** By running, the mouse is saving its own life, an example of self-preservation.

26. **(5)** The conscious decision by a human being to give up a dangerous activity is a good example of intelligent behavior.

27. **(2)** Nest building is an unlearned activity that is a natural part of a penguin's life cycle.

28. **(4)** The cigarette lighter and oven are both designed to be sources of heat. The lamp and candle are designed mainly to produce light, although both produce heat as well.

29. **(4)** The drawing indicates that *orbit* refers to the changing positions of the moon (or *path* of the moon) as it moves around Earth.

30. **(3)** An eclipse of the moon occurs only when the moon passes in the shadow of Earth. An eclipse can happen only when Earth is directly between the sun and the moon.

31. **(1)** When it moves into Earth's shadow, the moon is no longer struck by sunlight, and it seems to turn dark and disappear from view.

32. **(5)** The total volume of the statue can be measured only if the entire statue is under water when step 3 is carried out. Choices (1), (2), and (3) are irrelevant. If choice (4) were true, the experiment would be flawed.

33. **(2)** None of the choices except (2) would lead to an error in measuring the clay's volume. If the statue is hollow, the actual volume of clay may be much less than the volume of the statue itself.

Pre-Test Evaluation Chart

Use the answer key on pages 11–12 to check your answers to the Pre-Test. Then find the item number of each question you missed and circle it on the chart below to determine the reading skill and content areas in which you need more practice. Pay particular attention to areas where you missed half or more of the questions. The reading skills are covered on pages 17–79. These skills are absolutely essential for success on the GED Science Test. The numbers in boldface are questions based on graphics. For those questions that you missed, review the skill pages indicated.

Skill Area/ Content Area	Comprehension	Application	Analysis	Evaluation
Plant & Animal Biology (pages 81–111)	**4**, **5**, 6	24, 25, 26, 27		7, **14**, **15**, **16**
Human Biology (pages 113–143)	1, 2		**8**	3
Earth Science (pages 145–173)	**11**, **29**, **30**	12	**10**, **31**	**13**
Chemistry (pages 175–211)		18	9, 17, 19, 20	
Physics (pages 213–251)	21	22, 28	**32**	23, **33**

CRITICAL THINKING SKILLS
IN SCIENCE

- Comprehending Science Materials
- Applying Science Concepts
- Analyzing Science Materials
- Evaluating Science Materials

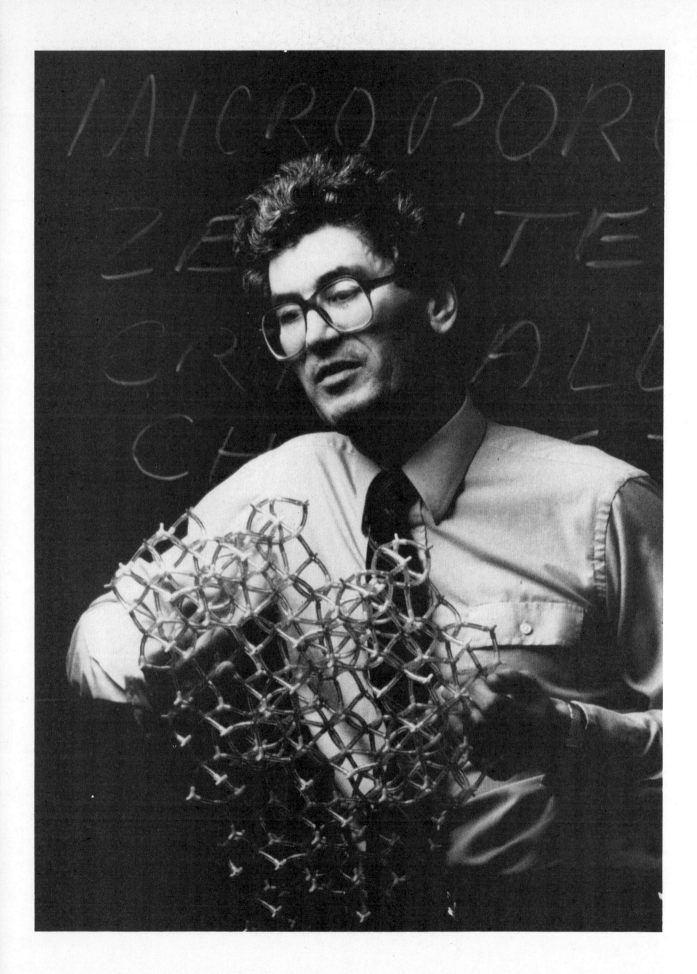

1 Comprehending Science Materials

The word ***comprehend*** means to understand. For example, when you comprehend, or understand, the game of soccer, you are able to watch the game and know what's going on. And, if you're watching with a friend who has never seen the game before, you are able to explain its rules. As you can see, comprehension means that you understand the general idea and have a good grasp of details. Comprehension in science is a measure of three abilities:

- the ability to summarize ideas

- the ability to restate information

- the ability to identify implications

SUMMARIZING THE MAIN IDEA

To ***summarize the main idea*** is to express briefly an author's key thought. You can summarize the sentences of a paragraph, or you can summarize several paragraphs of a longer passage. In each case, you sum up, in just a few words, the main point the author is trying to make. For example, you may have just read a long article on research done on vaccines for common wintertime respiratory infections. Though a lot of details are given, the key thought you'll remember is that "there is still no way to prevent the common cold!"

A MAIN IDEA MAY BE EXPRESSED IN A SINGLE SENTENCE

In many passages, the author expresses the main idea, or key thought, as a single sentence. Other sentences provide details to support the main idea. In this type of passage, the author will most often place the key thought near the beginning or near the end. By putting the main idea near the beginning of the passage, the author draws the reader's immediate attention to it. If the main idea comes near the end, it can serve as a summary of all the information that has come before it.

Try finding the key thought in the paragraph below. Underline the sentence that best expresses the author's main point.

The action of ocean waves can change the shape of a shoreline. Waves can erode the shore, breaking up land masses near the water. Waves can also move the eroding dirt and rocks great distances down the shoreline. Beaches will be formed when waves move more rock fragments toward the shore than away from it. Cliffs are formed when waves move more rock fragments away from the shore than toward it.

Did you underline the first sentence? You should have, because the changing shape of the shoreline is the author's key point. Each of the other sentences gives an example of how this change takes place. Each example is a detail that supports the key point.

Now try underlining the main idea sentence of this paragraph:

Imagine taking a microscope and looking at the edge of a piece of paper in the hope of seeing a single atom! Using the world's most powerful microscope, you still couldn't see one clearly. In fact, if you could see one, you would find that it takes about 1 million atoms, placed side by side, to cross a distance as short as the width of the edge of the paper. Atoms are so small that even scientists must be content with studying large numbers of them at the same time rather than trying to look at a single atom in the way that a doctor might look at a patient.

In the paragraph above, you should have underlined the final sentence. The author is making the point that atoms are very, very small. The first three sentences all emphasize this idea: the first sentence gets your interest, while the second and third sentences are details about the actual size of an atom.

A MAIN IDEA MAY NOT BE EXPRESSED DIRECTLY

In some passages, a main idea may not be expressed in any one sentence. However, when this is the case, you can usually express the key thought as a one-sentence summary of several points made by the author. Read the following passage.

The first action your body takes when you eat food is to begin the process of digestion. Digestion takes place in the mouth, stomach, and intestines. During digestion, food is broken down into small molecules. These molecules pass into the bloodstream when they reach the intestines. The step following digestion is called absorption. During absorption, food molecules leave your blood and enter your cells. The final step, assimilation, takes place within the cells themselves. During assimilation, cells use the food molecules for body growth and maintenance.

Write a sentence that summarizes this passage: _____

_____

Your answer will probably be something like the following: *Digestion, absorption, and assimilation are the three steps used by the body in making use of the food you eat.*

Notice that, because it is brief, a summary can't include many details. Instead, the summary expresses the main idea simply, using key words from the passage when possible.

EXERCISE 1

Directions: Read the passage below. Then choose the best answer to each question.

The possibility of life on the planets of distant stars has long been a favorite topic of science fiction writers and movie makers. Now this issue has drawn the serious interest of respected scientists.

Using specially designed telescopes that are able to pick up very weak radio waves, astronomers are scanning the sky above us every minute of each day and night. These radio telescopes can monitor over a million channels simultaneously as they search for any clue of a distant, advanced civilization broadcasting messages into space.

No one can predict if we'll ever receive a signal sent by intelligent beings from elsewhere in the universe. But one thing is sure. If we do receive such a message, we'll be hearing thoughts from the past! Any incoming signal would have to have been sent into space hundreds, thousands, or even millions of years ago. This is because it takes radio waves that long to travel the incredible distances that separate Earth from other planets that may contain life.

1. The main idea expressed in the final paragraph is that

   (1) intelligent beings may live on other planets
   (2) a message received from space would have been sent into space long ago
   (3) large distances separate the Earth from stars elsewhere in the universe
   (4) scientists are studying the possibility of life existing on other planets
   (5) we may receive a message from intelligent beings

2. The key thought of the passage is that

   (1) science fiction writers and movie makers were the first people to popularize the idea that life may exist on other planets
   (2) if distant civilizations were trying to contact us, they would use radio waves to send messages
   (3) scientists are beginning to investigate seriously the possibility that life exists elsewhere in the universe
   (4) astronomers' radio telescopes can receive messages from more than one million channels
   (5) life existed on planets elsewhere in the universe millions of years ago

ANSWERS ARE ON PAGE 302.

EXERCISE 2

Read the passage below and answer the question that follows.

Chimpanzees are highly intelligent members of the ape family and are similar genetically to human beings. Because of this similarity, chimpanzees are used as subjects in medical experiments. Researchers purposely infect chimpanzees with various diseases to study the effects of new drugs and to learn and practice new types of surgery. For example, chimpanzees purposely infected with the virus that causes AIDS do not become sick and die as do many human AIDS patients. By studying the properties of the chimpanzee's blood and immune system, researchers hope to eventually develop drugs that can help in the war against AIDS.

The main idea expressed in this passage is that chimpanzees

(1) are susceptible to many human diseases because of similarities in genetics
(2) are intelligent apes that do not differ in many ways from human beings
(3) are not harmed when medical experiments are performed on them
(4) are used in medical research because of their genetic similarity to human beings
(5) are not exposed to the AIDS virus while living in their natural habitat

ANSWER IS ON PAGE 302.

SUMMARIZING THE MAIN IDEA IN GRAPHICS

Graphics are used to present information visually, with pictures or numbers or both. The use of graphics makes it possible for an author to convey a lot of information in a compact way. And graphics make it easy for you to get a quick impression of this information without doing much reading.

The types of graphics we will work with in this book—and that are tested on the GED—are graphs, tables, charts, and diagrams. Each type of graphic is useful for certain types of information. You'll see sample uses of each as you read through the next four chapters.

Many of the sections on graphics begin with a Skill Builder. The purpose of each Skill Builder is to introduce you to a certain type of graphic. The questions about the graphic will be based on the reading skill you've just learned. For example, you just learned how to find the main idea and details. The questions in the Skill Builder below will require you to summarize the main idea of a circle graph and locate details on it. In this way, you'll be learning to read different types of graphics while you're practicing your question-answering skills.

▰ SKILL BUILDER
▰ Reading Circle Graphs

A *circle graph* looks like a divided pie. Each "slice," or segment, of the pie represents a part of a total amount. The total is represented by the whole circle. Most often, the amount of each segment is given as a percent, and the segments together add up to 100 percent. Because of their appearance, circle graphs are sometimes called pie graphs or pie charts.

Below is a circle graph. The title of this graph is "Earth's Surface." Each segment has a name and a percent value. Looking at this graph, you can see that the Pacific Ocean covers 33 percent of Earth's surface.

EARTH'S SURFACE

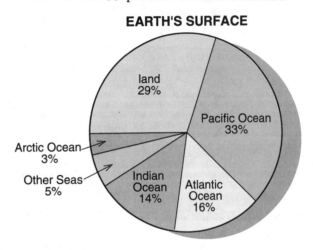

Try finding the following details on the graph above.

a. What percent of Earth's surface is land? _____

b. What total percent of Earth's surface is covered by the two largest oceans? _____

c. What total percent of Earth's surface is covered by water? _____

The answer to example a is *29 percent* and is found by reading the segment labeled "land." The answer to example b is *49 percent* and is obtained by adding the percents for the Pacific Ocean (33 percent) and the Atlantic Ocean (16 percent). The answer to example c is *71 percent* and is found either by subtracting 29 percent (the amount of land) from 100 percent or by adding all the percents given for bodies of water: 33% + 16% + 14% + 3% + 5% = 71%.

By comparing the amount of surface covered by water with the amount of surface covered by land, what would you say would be a key point made by this circle graph?

_____

_____

The key point of the graph is that *the surface of Earth is covered mainly by water.*

EXERCISE 3

Questions 1–4 refer to the following circle graph.

SOLID WASTE DISPOSAL IN THE UNITED STATES

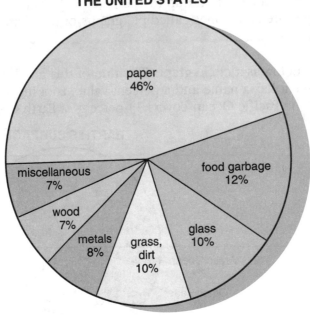

1. According to the graph, which material is the largest component of American garbage?

   (1) paper
   (2) glass
   (3) dirt
   (4) tin cans
   (5) pieces of wood

2. What total percent of solid waste produced in the United States is made up of glass and metals?

   (1) 10 percent
   (2) 14 percent
   (3) 18 percent
   (4) 22 percent
   (5) 26 percent

3. For every 100 pounds of solid waste produced in the United States, how many pounds are food garbage?

   (1) eight
   (2) twelve
   (3) twenty-four
   (4) thirty-eight
   (5) forty-six

4. An author used this graph in an article about the value of recycling paper, metal, and glass products. Which of the following statements best summarizes a key point made by the graph and supports the author's argument?

   (1) The United States produces more garbage than any other country in the world.
   (2) Garbage can be conveniently classified into seven broad categories.
   (3) A full 64 percent of American garbage consists of material that could be recycled.
   (4) Recycling efforts are failing because of the amount of recyclable material that is found in garbage.
   (5) Due to the presence of a large amount of dirt in garbage, most things that are thrown away are not recyclable.

ANSWERS ARE ON PAGE 302.

RESTATING INFORMATION

To **restate information** is to use different words and phrases to express the same idea. A restatement may not sound quite the same as the original statement, but it has the same meaning. Most often, you restate information in order to put it into words that are more familiar to you—words that make it easier for you to understand and remember what you're reading.

Here are two examples of restated information:

ORIGINAL	RESTATEMENT
Excess fat and carbohydrate consumption can lead to obesity.	You'll get fat if you eat too many fats and carbohydrates.
Rocks from the moon's surface show features characteristic of rocks found on Earth.	Moon rocks are very similar to Earth rocks.

Now you try it. Using your own words, restate each sentence below.

ORIGINAL	RESTATEMENT
a. Light reflected from the moon's surface indicates its spherical shape.	_____ _____
b. Touching the exposed electric wire, Jim's finger sensed the passage of a small amount of electricity, an experience that demonstrated the quick reaction of Jim's reflexes.	_____ _____ _____ _____
c. When exposed to air, blood forms fibrin, a fibrous substance that traps blood cells. If the blood flow is small, the mass of trapped cells restricts further blood flow.	_____ _____ _____ _____

Answers will vary, but here are three possibilities:

a. The moon looks round.
b. Jim jumped when he got a shock.
c. Fibrin helps small cuts stop bleeding.

Notice that each of these example answers restates information in a way more like the way you may talk or think. Yet, in each case, the information given is really about the same.

EXERCISE 4

Directions: Read the passage below and do the exercise that follows.

The two regions known as the Arctic and Antarctic are similar in that each lies at one of Earth's two geographical poles. Yet, in many ways, these two ends of Earth are very different from each other.

The Arctic, the region around the North Pole, is full of life. More than a hundred species of flowering plants grow there, as do many types of mosses and lichens. Many insects, birds, and mammals live there as well. The Arctic is also the home of about one million Eskimos and other peoples from North America, Europe, and Asia.

The Antarctic, the region around the South Pole, has much less life than the Arctic. Very few plants grow there because of the extremely harsh weather. In fact, the average monthly temperature is always below freezing, and winds of over a hundred miles per hour are common. These conditions make Antarctica a desert-like place that only penguins seem to love! Although these flightless birds make their home there, no mammals have done the same. The only exceptions are the few scientists who do research on this frozen continent and an occasional team of explorers.

Place a check mark before each statement below that is a restatement of information given in the passage. Be aware that a restatement may be a single sentence that combines information from more than one sentence in a passage. (Hint: Each statement below is a fact that you may already know. Be careful to check only those facts that are restatements of information presented above.)

_____ **1.** The Arctic is located at the North Pole and the Antarctic at the South Pole.

_____ **2.** The continent of Antarctica is as large as the United States and Canada combined.

_____ **3.** Because it is cold and windy, Antarctica is like a desert.

_____ **4.** Bears and seals live in the Arctic, while penguins live in the Antarctic.

_____ **5.** The Arctic has more plant and animal life than the Antarctic.

_____ **6.** The average temperature of the Arctic is below freezing.

_____ **7.** Penguins and a few mammals live on the continent of Antarctica.

_____ **8.** Scientists do research on the continent of Antarctica.

_____ **9.** Mosses and lichens grow only in the summertime in the Arctic.

_____ **10.** Eskimos live in both the Arctic and Antarctic regions.

ANSWERS ARE ON PAGE 302.

EXERCISE 5

Questions 1 and 2 refer to the following passage.

The success of modern agriculture is due in large part to our successful fight against crop diseases. To aid in the fight against diseases caused by insects, chemists developed special types of insect poisons called pesticides.

When pesticides first came out on the market, they were believed to be both safe and effective. Although a few pesticides are still safe enough to use, many of them are now known to cause both air and water pollution. One example is DDT, a once widely used pesticide that is now known to be so dangerous to animal life that its use has been banned in the United States.

Pesticides can be inhaled directly by animals and people living in areas where spraying takes place. Because of this, the spraying of many types of pesticides near residential areas is now strictly controlled and, in some cases, prohibited. Pesticides can also get into animal and human foods. For example, insect-eating animals, including game animals, absorb pesticides when they eat contaminated bugs. Contaminated game animals can pose a serious threat to human health. In addition, when cows eat grass that has been sprayed with pesticides, both milk and beef become contaminated. Still another problem occurs when pesticides are sprayed over crop fields. These pesticides soak into the ground and can be washed by rain into groundwater and local streams. Then the pesticides are eaten by fish and other aquatic animals.

1. According to the passage, which of the following is true about DDT?

   (1) DDT are the initials of the three people who invented a particular pesticide.
   (2) DDT is the most dangerous pesticide ever used in the United States.
   (3) DDT is still used in many European countries.
   (4) DDT is a pesticide that is now banned in the United States.
   (5) DDT has been found in samples of tuna and other ocean-dwelling fish.

2. According to the passage, what is one way that pesticides get into groundwater?

   (1) Birds carry pesticides to rivers when they go to drink.
   (2) Contaminated fish may bring pesticides to the rivers in which they swim.
   (3) Rain may wash pesticides in the soil into groundwater.
   (4) Wind may carry sprayed pesticides over residential areas and into the reservoirs of groundwater.
   (5) Sprayed insects contaminate groundwater reservoirs.

ANSWERS ARE ON PAGE 302.

RESTATING INFORMATION IN GRAPHICS

When you restate information found in graphics, you use words to express information that is presented in pictures or in numbers. Being able to restate information correctly is a skill needed for understanding all types of graphics. On the next few pages we'll show how this skill is used for understanding diagrams.

Look at the diagram below. This diagram contains both labels and a caption. Using your own words, describe the point you think the author is trying to make about translucent materials.

LIGHT RAYS

Reflected rays —

Absorbed rays —

Transmitted rays —

Transparent   Translucent   Opaque

Different types of materials transmit different amounts of light.

Your answer should be that *translucent materials transmit only part of the light that strikes them.* (As used here, *to transmit* means "to allow light to pass through.") Looking closely at the diagram, you can also see that the author makes the point that translucent materials reflect part of the light that strikes them. (When light reflects, it bounces off the object that it strikes.) An example of a translucent object is a piece of colored glass.

EXERCISE 6

Directions: Look again at the diagram above. What point do you think the author is trying to make about transparent and opaque materials? Also, think of an example for each type of material.

1. transparent: _____

  example: _____

2. opaque: _____

  example: _____

ANSWERS ARE ON PAGE 302.

EXERCISE 7

Questions 1–3 refer to the following diagram.

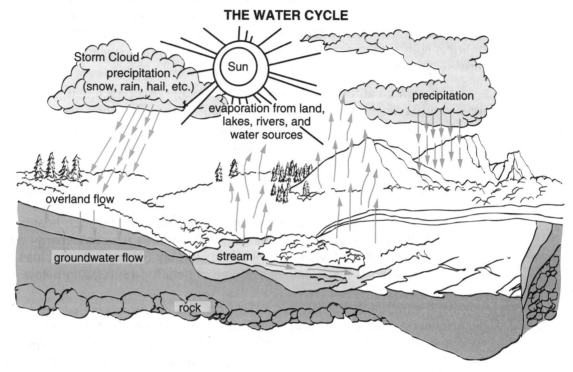

THE WATER CYCLE

1. According to the diagram, which of the following would be the best restatement of the label *precipitation*?

   (1) the mixture of gases that surrounds Earth
   (2) all sources from which moisture evaporates into the sky
   (3) the seeping of water into the rock layers of the land
   (4) all forms of moisture that fall to Earth
   (5) the flow of water over the surface of the land

2. What label on this diagram means the same thing as the expression "moisture that rises into the atmosphere from the land and from all water sources"?

   (1) stream
   (2) overland flow
   (3) groundwater flow
   (4) precipitation
   (5) evaporation

3. The artist's key point is that a water cycle is

   (1) the removal of fresh water from land by the actions of both runoff and the growth of vegetation
   (2) the evaporation of water from the land and rivers due to the sun's heat
   (3) the continual back-and-forth movement of water between Earth's surface and the atmosphere
   (4) the formation of storm clouds over a stream and land at the same time
   (5) the changing of the fresh water found in clouds to the salt water found in the oceans

ANSWERS ARE ON PAGE 302.

IDENTIFYING IMPLICATIONS

To *imply* means "to suggest." Therefore, an implication is a point of view or an idea that an author suggests. For example, an author who writes "Scientists may have invented nuclear weapons, but I sure don't want them to work on arms control!" *implies* that he does not have a lot of faith in the political ability of scientists. Although the author's point of view is not stated directly, you can tell how the writer feels about the subject.

Although an author may present many details in a passage, it is often left for you to figure out the additional information yourself. When you *infer*, you really are just making an educated guess at information that is not stated directly. An implied point of view, often called an *attitude*, is the way an author appears to feel about something.

For an example of an implied idea, read the following advertisement.

Many homes and businesses have installed Emerald solar heating units on their roofs. Our solar heating unit captures the sun's energy by letting sunlight heat water that circulates through darkly colored pipes. The hot water is then used as a source of heat for the building below.

An implied idea that you can infer from this paragraph is that the cost of heat obtained from an Emerald solar heating unit is less than the cost of a comparable amount of gas. Although cost is not mentioned, you can infer that this solar heating unit is used as a money-saving device because advertisers most often appeal to a potential customer's desire to save money.

EXERCISE 8

Directions: Read the following passage and see if you can identify its implications by answering the questions that follow.

One of the greatest inventions of the twentieth century is the robot. With its tiny electronic brain humming along, it can be programmed to do just about anything. Since we installed several robots, business has really picked up and we've saved a lot of payroll money.

A robot is a great investment. Robots don't take rest breaks, and they don't get sick. They don't require a lunchroom or a smoking area. You don't need to provide them with either medical insurance or retirement benefits. What's more, each robot can do the work of several regular employees, and you can run robots twenty-four hours a day, seven days a week.

1. How would you describe the author's attitude toward robots?

_____

2. What does the author imply about the yearly cost of operating a robot compared to the yearly salary of a regular employee?

_____

3. What can you infer about the quality of work done by a robot as compared to the quality of similar work done by a regular employee?

_____

4. From the way the passage is written, do you infer that the author is most likely an assembly-line worker or an owner?

_____

GED Practice
EXERCISE 9

Questions 1–3 refer to the passage below.

Extinction is the disappearance of a species from Earth. Some species become extinct because of a natural occurrence, such as an ice age. This is most likely what happened to dinosaurs about 70 million years ago. Other species become extinct because of the actions of human beings. The passenger pigeon, for example, was hunted to extinction during the 1800s. During that same century, the buffalo, now being raised in protected herds, was almost hunted to extinction.

Today, certain species of whales are in danger of being hunted to extinction. The panda is in danger of becoming extinct in the wild because its only source of food, the bamboo forests of Asia, is being cut down. Thousands of species of small land animals, insects, and plants are in danger of extinction because of the burning of Earth's tropical rain forests. Many of these forests are being cleared for the mining of gold and other minerals and for the grazing of livestock.

Some scientists believe that all organisms are on Earth for a limited time, after which better-adapted organisms take their place. Considering the way that humans have treated their home planet, you can't help wondering if we, by our own hand, are also destined for extinction.

1. Which word _least_ describes the author's attitude about how humans are treating other life forms on Earth?

(1) concerned
(2) disappointed
(3) proud
(4) upset
(5) interested

2. To which group below would the author most probably belong?

(1) a mining company
(2) a group protesting higher taxes
(3) a hunting club
(4) a group protesting government regulations
(5) an environmental protection group

3. What is the main point the author is trying to get across?

(1) Humans have no ability to control the natural disasters that cause extinction.
(2) Human actions can help save life on Earth or help destroy it.
(3) There is nothing humans can do to bring back extinct life forms.
(4) Most extinctions take place in tropical rain forests.
(5) If dinosaurs hadn't become extinct, they would rule Earth today.

ANSWERS ARE ON PAGE 302.

IDENTIFYING IMPLICATIONS IN GRAPHICS

When you identify an implication in a graphic, you're making a good guess at information that's not specifically given. In your study of science, you'll find that this skill is particularly useful when you work with line graphs.

SKILL BUILDER
Reading Line Graphs

A line graph shows information as points (often called ***data points***) that lie on a straight or curved line. This line of data points runs across the graph from left to right. A line graph contains both a labeled vertical axis (running up and down along the side of the graph) and a labeled horizontal axis (running across the bottom of the graph). Each data point on the line shows the relationship between two items of information, one taken from each axis. A line graph is especially useful in showing a trend.

The line graph above shows several temperature readings taken from a pan of water that was placed on a stove for 10 minutes. Each circle represents one data point—the water temperature after a certain time has passed.

As an example, the temperature of the water after 6 minutes is 60°Celsius (C). (Dotted lines have been drawn as a guide for your eyes.) To read this data point, first find the 6 minutes point on the horizontal axis. Next, move straight up from this point to the indicated data point. Now, from this data point move directly across to the vertical axis. The point you read on the vertical axis is about 60°C.

You can also find the temperature of the water after 6½ minutes even though there is no recorded data point at 6½ minutes. As the second pair of dotted lines show, you treat this point just as you would treat an actual data point. First you find the 6½ minutes point on the horizontal axis. Next, move straight up to a point on the data line—even though this point is not indicated by a circle. Then, read directly across to the temperature scale on the vertical axis. The temperature after 6½ minutes is about 70°C.

Now try identifying a point on the line.

About what temperature is the water when 7 minutes have passed? Your answer should be *80°C.*

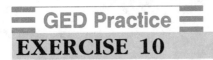

EXERCISE 10

Questions 1–3 refer to the following line graph.

TRAY OF WATER PLACED IN FREEZER

1. About what temperature is the water after 20 minutes have passed?

   (1) 48°F
   (2) 41°F
   (3) 35°F
   (4) 24°F
   (5) 15°F

2. About how long does it take the tray of water to reach a temperature of 32°F?

   (1) 10 minutes
   (2) 20 minutes
   (3) 28 minutes
   (4) 45 minutes
   (5) 55 minutes

3. After the tray had been in the freezer for 50 minutes, its contents would most probably be

   (1) all water at a temperature slightly above 32°F
   (2) all water at a temperature slightly below 32°F
   (3) partly water and partly ice, all at a temperature of 32°F
   (4) all ice at a temperature of 32°F
   (5) all ice at a temperature slightly above 32°F

ANSWERS ARE ON PAGE 303.

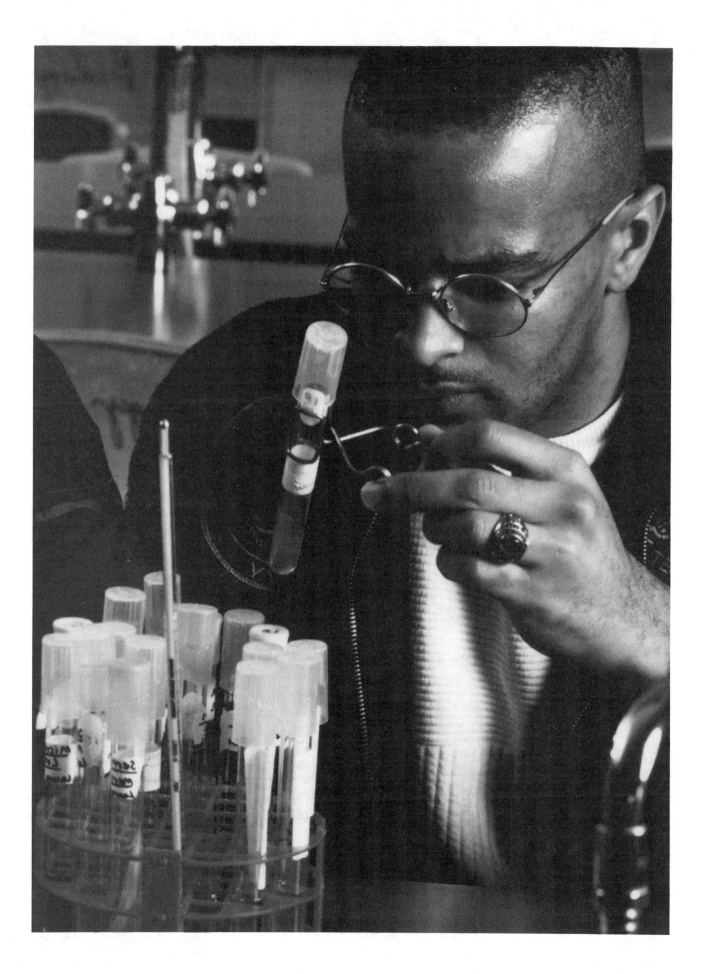

2 Applying Science Concepts

Much of what you learn is not learned purely for the sake of knowing something but for the purpose of applying that knowledge. For example, you read a first aid manual in order to help an injured or ill family member or friend. You read about bandaging a serious wound to stop it from bleeding, and you learn how to clear a person's airway to make sure he or she doesn't suffocate. The quick application of this knowledge can save a life.

On the GED Test, you'll be asked to apply knowledge to new situations. This application of reading skills is a measure of two abilities:

- the ability to apply given ideas in a new context
- the ability to apply remembered ideas in a new context

APPLYING GIVEN IDEAS

Many principles in science apply in a lot of different contexts (situations). One principle you might know about is often called ***stimulus-response***. According to this principle, an organism will respond in some way when acted on by a stimulus (something that can be felt, seen, heard, smelled). For example, if you hit your thumb with a hammer, you pull your thumb back and probably yell. Here, the act of hitting your thumb is the stimulus, and pulling your thumb back and yelling is the response.

Identify the stimulus and response in each of the next two examples:

a. A child throws a cracker into the pond, and several ducks quickly swim over to get the cracker.

Stimulus: _____

Response: _____

b. While driving, Julia hit the brakes after seeing a dog dart in front of her car.

Stimulus: _____

Response: _____

In example a, the stimulus is *the cracker hitting the water*, and the response is *the ducks swimming over*. In example b, the stimulus is *the dog darting in front of the car*, and the response is *Julia hitting the brakes*. Notice that the stimulus always occurs before the response, even if the response is described first in the sentence.

EXERCISE 1

Directions: Read the paragraphs below and do the exercise that follows.

Inherited traits are characteristics that are passed on from parents to children. For example, hair color is an inherited trait. Dark-haired parents are likely to have a dark-haired child.

Traits that are a result of changes you make yourself cannot be passed on. For example, if a dark-haired mother dyes her hair blond, *she* will have blond hair, but this characteristic cannot be passed on to any children she might have.

Check the following traits that most probably were inherited by children.

_____ **1.** Kani has pierced ears, just like her mother.

_____ **2.** Jeremy has blue eyes, the same color as both his mother's and father's.

_____ **3.** Joe and his parents go jogging every day, so Joe has developed strong leg muscles.

_____ **4.** Julius stands six feet nine inches tall, two inches taller than his father.

_____ **5.** When he turned thirty, Arnold noticed he was beginning to lose his hair, just as his father had at that age.

EXERCISE 2

Directions: Read the paragraph below and answer the questions that follow.

In a science class, you have learned that one general principle of science is that objects expand when they are heated and contract when they are cooled. A rock exposed to the weather will expand in high temperatures and contract in low temperatures. In fact, it is this expansion and contraction that causes many large rocks to crack and break apart.

Check each action below that is an application of the expansion/contraction principle.

_____ **1.** To help keep it from cracking, a sidewalk is made in sections, with a small space between sections.

_____ **2.** Richard noticed that the metal screen door on his house shuts more easily on a cold day than on a hot day.

_____ **3.** By wearing a white shirt on a hot summer day, Tu'ong kept cooler than he would have been had he worn a dark shirt.

_____ **4.** To open a "stuck" jar of jam, Emmy ran hot water over the metal lid.

_____ **5.** In order to save energy, Yoko replaced her 100-watt light bulbs with special 50-watt bulbs that gave off the same amount of light but didn't get as hot.

ANSWERS ARE ON PAGE 303.

EXERCISE 3

Questions 1 and 2 refer to the following passage.

The study of the development of different species of animals is filled with fascinating questions. One of the most interesting concerns the discovery of vestigial organs. A *vestigial organ* in an animal is an organ that seems to have no purpose.

An example of a vestigial organ is the presence of leg bones inside a snake. These small bones are absolutely useless to snakes that exist at the present time. One possible explanation of vestigial organs is that present-day animals evolved from ancestors who needed these organs. According to this idea, snakes inherited the genes that produce leg bones from some ancestral relative among ancient reptiles that did have legs.

1. Which of the following is true about a vestigial organ? A vestigial organ

   (1) is usually very large and easily identified
   (2) is not present in any life form today
   (3) is not passed down from one generation to the next
   (4) has only one use in the life form in which it is present
   (5) has no known use in the life form in which it is present

2. Which of the following is the best example of a vestigial organ?

   (1) a frog's spleen, an organ that helps destroy germs
   (2) the hoof of a horse, an organ to which a metal horseshoe is often attached
   (3) the tailbone of a human, a bone having no known use
   (4) the shell of a turtle, a heavy object the turtle must carry
   (5) eyes of a bat, an animal that flies mainly at night

Questions 3 and 4 refer to the following passage.

A sound wave causes the atoms and molecules of a substance to vibrate. By bumping into their neighbors, vibrating atoms and molecules transmit the sound wave throughout the entire substance. Sound waves cannot travel through outer space or any other space that does not contain air or some kind of matter.

The speed that sound travels depends on the density and temperature of a substance. Dense substances such as solids have a tightly packed structure and transmit sound at higher speeds. Substances at higher temperatures have faster-moving particles and also transmit sound at higher speeds. Loosely-packed substances such as cool gases transmit sound at slower speeds.

3. In which substance would you expect the speed of sound to be the greatest?

   (1) warm water at 120°F
   (2) a piece of iron at 212°F
   (3) boiling water at 212°F
   (4) a piece of iron at 120°F
   (5) a piece of wood at 212°F

4. At which location would sound waves *not* be present?

   (1) at the North Pole
   (2) high in Earth's atmosphere
   (3) deep in the Pacific Ocean
   (4) just above the clouded surface of Venus
   (5) in space, between Earth and the moon

ANSWERS ARE ON PAGE 303.

CLASSIFICATION QUESTIONS

One special use of application questions is with a passage that defines classes of things. The passage is followed by several questions that ask you to apply these definitions in new contexts.

When animals and plants live together in the same environment, such as a forest or a lake, special nutritional relationships develop among many of the different organisms. These relationships can be classified as follows:

predator-prey relationship—one organism kills and eats a second organism.

saprophytic relationship—an organism takes nutrients from the remains of dead organisms it finds.

parasitic relationship—one organism takes nutrients from the living body of another organism and, in doing so, may harm, but not kill, the other organism.

mutualistic relationship—organisms live together in a way that nutritionally benefits all of the organisms.

commensal relationship—one organism nutritionally benefits from a second organism, while the second organism neither benefits nor is harmed.

Compare the following relationship with the definitions above:

In a freshwater lake, bass live by eating minnows and small crustaceans.

What is the nutritional relationship of bass to minnows and small crustaceans? _____

You are correct if you answered *predator-prey.* One organism (the bass) kills and eats the other organisms (the minnows and small crustaceans).

Here is another example:

Many tiny lice can live on the body of a bird by slowly eating its feathers. Although lice damage the feathers, they do not kill the bird. However, the bird does not benefit in any way from this relationship.

What is the relationship of the lice to the bird? _____

To answer this question, notice that the bird is harmed but not killed by the lice. You can rule out predator-prey, saprophytic, and commensal as possible answers. Also, since the bird does not benefit from the relationship, mutualistic is not a possible answer either. You are left with *parasitic* as the correct answer. The lice do take nutrients from part of the body of a living bird and do harm—but not kill—the bird.

EXERCISE 4

Questions 1–5 refer to the definitions on page 36.

1. As uninvited guests, small beetles often live in the nest of an ant colony, helping themselves to food supplies built up by the ants. During a prosperous season, when the portion taken by the beetles is not missed, the relationship of beetles to ants is best classified as

   (1) predator-prey
   (2) saprophytic
   (3) parasitic
   (4) mutualistic
   (5) commensal

2. A fungus causes the disease chestnut blight in the native American chestnut tree. This fungus takes nutrients from the tree and damages plant tissue on any part of the tree on which it grows. Fortunately, chestnut trees usually do not die from this disease. The relationship of the chestnut-blight fungus to the chestnut tree is best classified as

   (1) predator-prey
   (2) saprophytic
   (3) parasitic
   (4) mutualistic
   (5) commensal

3. Decay bacteria play an important role in bringing nitrogen, needed for plant growth, back into the soil. These bacteria take nutrients from plant and animal remains, break down the proteins, and release ammonia, a nitrogen compound, into the soil. The relationship of decay bacteria to dead plants and animals is called

   (1) predator-prey
   (2) saprophytic
   (3) parasitic
   (4) mutualistic
   (5) commensal

4. While a herd of gazelle graze close by, a solitary lioness lies quietly in the grass. With a powerful but graceful lunge, the lioness brings down a gazelle that strays too far from the herd. The gazelle provides needed meat for the lioness and its cubs. The relationship of lioness to gazelle is known as

   (1) predator-prey
   (2) saprophytic
   (3) parasitic
   (4) mutualistic
   (5) commensal

5. Some algae live in such close association with a fungus that the two plants together are given the name *lichen*. In a lichen, the fungus captures moisture for the algae and provides a protective skinlike covering. The algae produce the food necessary to support the life of both plants. The relationship of fungus to algae in a lichen is best classified as

   (1) predator-prey
   (2) saprophytic
   (3) parasitic
   (4) mutualistic
   (5) commensal

ANSWERS ARE ON PAGE 303.

APPLYING REMEMBERED IDEAS

Some of the questions on the GED Science Test will draw on knowledge you might have from experience or reading. Below is an example of this type of question. Read it carefully and choose the most reasonable answer.

An animal's color may be related to its need for

(a) absorption of sunlight
(b) protection from predators
(c) easy identification

You are correct if you chose (b) as your answer. A general principle of science is that animals adapt to their environment in a way that gives them the best chance of survival. If an animal's coloring matches its environment, it is less likely to be seen by a predator.

Both in this book and on the GED Test, you may sometimes find that you are just not familiar with the principle or example. Remember that you will learn a lot of background information in science as you read this book. If you see a question you're unable to answer, make the most reasonable guess you can and then move on to the next question.

EXERCISE 5

Directions: Both questions below require that you apply a remembered idea in one way or another. Choose the best answer for each question.

1. In the autumn of each year, ducks and geese gather in huge flocks and begin a long journey to a warmer climate before winter begins. This annual journey is for the purpose of

   (1) escaping from natural predators
   (2) leaving before bird hunters begin the fall hunt
   (3) finding food or going to a mating area
   (4) exercise
   (5) teaching the young how to fly

2. Erosion is the wearing away of land formations by the actions of nature. Which of the following is *not* one of the causes of erosion of the Rocky Mountains?

   (1) the action of rain water
   (2) the action of wind
   (3) the action of the tides
   (4) the action of rivers and streams
   (5) the action of seasonal temperature changes

ANSWERS ARE ON PAGE 303.

EXERCISE 6

Choose the best answer for each question below.

1. In a recent magazine advertisement, a national corporation made these statements:

   A. Nuclear power is safe, clean, and efficient.
   B. Nuclear power is now America's second most important power source.
   C. Fuel for nuclear power plants is almost unlimited.

   What serious disadvantage of nuclear power plants does this "pro-nuclear" advertisement fail to point out?

   (1) A nuclear power plant requires a large plot of valuable land for its development.
   (2) Nuclear power plants produce a deadly form of radioactive waste that can't be disposed of safely.
   (3) Nuclear power plants use steam-driven turbines to turn electric generators.
   (4) The energy produced by a nuclear power plant comes from the splitting of atoms.
   (5) Certain religious groups oppose the use of electricity, whatever the type of power plant that's used to produce it.

2. Which of the following is *not* an effort to reduce the amount of air pollution to which the general public is exposed?

   (1) developing efficient engines that use unleaded fuel
   (2) inventing emission control devices that limit exhaust pollutants from automobiles
   (3) restricting the number of hours allowed each day for using wood stoves in certain areas of the country
   (4) reducing the amount of money spent on the problem of acid rain in order to cut down on government spending
   (5) limiting the spraying of pesticides near residential areas

3. Space flight is one of the most exciting and risky adventures undertaken by science in the last half of the twentieth century. What has proved to be the main danger of space flight to astronauts?

   (1) the high cost of each space mission
   (2) an explosion of rocket fuel
   (3) the possibility of getting lost
   (4) serious illness while in space
   (5) the long training to become an astronaut

4. Viruses that cause the common cold can survive several hours outside the human body. When you have a cold, each of the following is a way to help avoid spreading cold viruses *except*

   (1) covering your mouth when you cough
   (2) sneezing into a tissue
   (3) dressing extra warmly
   (4) keeping your hands clean
   (5) avoiding getting too close to others

5. When treating a person who accidentally swallowed liquid from a bottle marked "poison," a doctor would need to know each of the following *except*

   (1) the amount of liquid swallowed
   (2) the chemical makeup of the liquid
   (3) the time the liquid was swallowed
   (4) whether the person had eaten or drunk anything since swallowing the liquid
   (5) where the liquid was purchased

ANSWERS ARE ON PAGE 303.

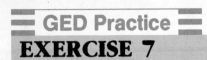

EXERCISE 7

Questions 1–4 refer to the following diagram.

HUMAN TEETH AND THEIR USES

incisors— for biting off pieces

canine — for cutting or tearing

molars — for hard chewing or for grinding

premolars — for light chewing

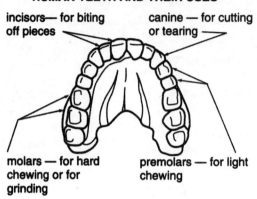

1. Which teeth would you use the most in chewing a cut piece of steak before swallowing?

    (1) incisors
    (2) canines
    (3) molars
    (4) both incisors and canines
    (5) both incisors and premolars

2. Which teeth would you be most apt to use to bite off a piece of chicken from a drumstick?

    (1) incisors
    (2) canines
    (3) premolars
    (4) molars
    (5) both premolars and molars

3. Which teeth are you most likely to use for the purpose of cutting a string into two pieces?

    (1) incisors
    (2) canines
    (3) premolars
    (4) molars
    (5) both premolars and molars

4. Which teeth are most likely to be the hardest to clean while brushing?

    (1) incisors
    (2) canines
    (3) premolars
    (4) molars
    (5) incisors and canines

Questions 5–8 refer to the following diagram.

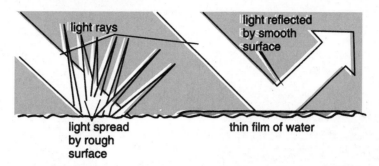

light rays

light reflected by smooth surface

light spread by rough surface

thin film of water

5. In which case are you most likely to see light reflecting off a thin film of water?

(1) taking a bath
(2) driving on a wet highway
(3) swimming in a pool
(4) walking in the rain
(5) hiking on a mountain

6. Another substance with reflective properties similar to a thin film of water is

(1) sandpaper
(2) wood stain
(3) laundry soap
(4) furniture polish
(5) candle wax

7. The property that the surface of a pane of glass and a thin film of water have in common is their

(1) color
(2) weight
(3) smoothness
(4) roughness
(5) temperature

8. In order for a room to reflect as much ceiling and lamplight as possible into all directions, the finishing texture should be

(1) smooth on both the ceiling and walls
(2) rough on the ceiling but smooth on the walls
(3) rough on both the ceiling and walls
(4) smooth on the ceiling but rough on the walls
(5) rough on the ceiling and two walls, smooth on two walls

ANSWERS ARE ON PAGE 303.

3 Analyzing Science Materials

When you analyze something, you look at all of its parts in order to get a better understanding of the whole. On the GED Science Test, you will be tested on your ability to analyze a passage or illustration in four ways:

- distinguishing facts from hypotheses and opinions
- recognizing unstated assumptions
- identifying cause-and-effect relationships
- distinguishing a conclusion from supporting statements

DISTINGUISHING FACTS FROM HYPOTHESES

To begin this section, become familiar with the following definitions:

- A scientific *fact* is a statement, based on evidence, that scientists can agree on. For example, it is a scientific fact, based on geological evidence, that dinosaurs became extinct about 70 million years ago.

- A *hypothesis*, on the other hand, is a reasonable explanation of a scientific fact. Some scientists hypothesize that the dinosaurs became extinct because of the sudden occurrence of an ice age.

- An *opinion* is a personal belief that is often based on a person's own feelings of the way things should be. As an example, a person may have the opinion that the study of dinosaurs is a waste of time and taxpayers' money.

Try classifying each of the following as fact, hypothesis, or opinion. Write *F*, *H*, or *O* on the line before each statement.

_____ **a.** Although any person can lose his or her hair, baldness is much more common in men than in women.

_____ **b.** Because of superior intelligence, human beings are the most important animals that have ever lived.

_____ **c.** The reason that human beings and other primates show genetic and physical similarities may be that each evolved from a common ancestor millions of years ago.

Statement a is a *fact*. Statement b is an *opinion*. Statement c is a *hypothesis* that gives a possible explanation for an observed fact.

EXERCISE 1

Directions: Write *F*, *H*, or *O* on the line preceding each statement below to classify the statement as a fact, hypothesis, or opinion.

_____ **1.** Because many people are frightened by snakes, there should never be an effort to save any species of snake.

_____ **2.** Moonlight is actually light from the sun that is reflected off the moon's surface.

_____ **3.** The reason that moon rocks are similar to Earth rocks may be that the moon and Earth were once part of the same cloud of matter in space.

_____ **4.** During winter months, tree roots store food that is used by the plant as it grows new leaves and stems in the spring.

_____ **5.** Regardless of what chemists claim, vitamins produced in a laboratory can't possibly be as healthful as vitamins naturally found in foods.

_____ **6.** The reason that one person is often so strongly attracted to a second person may be smell rather than good looks or personality.

_____ **7.** Air pollution is a negative by-product of the Industrial Revolution.

EXERCISE 2

Directions: A passage may contain facts, hypotheses, and opinions. As you read the passage below, try your skill at identifying each. On the lines below, write a fact, hypothesis, and opinion found in the passage.

Can a computer be made to think? This is the question being asked by artificial intelligence researchers around the country. Although even home computers can do thousands of routine calculations each second, it is not known whether a computer can ever be designed that will actually think for itself. In support of the idea, some scientists suggest that a computer is already similar to the human brain. Based on their observations, these scientists believe that the human mind stores and sorts information in the same way a computer does. What's more, they point out, a thinking computer would be a great benefit to our society. One use, for example, would be to provide companionship to lonely people!

1. Fact: _____

_____

2. Hypothesis: _____

_____

3. Opinion: _____

_____

ANSWERS ARE ON PAGE 303.

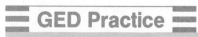
EXERCISE 3

Questions 1–3 refer to the following passage.

Before the year 2000, biologists and chemists may develop vaccines that can rid Earth of many diseases we now have.

A vaccine is used to prevent a disease, not to cure it. A *vaccine* is a dose of a germ that is enough to trigger your immune system into action but not enough to make you sick. For example, a flu vaccine consists of a small dose of flu virus. Once this vaccine is taken, your body responds by making antibodies, a form of protein that acts as a virus fighter. These antibodies prevent more of the same flu virus from entering and attacking cells in your body.

Vaccines that have been very successful are the DPT vaccine that has all but eliminated the three long-feared childhood diseases—diphtheria, tetanus, and pertussis (commonly known as whooping cough)—and vaccines for pneumonia, influenza, polio, measles, mumps, German measles, and smallpox. The effectiveness of vaccines is most obvious when parents fail to have their children immunized at proper times. When this happens, the number of children stricken with polio and other diseases once again rises.

Although vaccines are usually safe, there is an element of risk. A small number of people who take a vaccine actually get the disease itself. For example, it is estimated that one child in 310,000 who takes the DPT vaccine will become ill and suffer brain damage. Yet, without the DPT vaccine it is claimed that the incidence of death due to whooping cough would be nineteen times higher than it is now and the incidence of brain damage would be four times as high. Because of the potential danger of vaccines, medical research in studies of vaccine safety is continuing. Parents are advised to check with their own doctor or with a local health clinic to see which vaccines are appropriate for their children.

1. Which of the following is a fact that the author could prove by citing scientific evidence?

(1) Most diseases caused by viruses will someday be curable by vaccines.
(2) By the year 2000, scientists will discover a vaccine that will prevent all cancers.
(3) The beneficial effect of a vaccine occurs because of the production of a person's own antibodies.
(4) A vaccine is made up of antibodies designed to fight viruses and bacteria.
(5) A flu virus prevents a person who has the flu from being able to infect other people.

2. Which of the following is a hypothesis based on the passage?

(1) A vaccine is a dose of a germ that triggers your immune system into action.
(2) Someday vaccines will be invented that can cure diseases as well as prevent them.
(3) About one child in every 310,000 that takes the DPT vaccine will be made ill by it.
(4) Without vaccines, civilization could not survive another 1,000 years.
(5) The decrease in childhood diseases during this century has most likely resulted from the use of vaccines.

3. Which of the following is an opinion that can neither be proved nor disproved with evidence?

(1) Vaccines have been very successful in preventing many diseases caused by viruses and bacteria.
(2) Because of the risk, all vaccinations should be halted until vaccines can be perfected.
(3) Many cancers are believed to be caused by viruses, and work is being done on possible types of cancer vaccines.
(4) The success of vaccines has been due to the work of chemists involved in medical research.
(5) By failing to get their children vaccinated as directed by their doctor, parents risk the health of their children.

ANSWERS ARE ON PAGE 304.

FACTS, HYPOTHESES, AND OPINIONS IN GRAPHICS

Questions about facts, hypotheses, and opinions may also be asked about information presented in graphics. Following the Skill Builder, we'll discuss how these types of questions may apply to information on bar graphs.

SKILL BUILDER
Reading Bar Graphs

A **bar graph** gets its name from the bars it uses to present information. The bars may run horizontally (from left to right) or vertically (up and down). In each type of bar graph, a bar represents a value that is determined by two things: (1) the length (or height) of the bar, and (2) the bar's position along an axis.

As an example, look at the horizontal bar graph below.

CALORIE USAGE PER HOUR PER ACTIVITY

The length of the bar indicates the number of calories used per hour—a value that is read on the horizontal axis directly below the end of the bar. For example, find the end of the bar labeled "Walking" and look straight down. You'll see that walking uses about 200 calories per hour.

Now label the following as fact, opinion, or hypothesis.

_____ **a.** Moderate work uses fewer calories than fast running.

_____ **b.** Exercises that use more calories are more fun than exercises that use fewer calories.

_____ **c.** Some people feel better when they exercise because exercise uses up calories that might otherwise be used for an unhealthy activity such as too much worrying.

Statement a is a *fact* based on the graph. Statement b is an *opinion*. The bar graph can't give any information about comparative fun. Statement c is a *hypothesis* because it is a possible explanation of an observed fact.

≡ GED Practice ≡
EXERCISE 4

Questions 1–3 refer to the vertical bar graph below.

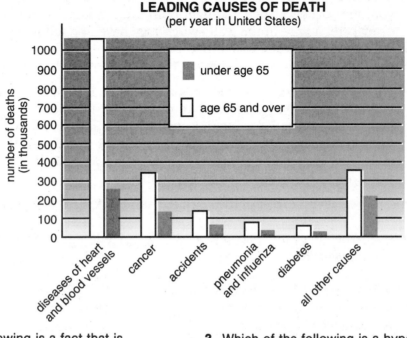

LEADING CAUSES OF DEATH
(per year in United States)

1. Which of the following is a fact that is supported by information given by the graph?

   (1) For people under age 65, accidents are the leading cause of death.
   (2) Cancer is the second-leading single cause of death in people age 65 and older.
   (3) Diabetes is responsible for more deaths in all age groups than are pneumonia and influenza.
   (4) Most people suffering from cancer are hospitalized unnecessarily.
   (5) More money is spent on heart disease research than on any other area of medical study.

2. Which of the following is an opinion?

   (1) Cancer is the most feared of all diseases.
   (2) The average hospital stay for cancer is longer than the average hospital stay for heart disease.
   (3) The cost of heart transplant operations is now being covered by some insurance companies.
   (4) Many terminally ill patients are encouraged to spend their remaining time at home with family members when possible.
   (5) In schools where there is accident prevention instruction, accidental student deaths have been reduced.

3. Which of the following is a hypothesis?

   (1) The cure rate for certain types of cancer has increased by more than 50 percent during the last twenty-five years.
   (2) Recent evidence suggests that heart disease is on the decrease.
   (3) Drunk drivers are responsible for more than half of all highway accident deaths.
   (4) The American diet, high in fat and sugar, is very possibly the main reason why so many Americans die from heart problems.
   (5) By the year 2000, heart disease will no longer be the leading cause of death in the United States.

ANSWERS ARE ON PAGE 304.

UNSTATED ASSUMPTIONS

When you make an *assumption*, you act as if something is true without checking to see if you're right. For example, when a light goes out in a room, you immediately change the light bulb even though the problem could be elsewhere. A wire in the wall switch may have popped loose, or the light socket itself may be broken. But, because the problem is most often a burned out light bulb, we all assume that the bulb needs to be changed.

When you read a science passage, it is important to be aware of the author's unstated assumptions. An unstated assumption is something the writer just seems to take for granted. It may even be an idea the writer just didn't think of. Other times it may be a point of view that the writer wants you to take. This is a technique used by salespeople, by politicians, and by others who want you to believe and act in a certain way.

See if you can spot the unstated assumption in the statement below.

When the world's supply of oil runs out, automobile use will decrease drastically.

What unstated assumption is the author making? The writer is assuming that *scientists will not be able to find an energy source for automobiles other than the gasoline we now use.*

EXERCISE 5

Directions: In the space following each passage below, answer the question by identifying the unstated assumption indicated by the writer.

1. When life is discovered on another planet, its form will be much different from any of the life forms on Earth.

   What is the writer assuming about other planets? _____

   _____

2. An astronaut stated, "Manned space travel is absolutely necessary if we are to learn about the planets outside of our own solar system."

   What assumption is the astronaut making about information obtained from

   unmanned space travel? _____

3. To make ice in her freezer as quickly as possible, Rhoda first ran the tap water until it was as cold as she could get it. She then placed a tray full of this cold tap water into the freezer.

   What assumption is Rhoda making about the fastest way to make ice? _____

   _____

4. Most people take aspirin for a headache or take other medicinal drugs for specific purposes.

What assumption are they making about these drugs?

_____

_____

5. Doctors recommend that pregnant women do not take any medication of any kind unless specifically advised by a doctor. This includes common drugs such as aspirin, cold medicine, allergy medicine, and so on.

Upon what unstated assumption do doctors base this recommendation? _____

_____

6. Astrology, though not a real science, did help advance the early study of astronomy. Astrologers predict the future by looking at the position of the stars and planets. This is commonly called reading a person's horoscope.

What is an unstated assumption made by astrologers? _____

_____

EXERCISE 6

Directions: Read the passage below and do the exercise that follows.

While taking an afternoon hike up a mountain trail, Jerry and DeShawn had a strange encounter with bees. On the way up the mountain, several bees were always buzzing around Jerry but not around DeShawn. To see what would happen, Jerry and DeShawn switched shirts for the walk back down. Jerry gave his orange shirt to DeShawn, and Jerry wore DeShawn's brown shirt. Interestingly, on the way down the mountain, several bees now buzzed around DeShawn but not around Jerry. Jerry concluded that bees are attracted to the color orange but not to the color brown.

Place a check before each statement below that is an unstated assumption that Jerry has made in reaching his conclusion.

_____ **1.** Bees can distinguish one color from another.

_____ **2.** The bees buzzed around Jerry on the way up the mountain and around DeShawn on the way down.

_____ **3.** Jerry and DeShawn switched shirts at the top of the mountain.

_____ **4.** It was the color of the shirt and not something else such as shape or smell that attracted the bees.

_____ **5.** Bees have a very good sense of smell.

ANSWERS ARE ON PAGE 304.

GED Practice
EXERCISE 7

Questions 1–3 refer to the following passage.

When scientists first developed nuclear power, it was hailed as the energy source of the future. People saw only the positive side of its use: an inexpensive, almost inexhaustible source of energy. Little was said about the radioactive waste that nuclear power plants produce.

Today, the nuclear waste issue is one of the most serious issues of our time. Scientists still know of no way to safely dispose of radioactive waste. If this waste gets into the air or into our drinking water, it could cause cancer, genetic mutations, and death. Therefore, nuclear waste must be stored for the thousands of years that it remains harmful to life. Storage sites must be watched carefully to guard against contamination of the atmosphere and of the groundwater and to guard against the possibility of terrorism. Many communities have resisted the building of storage sites in their area, so it is becoming difficult to find places to store nuclear waste. A growing number of scientists and other citizens are demanding that no more nuclear power plants be built.

1. An unstated assumption made by those who favor further development of nuclear power is that

    (1) the demand for electrical energy will decrease in the future due to more efficient consumer products
    (2) nuclear power companies are more concerned about radioactive waste than the general public is
    (3) scientists will someday invent safe methods of disposal of radioactive waste
    (4) nuclear power plants do not produce radioactive waste
    (5) scientists who don't work in the nuclear industry are only trying to scare the public

2. Which of the following was most likely true when nuclear power was first developed?

    (1) Scientists did not realize how difficult and dangerous it would be to store radioactive waste.
    (2) Scientists did not know that radioactive waste was dangerous to human life.
    (3) Scientists did not know that nuclear power plants would create radioactive waste.
    (4) Scientists believed that no one would discover the danger of the radioactive waste.
    (5) Scientists believed that safe storage facilities would be created before the public found out about the dangers of radioactive waste.

3. Which assumptions are most likely made by those who favor shutting down nuclear power plants in the United States?

    A. Shutting down nuclear power plants will permanently put thousands of people out of work.
    B. Public officials will act to shut down nuclear power plants if enough people demand it.
    C. Nuclear power provides only a small part of the energy used in the United States.
    D. There is already a dangerous amount of radioactive waste in temporary storage sites in the United States.

    (1) A and B only
    (2) A, B, and C only
    (3) B and C only
    (4) B and D only
    (5) B, C, and D only

ANSWERS ARE ON PAGE 304.

IDENTIFYING CAUSE AND EFFECT

On the evening news we hear that an earthquake in southern California caused extensive damage to nearby cities and towns. During the next few weeks, we hear that frightened residents now demand that earthquake-proof buildings be built to replace those destroyed by the quake.

The earthquake and the later demands by the citizens are a good example of a cause-and-effect relationship. In this type of relationship, you can identify an event (the *effect*) with the condition (the *cause*) that made the event occur. In the example above, the cause is the earthquake and the effect is the action taken by the citizens.

In many cases, one cause leads to an effect that then itself becomes the cause of a second effect, and so on. This is called a chain of causes and effects. Below is listed a chain of causes and effects that might be started by an earthquake.

CAUSE	EFFECT
Earthquake	Damaged buildings
Damaged buildings	Action taken by citizens
Action taken by citizens	New building codes
New building codes	Safer buildings

On the line provided, write an effect that might result from the construction of safer buildings.

CAUSE	EFFECT
Safer buildings	_____

Several answers are possible. Here are two of them: (1) *citizens feel safer*, and (2) *the new buildings don't get destroyed in the next earthquake.*

In any chain of events, a cause always occurs before the effect. It is important to remember this because a passage may mention the effect first. Look at this sentence:

> Jimmy had several fillings before he was six years old because he ate too much candy and did not brush his teeth daily.

See if you can identify the two causes that lead to a single effect.

CAUSE	EFFECT
_____	_____
_____	

As you probably wrote, the two causes are Jimmy's *eating too much candy* and his *failure to brush his teeth*. The effect is that *he needed work done on his teeth*.

EXERCISE 8

Directions: Read the passage below and do the exercise that follows.

During times of unexpected stress or fright, the human body reacts in a most protective, amazing way. First, the adrenal glands give off into your bloodstream two hormones, adrenaline and noradrenaline. These adrenal hormones can give you extra strength and endurance. When you get a "rush of adrenaline," you might experience some of these changes:

- Your heart beats faster.

- The pupils of your eyes dilate (become wider).

- The liver releases stored sugar, so there is an increased energy supply to the muscles.

- Digestive processes slow down.

- The blood vessels near the surface of your skin constrict (become more narrow), slowing the bleeding of any surface wounds and causing a greater flow of blood to the muscles, brain, and heart.

- The bronchial tubes in your lungs dilate, increasing the rate at which you're able to absorb oxygen.

Because your adrenal glands have this effect, they are often called the glands of "fight or flight." This refers to the fact that a surprised, scared animal will usually flee if given the chance but will fight if it has no choice. The adrenal hormones prepare the animal for either course of action.

Match each effect listed in the column on the right with its cause listed on the left. Write the correct letter in the space before each number.

Cause

_____ **1.** unexpected stress or fright

_____ **2.** adrenal hormones in blood

_____ **3.** dilation of bronchial tubes

_____ **4.** release of stored sugar by liver

_____ **5.** constriction of surface blood vessels

Effect

(a) increased muscle energy

(b) increased absorption of oxygen

(c) the adrenal glands give off two adrenal hormones

(d) increased blood flow to the heart

(e) increased heart rate

ANSWERS ARE ON PAGE 304.

EXERCISE 9

Directions: Read the passage below and answer the questions that follow.

One of the unique features of Earth, "the blue planet," is the presence of liquid water on its surface. The temperature at Earth's surface makes this possible. If Earth were much hotter, the oceans would evaporate and water would be found only as a gas in the atmosphere. If Earth were much colder, the oceans would freeze and remain as an ice blanket.

According to the passage, what effect would follow each of these occurrences?

1. A great increase in Earth's average temperature

_____

2. A great decrease in Earth's average temperature

_____

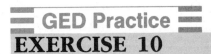

EXERCISE 10

Questions 1–3 refer to the following passage.

The Mesozoic era, called the Age of the Reptiles, began about 225 million years ago. During this era, the giant reptiles called *dinosaurs*—from the Greek words meaning "terrible lizard"—roamed Earth. For over 150 million years, these wondrous and feared creatures dominated all other life forms. Then, about 70 million years ago, the dinosaurs suddenly disappeared. In fact, the only reptiles that survived this period were the ones we today know as snakes, lizards, turtles, and crocodiles.

The reason for the dinosaurs' extinction remains one of the strangest mysteries in science. According to one popular theory, Earth collided with a large asteroid or comet from space. This collision kicked a lot of dirt up into the atmosphere. With only a little sunlight able to get through the darkened atmosphere, the temperature of Earth's surface rapidly decreased. Before long, possibly only a few months, the whole Earth froze, and an ice age began. All tropical forests quickly died, as did all of the animals, such as the dinosaurs, that depended on the lush vegetation for their survival.

With the disappearance of the dinosaurs, another animal form became dominant. This next era, called the Age of the Mammals, is the one we're still in.

1. One effect of an ice age, mentioned in the passage, would be

(1) the beginning of the Mesozoic era
(2) a drop in temperature at Earth's surface
(3) a collision between Earth and a comet
(4) the emergence of mammals
(5) the death of tropical forests

2. According to the passage, a cause of the end of the Mesozoic era could have been

(1) the disappearance of dinosaurs from Earth
(2) the sudden occurrence of an ice age
(3) the survival of snakes, lizards, and turtles
(4) the beginning of the Age of the Mammals
(5) the rise of humans as a dominant life form

3. According to the theory presented in the passage, what exactly was the cause of the dinosaurs' death?

(1) the collision of Earth with an object from space
(2) the emergence of mammals
(3) the extremely low temperature of the air
(4) the disappearance of their food supply
(5) the lack of sunlight by which to see

ANSWERS ARE ON PAGE 304.

IDENTIFYING CAUSE AND EFFECT IN GRAPHICS

A cause-and-effect relationship might be indicated in a graphic as illustrated below. These pictures show two orientations of an outdoor plant at two different times of the day and the position of the sun in the sky at each of these times.

The illustration at right shows a cause-and-effect property of plants known as **phototropism**, the movement and growth of plants toward a source of light. As shown here, the movement of the sun (the cause) is followed by the movement of the plant (the effect).

10:00 A.M.   4:00 P.M.

EXERCISE 11

Directions: The drawings below show the steps of cavity formation in a tooth. Study the drawings and then complete the exercise that follows.

Leftover food particles lead to plaque on tooth.

Bacteria grow in plaque and eat tooth enamel.

Cavity forms.

Cavity grows and exposes nerves in tooth.

Toothache felt.

Bacterial infection reaches tooth root.

Abscess occurs.

Use the information pictured above to fill in the causes in the blanks below.

Cause

1. _____

2. _____

3. _____

4. _____

Effect

Food particles are left on tooth.

A cavity forms in the outer layer (the enamel) of the tooth.

A toothache occurs.

Tooth abscess (swollen inflammation) occurs.

ANSWERS ARE ON PAGE 304.

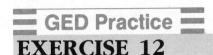

EXERCISE 12

Questions 1–4 refer to the following diagram.

SOLAR HEATING SYSTEM

Sun's rays

solar panel, mounted on roof

heated air

coiled tubes inside solar panel

fluid pump

heated fluid

heat exchange

cooled fluid

heat storage device

1. Which statement best describes what takes place in the solar heating system?

   (1) Heat exchangers produce heat that is used to heat a house and a solar panel.
   (2) A heat storage device is used to heat a solar panel.
   (3) Energy from the sun warms a fluid that is circulating in the heating system.
   (4) Pumps heat a fluid which circulates through both a solar panel and several heat exchangers.
   (5) The solar panel acts as an air conditioner by removing heated air from a house.

2. If fluid stops circulating through the system on a cold day, the most likely cause is

   (1) a lack of sunshine
   (2) a faulty pump
   (3) a closed air vent
   (4) the presence of another heat source
   (5) a cold heat storage device

3. The purpose of the heat exchanger is to

   (1) warm the house by transferring heat from the fluid to the air around the heat exchanger
   (2) cause the fluid to circulate through the heating system
   (3) capture the sun's energy and heat the circulating fluid
   (4) store heat for later use
   (5) measure the temperature in the house

4. The most likely purpose of the heat storage device is to

   (1) store heat in case the system breaks down
   (2) remove excess heat from the fluid so that the house does not get too hot
   (3) provide a source of heat to warm the fluid at night
   (4) provide a source of heat during winter months when the sun doesn't shine
   (5) serve as a source of extra fluid in case the system develops a leak

ANSWERS ARE ON PAGE 304.

DRAWING CONCLUSIONS

You know that the directions on a map, read clockwise, are north, east, south, and west. If a map is oriented so that the top is pointing toward north, what direction will be to the left side?

You know that the answer to this question is *west*. You correctly conclude this from the detail given in the question that tells you north is at the top. You can also conclude that south is at the bottom and east is at the right.

Answering the above question is an example of drawing a conclusion from details. When you ***draw a conclusion***, you express an unstated idea that is logically connected to the information you are given.

What conclusion can you draw from the following passage?

> Fossils are the hardened remains or traces of any plant or animal that lived in previous times. Many fossils have been found in the layers of sedimentary rock that make up the cliff faces of the Grand Canyon. Some of the 200-million-year-old rocks contain predominantly fossils of reptiles; the 400-million-year-old rocks contain mainly fossils of fishlike animals; and the even older rocks contain only the fossils of worms.

Check each statement below that is a conclusion that can be drawn from the details given in the passage.

_____ **a.** Ancient fishlike animals fed on worms and were themselves devoured by reptiles.

_____ **b.** Each geological time period is characterized by the types of life forms that predominated during that period.

_____ **c.** Only the remains of small animals are preserved in fossils.

Only statement b is a conclusion you can draw from this passage. Fossil evidence allows you to conclude that different types of animals predominated during widely separated time periods. However, this evidence does not allow you to conclude that either statement a or statement c is true. Statement a is an interesting hypothesis but not a conclusion that can be drawn. The passage doesn't give any information about the diets of different animal forms. Statement c is not true and could not be concluded from the passage. The passage does not describe the sizes of the fossils.

EXERCISE 13

Directions: Read the following paragraph. Then read the statements that follow. Check the statements that are conclusions that can be drawn from the details given in the paragraph.

Smoking during pregnancy is known to affect fetal development. Babies born to mothers who smoke have lower average birth weights and have a higher probability of being born with a lung illness or a birth defect. Also, more miscarriages and stillbirths occur in babies whose mothers smoked during pregnancy.

_____ **1.** To do everything that she can to ensure a healthy baby, a woman should not smoke during pregnancy.

_____ **2.** A child born to a mother who smokes will also have a dependency on cigarettes.

_____ **3.** Women who smoke during pregnancy are likely to suffer more morning sickness than nonsmokers.

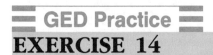

EXERCISE 14

Questions 1 and 2 refer to the following two passages.

Electricity and water can be a deadly combination. Making contact with an electric current while standing in water, on wet ground, or on a wet floor can cause serious injury or death. Contact with an electric current occurs when you touch an exposed electric wire. It can also occur when an electric appliance shorts out (has some kind of an electrical breakdown inside). You can be injured when the electric current flows from the point of contact through your body and out to the ground by passing through the wet surface.

1. From the information given in the passage, you can conclude that a good safety rule to follow is

   (1) always wear dry shoes inside your house
   (2) turn off all electrical appliances when it's raining
   (3) don't use an electrical product when you're in contact with a wet floor or any other source of water
   (4) don't take a bath or shower when the television is on
   (5) don't use a hair dryer after you shower or bathe

For any substance to burn in air, oxygen gas must be present. Without oxygen, a flame will simply go out. For example, when Erin's science class placed a burning candle in a jar and then placed a lid on the jar, the candle burned for only thirty-five seconds, and then the flame died out.

2. From this observation it is reasonable to conclude that

   (1) an open jar contains less oxygen than a closed jar
   (2) if the space above a candle flame is blocked, the candle cannot burn for more than thirty-five seconds
   (3) a shorter candle would burn for more than thirty-five seconds before going out
   (4) a candle will not stay lit in a jar either open or closed
   (5) in thirty-five seconds, a candle flame uses up all the oxygen in the jar

ANSWERS ARE ON PAGE 305.

DRAWING A CONCLUSION FROM A GRAPHIC

To draw a conclusion from a graphic, you express an idea that follows from the graphic itself. This skill is particularly useful for reading a table or chart.

Below is a nutrition chart for six-ounce servings of different foods.

NUTRITIONAL INFORMATION FOR SIX-OUNCE SERVINGS OF FOOD				
	Calories	Protein (grams)	Fat (grams)	Carbohydrates (grams)
Chicken				
light meat	191	36	4	0
dark meat	203	32	7.3	0
Ham	637	39	52.13	0
Round steak	443	49	26	0
Broccoli	44	5.3	0.5	7.6
Corn	58	2	0.7	13.4
Tofu (soy bean curd)	61	6.8	3.6	2.1
Apples	70	0.3	0.7	17.6
Pears	106	1.2	0.7	26.7

To read a value from the chart, find the row (or column) of the item you're interested in and then read across (or up and down) and stop at the appropriate point. For example, to find the number of calories in a six-ounce serving of ham, you would go to the row labeled *Ham* and look across to the column labeled *Calories*. As you can see from the shading, there are 637 calories in a six-ounce serving of ham.

Now try reading the chart in order to answer the following questions:

a. How many grams of protein are in a six-ounce serving of round steak? _____

b. How many grams of carbohydrates are in a six-ounce apple? _____

c. Which type of meat contains 7.3 grams of fat in a six-ounce serving? _____

To answer question a, find the row labeled *Round steak* and then read over to the column labeled *Protein*. The answer is *49*.

By following the same method, you can see that the answer to question b is *17.6*. To find answer c, look at the column labeled *Fat*. Next, read down the column until you come to the number 7.3. You'll find that 7.3 is in the row labeled *dark meat* (under chicken).

d. What can you conclude about the fat content of meat compared to the fat content of fruit? _____

e. Which type of food (meat, vegetables, or fruit) contains the highest percentage of carbohydrates? _____

f. What conclusion can you draw about the calorie content of fat? _____

_____

Answer d is that *meat has a much higher fat content than fruit*. Answer e is *fruit*. Answer f is that *fat is very high in calories*.

EXERCISE 15

Directions: The Beaufort scale below is used to measure wind force. Answer each question by circling the choices given in parentheses.

Type of Wind	Wind Speed (miles per hour)	What Happens
no wind	0	Smoke rises straight up.
light breeze	1–12	Leaves and twigs move.
moderate breeze	13–24	Small trees sway.
strong breeze	25–36	Wind is hard to walk against.
gale	37–48	Branches break on trees. Store windows break.
strong gale	49–72	Trees are uprooted.
hurricane	above 73	Buildings are greatly damaged.

1. What kind of wind would be considered safe for children to play in? (*moderate breeze, gale, strong gale*)

2. For which type of predicted wind would it be wise to cover the windows of your house if you live in a wooded area? (*moderate breeze, strong breeze, gale*)

3. If 60-mile-per-hour winds are expected, what type of wind is being predicted? (*strong breeze, strong gale, hurricane*)

ANSWERS ARE ON PAGE 305.

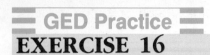

EXERCISE 16

Questions 1–4 refer to the following table about the planets in our solar system.

Name of Planet	Distance from Sun (in miles)	Diameter (in miles)	Length of Year* (in Earth days)	Length of Day** (in Earth days)	Main Elements of Which Planet Is Composed
Mercury	36,187,500	3,050	88	59	nickel, iron, silicon
Venus	67,625,000	7,560	225	243	nickel, iron, silicon
Earth	93,500,000	7,973	365	(1 day = 24 hr.)	nickel, iron, silicon
Mars	142,120,000	4,273	687	1	iron, silicon
Jupiter	486,120,000	89,500	4,329	(10 hr.)	hydrogen
Saturn	891,875,000	75,000	10,585	(10 hr.)	hydrogen
Uranus	1,793,750,000	32,375	30,660	(16 hr.)	hydrogen, helium
Neptune	2,810,625,000	30,937	60,225	(19 hr.)	hydrogen, helium
Pluto	3,687,500,000	1,875	103,660	9	unknown

*A year is the length of time it takes a planet to make one complete orbit around the sun. This time is also called the period of revolution.
**A day is the length of time it takes a planet to make one complete turn on its own axis. This time is also called the period of rotation.

1. The planet that is closest in size to Earth is

   (1) Mercury
   (2) Venus
   (3) Mars
   (4) Jupiter
   (5) Pluto

2. From the information shown in the table, which of the following can you conclude to be true?

   (1) Earth is one of the three largest planets in the solar system.
   (2) The elements found on Earth are not found on any other planet.
   (3) Earth is the largest of the five small planets in our solar system.
   (4) Earth is the closest planet to the sun.
   (5) Earth is the farthest planet from the sun.

3. Not counting the sun, the largest planets contain most of the matter in the solar system. Which two elements make up most of the matter in the solar system?

   (1) iron and silicon
   (2) iron and hydrogen
   (3) silicon and helium
   (4) nickel and iron
   (5) hydrogen and helium

4. From the table, you can conclude that the two planets that rotate (spin on their axes) most slowly are

   (1) Mercury and Venus
   (2) Uranus and Neptune
   (3) Earth and Mars
   (4) Jupiter and Saturn
   (5) Pluto and Mercury

ANSWERS ARE ON PAGE 305.

HEARTBEAT RATES DURING EXERCISE

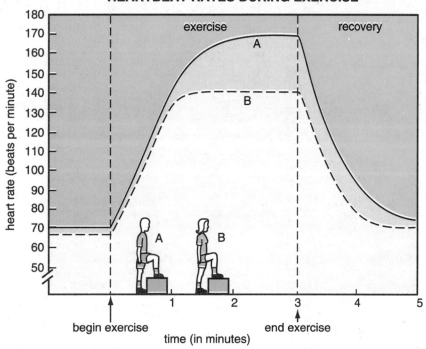

Questions 5–9 refer to the following passage and line graph.

Two students (indicated as student A and student B) are doing a step exercise as part of a conditioning class. Their heartbeat rates before, during, and after the exercise are shown on the line graph above.

5. How long did the step exercise last?

  (1) less than one minute
  (2) exactly one minute
  (3) more than one but less than three minutes
  (4) exactly three minutes
  (5) more than three minutes

6. At what point does the greatest difference between the heartbeat rates of student A and student B occur?

  (1) just before beginning the step exercise
  (2) just after beginning the step exercise
  (3) just before stopping the step exercise
  (4) just after stopping the step exercise
  (5) after recovery is complete

7. If the stepping exercise were to be continued for five minutes, you can conclude that student A's heart rate at that time would be about

  (1) 70 beats per minute
  (2) 90 beats per minute
  (3) 120 beats per minute
  (4) 150 beats per minute
  (5) 170 beats per minute

8. What heart rate will student A most likely have one hour after quitting the step exercise?

  (1) 70 beats per minute
  (2) 90 beats per minute
  (3) 120 beats per minute
  (4) 150 beats per minute
  (5) 170 beats per minute

9. To compare the physical condition of student A with that of student B, you must assume that the two students

  (1) are the same sex
  (2) are exactly the same height
  (3) are exactly the same age
  (4) are exercising at the same rate
  (5) are exercising at the same time

ANSWERS ARE ON PAGE 305.

4 Evaluating Science Materials

What do you think when you hear a tobacco company spokesperson make a statement like "Smoking never hurt anyone"? Would you agree with this person? Before you can answer yes or no, you need more information.

First, you need to know what evidence is available. (**Evidence** is any item of information that either supports or opposes a particular point of view.) For example, you need to know about the medical evidence that links smoking to many respiratory diseases and to lung cancer. You also need to know about any evidence that the tobacco company may have that disagrees with or questions the medical findings. Only then, after you've considered both points of view, will you be ready to give an informed opinion yourself.

When you hear or read something, you know you can't always assume it to be true. Too often people are influenced by more than just the facts. And people often don't know all the facts that are necessary in order to reach a sound conclusion. Because of this, it is important in our own decision making to learn to evaluate (judge) evidence objectively.

Scientists also rely on the objective evaluation of evidence. In fact, they have developed a special research method for collecting, organizing, and evaluating evidence. The **scientific method** is simply a logical way to do experiments and reach correct conclusions.

On the GED Science Test, evaluation questions measure your ability to make judgments about the information that's presented to you. On the pages ahead, you'll learn to do this in three ways. Then you'll see how a scientist uses the same skills to do experiments. This section is divided into four parts:

- judging the value of information
- judging the adequacy of information
- recognizing the influence of values
- the scientific method

JUDGING THE VALUE OF INFORMATION

Before making a decision or drawing a conclusion, you must judge the value of all available information. Most often this means distinguishing *relevant information* from *irrelevant information*. Relevant information includes any facts that directly affect your decision. Irrelevant information includes any facts that do not affect your decision.

For example, suppose you want to know if you can successfully grow a small garden on a plot of land near your home. You know that one item of relevant information is the answer to the following question.

Is the type of soil on the land fertile, garden-type soil?

An item of irrelevant information would be the answer to this question:

Should corn be planted before beans are planted?

Notice that this second question may be of interest, but it is not information that will tell you whether or not a garden is possible.

Now you try it. Place a check before each question below that is relevant to whether you'll be able to grow that garden.

_____ **a.** Is there a source of water for the proposed garden?

_____ **b.** How much snow do you get during winter months?

_____ **c.** Should you start the garden from seeds or seedlings?

_____ **d.** Does the plot receive adequate daily sunshine?

_____ **e.** Which store has the best buy on garden supplies?

Only questions a and d should be checked. Water and sunlight are both needed for crops to grow. Questions b, c, and e are not relevant to the needs of crops.

EXERCISE 1

Directions: Put a check next to each question that asks for relevant information about the health risks associated with smoking.

_____ **1.** What is the cost of a pack of cigarettes?

_____ **2.** Is there evidence that links lung cancer to smoking?

_____ **3.** How many different brands of tobacco are on the market today?

_____ **4.** Is smoking a socially acceptable activity?

_____ **5.** Is it true that heart attack risk doubles if a person smokes?

ANSWERS ARE ON PAGE 305.

EXERCISE 2

Questions 1 and 2 refer to the following passage.

Alcohol is a chemical that interferes with the normal functioning of the human body. Its effects can range from loss of coordination to unconsciousness to death. As the following story shows, alcohol does not mix well with driving.

After having five beers during the first hour at a party, Larry got mad at the hostess and left. Even though he was an alcoholic who had received medical treatment for drinking problems, Larry felt he could "hold his booze." While on the way home, he was stopped by a police officer who noticed that Larry's car had one headlight burned out and was weaving down the highway. The officer gave Larry a breathalyzer test that showed his blood-alcohol level to be at .15 percent, .05 percent greater than .10 percent (the level at which a person is legally considered to be too drunk to drive).

1. Which of the following facts would be most relevant to the officer when he has to decide whether Larry is *legally* too drunk to drive?

    (1) Larry is an alcoholic.
    (2) Larry had consumed five drinks.
    (3) Larry's blood-alcohol level was above .10 percent.
    (4) Larry had previously received medical treatment.
    (5) Larry's car was weaving down the highway.

2. Which of the following facts is probably *not* related to Larry's drunk driving?

    (1) Larry was unable to drive his car in a straight line.
    (2) Larry took a breathalyzer test.
    (3) Larry's blood-alcohol level was above .10 percent.
    (4) Larry's car had a burned-out headlight.
    (5) Larry was stopped by a police officer.

Question 3 refers to the following passage.

Although light and sound are both forms of wave energy, the speed of light is much greater than the speed of sound. In fact, light travels at about 186,000 miles per second, while sound travels at only about 1,100 feet per second. One way to see the difference between the speeds of light and sound is to watch a lightning storm.

Lightning is caused by separated electrical charges rushing together in the atmosphere. At the instant the charges come together, both a flash of light and a loud sound are created. Although the flash of lightning reaches your eyes almost at once, the thunder may not reach your ears until several seconds later.

You can use the relative speeds of light and sound to find out how far away the lightning is. When you see a flash of lightning, start counting slowly, spacing your counts one second apart. For each five seconds you count before you hear the thunder, you can figure that the lightning is about one mile away. (In five seconds, sound travels a distance of about 5,500 feet which is just a little farther than one mile—5,280 feet.) If you see a flash and don't hear thunder until you've counted to ten, you know that the lightning flash occurred about two miles from you.

3. Assume you know that both light and sound are created at the instant that lightning occurs but that you do not know either the speed of light or the speed of sound. From which fact below can you deduce that light travels faster than sound?

    (1) As you move farther away from a lightning storm, the sound of thunder becomes fainter.
    (2) You always see a lightning flash before you hear the thunder that is created with it.
    (3) The speed of sound is about 1,100 feet per second.
    (4) Light and sound are both forms of wave energy.
    (5) One mile is a distance of exactly 5,280 feet.

ANSWERS ARE ON PAGE 305.

JUDGING THE VALUE OF INFORMATION IN GRAPHICS

Being able to identify relevant information is especially useful when you're looking at a graphic. To avoid confusion, remember to look for just the information you need. In the example below, the locations and directions of other wind patterns are not relevant to the question you're answering.

**PREVAILING WINDS DURING
JULY OF EACH YEAR**

Now try answering this question: In July, in what direction do the prevailing winds blow over the eastern United States? _____

The answer is *from south to north*. To find this answer you need to look only at the eastern part of the United States. Then see in which direction the arrows are drawn.

EXERCISE 3

Directions: The following questions refer to the diagram above.

1. In what direction do the prevailing July winds blow over the western part of the United States? _____

2. In what direction do the prevailing July winds blow off the southern tip of South America? _____

3. In which of the following studies would the diagram above be of *least* relevance?

   (1) ocean water current movement
   (2) the prediction of weather
   (3) the prediction of volcanic eruptions
   (4) ocean navigation

ANSWERS ARE ON PAGE 305.

EXERCISE 4

Questions 1–5 refer to information from the illustration below.

BEAK STRUCTURES OF NORTH AMERICAN BIRDS

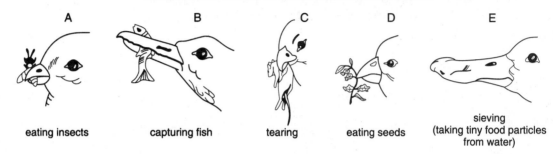

A	B	C	D	E
eating insects	capturing fish	tearing	eating seeds	sieving (taking tiny food particles from water)

1. Which two drawings above would be of most interest to someone studying different beak structures of birds that get their food from rivers and lakes?

   (1) A and C
   (2) B and D
   (3) C and E
   (4) B and E
   (5) D and E

2. Which drawings above show beak structures that are best adapted for eating small land animals?

   (1) A and C
   (2) A, B, and C
   (3) B and D
   (4) C and E
   (5) D and E

3. Which beak structure is most adapted to a vegetarian diet of land plants?

   (1) A
   (2) B
   (3) C
   (4) D
   (5) E

4. Which beak structure is found on birds that have the least dependence on keen eyesight for food gathering?

   (1) A
   (2) B
   (3) C
   (4) D
   (5) E

5. The drawings would have the *least* relevance to a person interested in

   (1) the eating habits of birds
   (2) the way animals have adapted to their environments
   (3) the beak structure of birds
   (4) bird-watching
   (5) the brain sizes of different birds

ANSWERS ARE ON PAGE 305.

JUDGING THE ADEQUACY OF INFORMATION

In the previous section, you read about distinguishing between relevant and irrelevant information. A closely related skill is the ability to determine if there is enough information to support a conclusion. For example, suppose that during a storm the power goes off in your house just a second after you plugged in an old toaster. What can you conclude? Not really anything! There may be trouble with the power lines because of the storm, or your own house power may have switched off because of a faulty toaster. Until you have more information, you can't be sure what the trouble is.

Read the next passage and answer the following question.

A tide is the alternate rising and falling of the surface of the ocean. At any point along a coast, a rising tide occurs at a regular interval and is later followed by a falling tide. A rising tide is called a *flood tide*, and a falling tide is called an *ebb tide*. Oceanographers often keep tide tables to tell you when tides occur.

Which item of information below would you need to know in order to be sure of what type of tide will next occur in Depoe Bay?

(a) how long it's been since the last tide
(b) whether the previous tide was an ebb tide or a flood tide
(c) the highest water level of the last flood tide

According to the passage, an ebb tide follows a flood tide, and vice versa. Thus, answer (b) is the information you need. If, for example, the previous tide was an ebb tide, then the next tide will be a flood tide. Answers (a) and (c) refer to the tide but do not help you determine what type of tide the next one will be.

EXERCISE 5

Directions: Check your skill at identifying missing information in the passage below. Read the passage and question and then choose your answer.

Competition for food determines where animals can live in a forest. When two different animals eat the same foods, each animal may have to find its own region of the forest where it has sole access to that particular food supply.

Which item of information below would you need to know in order to decide whether owls and hawks can live in the same part of the forest?

(1) whether owls and hawks use the same hunting methods
(2) whether owls and hawks eat the same daily amount of food
(3) whether owls and hawks eat the same sources of food

ANSWER IS ON PAGE 305.

EXERCISE 6

Questions 1 and 2 refer to the following passage.

Scientists have discovered that all forms of chemical pollutants that enter the human body seem to prefer lodging in our bodies' fat cells. By reducing excess body fat, we actually reduce the amount of pollutants in our bodies.

Scientists have also discovered that the concentration of pollutants increases as you move up the food chain. Root vegetables contain the least amount of pollutants, followed by grains, legumes, fruits, and vegetables. The most polluted foods are meat, fish, and poultry, followed by dairy products. People who eat large amounts of fatty animal meat and fish add to their own body fat *and* at the same time consume the concentrated chemical pollutants in the tissues of these animals.

1. Which of the following facts may lead you to conclude that you should reduce your consumption of fatty beef, pork, and fish?

   (1) Many chemical pollutants cause no known harmful effects.
   (2) An increased cancer risk is related to a high-fat diet.
   (3) Organically grown foods contain very low levels of chemical pollutants.
   (4) Cooking destroys many types of chemical pollutants found in meat.
   (5) Shellfish contain higher levels of chemical pollutants than other fish.

2. Which of the following facts would lead a thirty-five-year-old man to reduce his body fat by dieting?

   (1) He can afford the monthly cost of joining a weight-loss clinic.
   (2) He feels fine, exercises each day, and doesn't smoke.
   (3) His family says he looks great and has no reason to diet.
   (4) He weighs forty pounds more than his doctor recommends.
   (5) He used to weigh thirty pounds more than he weighs now.

Questions 3 and 4 refer to the following passage.

The density (weight per unit volume) of one liquid can often be compared with the density of a second liquid by combining the liquids in the same container. When two liquids are combined, either one liquid will float on the other, or the liquids will mix freely. When one liquid floats on the other, you know that the liquid on top has the lesser density. As an example, oil floats on water, so you can conclude that oil is less dense than water.

Liquids that freely mix together are said to be *miscible*. When two liquids are miscible, simply combining them won't give you any information about which liquid has the lesser (or greater) density. For example, water and alcohol are miscible in all proportions. Mixing them tells you nothing about whether alcohol is more dense than water or vice versa.

3. Which of the following facts would enable you to conclude that the density of water is greater than the density of gasoline?

   (1) Gasoline and alcohol are miscible.
   (2) Gasoline and oil are miscible.
   (3) Water that condenses in a car's gas tank can prevent the car from starting.
   (4) Gasoline will float when combined with water.
   (5) Water will not put out a gasoline fire.

4. Which of the following items of information would you need to know in order to determine whether alcohol will float on oil?

   A. whether or not oil and alcohol are miscible
   B. whether the density of alcohol is less than the density of water
   C. whether the density of alcohol is less than the density of oil

   (1) A only
   (2) B only
   (3) C only
   (4) A and B only
   (5) A and C only

ANSWERS ARE ON PAGE 305.

ADEQUACY OF INFORMATION FROM GRAPHICS

The question of the adequacy of information also occurs with all types of graphics. Most often, you'll be asked to decide whether a graphic contains enough information to support a certain conclusion. For example, look at the following chart.

AVERAGE WEIGHTS FOR MEN AND WOMEN		
	Weight in Pounds	
Height	Women	Men
5'4"	124–138	135–145
5'5"	127–141	137–148
5'6"	130–144	139–151
5'7"	133–147	142–154
5'8"	136–150	145–157
5'9"	139–153	148–160

See if you can decide which of the following statements are conclusions that are supported by the data given.

a. At birth, baby girls tend to be shorter than baby boys.
b. Between age two and age five, girls and boys are about equal in weight.
c. Adult men tend to be heavier than adult women of the same height.
d. Six-foot-tall men and women of average weight differ in weight by less than 10 pounds.
e. Between the heights of 5'4" and 5'9", women tend to be closer to their recommended weights than men.
f. At each height shown, the difference between high and low weight values is greater for women than for men.

Only conclusions c and f are supported by data given in the chart. The chart supports c because at each height the weight range for men starts and ends at higher values than those for women. To see that the chart supports statement f, subtract the low value from the high value at each weight level. The spread in values is always higher for women than for men.

Statements a and b are true, but the chart says nothing about comparative sizes of babies or children. Statements d and e may or may not be true. But, the chart gives no information on six-foot-tall people nor on *recommended* weights.

Although you may know a statement is true, your own knowledge is not what's being tested on this type of question. To get correct answers, you must consider only the data given on the graphic itself.

EXERCISE 7

Directions: Look at the chart below. Then place a check next to each of the statements listed that is supported by information from the chart.

PROPERTIES OF METALS AND NONMETALS		
Properties	*Metals*	*Nonmetals*
Common Phase (at room temperature)	Solids, except mercury (a liquid) Examples: copper, iron, gold, aluminum	Solids, liquids, or gases Examples: glass, wood, plastic, oxygen
Luster	Bright and shiny	Dull-looking
Color	Silver-gray, except for gold and copper	Various colors
Electrical Conductivity	Very good conductors	Very poor conductors
Heat Conductivity	Very good conductors	Very poor conductors

_____ **1.** Iron, a metal, is a better conductor of heat than is glass, a nonmetal.

_____ **2.** Gold is not considered a metal because it does not have the normal silver-gray metallic color.

_____ **3.** Of the two metals, copper is a better conductor of electricity than aluminum.

_____ **4.** Mercury is an example of a liquid metal.

_____ **5.** Many gases are considered to be metals.

_____ **6.** At room temperature, aluminum is a solid.

_____ **7.** Iron is a very poor conductor of electricity.

_____ **8.** Glass is classified as a nonmetal.

_____ **9.** Oxygen, a gas, is a very poor conductor of heat.

_____ **10.** Wood is a better conductor of heat than aluminum.

ANSWERS ARE ON PAGE 306.

EXERCISE 8

Questions 1 and 2 refer to the following drawings.

1. Assume that levers A and B are balanced. You can conclude that for a lever to be balanced,

    (1) equal weights must be placed on each side
    (2) weights must be placed at equal distances from the fulcrum
    (3) the sum of the two weights must not be greater than 200 pounds
    (4) the product of each weight times its distance from the fulcrum must be the same on both sides of the lever
    (5) the larger weight must be placed twice as far from the fulcrum as is the smaller weight

2. Assume that the teeter-totter in drawing C is moving. What item of information would you need to know in order to determine whether the teeter-totter will balance when the children stop it?

    (1) the sum of the weights of the children
    (2) the height of each child
    (3) the average weight of the children
    (4) the weight of the teeter-totter
    (5) the weight of each child

ANSWERS ARE ON PAGE 306.

RECOGNIZING VALUES

A *value* is a personal belief about the way to live one's own life. It can be a religious belief, or it can be the way a person believes he or she should act when around other people.

People often express their values by writing letters to newspapers, by voting for certain political candidates, or by donating money or time to organizations that have values similar to their own. For example, many people donate money and time to work on cleaning up public parks. These people see this as a way to show the high value that they place on having a clean and enjoyable recreation area for themselves and their neighbors.

Values affect the way each of us makes decisions. One way this can occur is when a personal belief does not agree with what scientists tell us is a fact. A good example is the question of evolution. Though scientific evidence strongly supports the basic principles of evolution, many religious groups oppose these ideas on the grounds that evolution does not agree with religious teachings. In this case, a person may be forced to decide between two competing values: the value a person places on certain religious teachings versus the value the person places on certain scientific evidence.

Here's an example for you to try. The paragraph below describes a situation. On the line beneath the paragraph, write the two competing values you think are in conflict in this situation.

> Reggie is nineteen and has a job at a factory. The men he works with all chew tobacco. To feel "like the other men," Reggie also started to chew tobacco about three weeks ago. Last night, for the first time, Reggie heard about medical evidence that strongly indicates that chewing tobacco can cause cancer of the mouth. Because Reggie is concerned about his health, he finds himself having to make an uncomfortable choice.

What two values are in conflict in Reggie's situation?

_____

Reggie is in a very common situation. He is faced with choosing between (1) *the value he places on wanting to feel accepted by the group he works with* and (2) *the value he places on his health.*

EXERCISE 9

Directions: In each situation described below, a person must choose between two competing values. On the line beneath each paragraph, express in your own words the values you believe are in conflict.

1. According to Betty's religious beliefs, she is not allowed to have a medical operation of any type. Recently, though, Betty found out that she needs an operation on her fallopian tubes if she ever wants to give birth to a child, a lifelong dream of hers.

_____

2. Jay, a physicist, has just found out that the company he works for has accepted a government contract to do work in nuclear weapons research. Jay is strongly opposed to the use of nuclear weapons, and he refuses to take part in the project.

_____

3. Rosario, a housewife on a limited income, drives an older car. She has been told that she can use either regular gas or unleaded gas. Regular gas is about 10 cents less per gallon, but it creates a dangerous form of air pollution because it contains lead. Unleaded gas is good for her older engine and is safer for the environment, but it costs more.

_____

ANSWERS ARE ON PAGE 306.

THE SCIENTIFIC METHOD

The steps followed by scientists in the ongoing search for knowledge are part of a logical process called the **scientific method**. As we identify each of the five steps of the scientific method, we'll show how each might actually be used in a real experiment.

1. The first step of the scientific method is to *identify the problem*.

   Suppose a biologist notices that the tomato plants in her lab are growing at a faster rate than usual. She wants to find out why.

2. The second step is to *collect information*.

   The biologist asks the lab assistants if anything unusual has happened to the tomato plants lately. She also checks the records. She discovers that the plants had been accidentally treated with a certain synthetic hormone. She researches this hormone.

3. The third step is to *make a hypothesis*, or an educated guess.

   The biologist's hypothesis is that the synthetic hormone causes tomato plants to grow at a faster rate.

4. The fourth step is to *test the hypothesis* by trying an experiment and recording the results.

   The biologist tests her hypothesis by doing the following experiment: She grows tomato plants in two planters. One group of plants, called the experimental group, will be treated with the synthetic hormone. The second group of plants, called the control group, will not be treated with the hormone. Both the experimental group and the control group will be given equal amounts of water and sunshine.

   The purpose of the control group is to let the biologist know what would happen to the plants if they stayed in their natural state and did not receive hormones. Only by comparing the growth rate of the plants in the experimental group with that of the plants in the control group can the biologist find evidence of an increased growth rate.

   On a weekly basis, the biologist measures and records on graphs the height of each plant in both the control and experimental groups.

5. The fifth step is to *draw conclusions.*

After two months, the plants in the experimental group are taller, on the average, than the plants in the control group. From the data obtained, the biologist concludes that the synthetic hormone does in fact increase the rate at which tomato plants grow.

(If there had been no difference in size between the experimental group plants and the control group plants, the biologist would probably conclude that the synthetic hormone did not cause the increased growth rate. Then she would have to throw out her hypothesis and form a new hypothesis about why the plants had started growing more quickly. She would have to repeat the whole process, running a new experiment to test her hypothesis and drawing conclusions based on the new experimental results.)

The biologist will want to run this experiment a second time to make sure that the same results can be obtained. When she does the experiment again, she will use new seeds and new soil. This helps ensure that the only difference between the two groups of plants is the use of the synthetic hormone.

Before reaching a conclusion, the biologist must make sure there are no **unwanted variables**. An unwanted variable is any unplanned difference that exists between the experimental group and the control group. An unwanted variable can affect the outcome of an experiment and can cause the reported results to be meaningless. In the experiment described above, an unwanted variable would be any difference other than the use of synthetic hormone on the experimental plants.

Place a check beside each statement below that identifies an unwanted variable in the experiment described above.

_____ **a.** Both the experimental group and the control group received equal amounts of sunshine.

_____ **b.** The planter in which the control group was planted was not watertight, while the experimental-group planter was watertight.

_____ **c.** The soil of the control group contained more rocks than did the soil of the experimental group.

_____ **d.** The experimental group and control group were both watered at the same time each day.

_____ **e.** The experimental-group planter was closer to the space heater (used to keep the laboratory warm at night) than the control-group planter.

You should place check marks by statements b, c, and e. Each of these describes a difference (unwanted variable) between the experimental plants and the control plants. Before the biologist can be sure of her conclusion about the effect of the hormone, she must be sure that none of these three unwanted variables was really the cause of the faster growth in the experimental-group plants.

EXERCISE 10

Directions: Answer each of the following questions.

1. Following are phrases that summarize each of the five steps of the scientific method. Write these phrases in the correct order: draw conclusions, collect information, perform experiments, identify a problem, form a hypothesis

   a. _____

   b. _____

   c. _____

   d. _____

   e. _____

2. In the plant hormone experiment, why did the biologist grow a control group of plants as well as the experimental group of plants?

   _____

3. Why is it better that the biologist grew several plants in each planter rather than just one plant in each?

   _____

ANSWERS ARE ON PAGE 306.

 GED Practice

EXERCISE 11

Questions 1–4 refer to the following chart and information.

Experiment	Objects Dropped	Observed Results
1	3-lb. brick and 1-lb. rock	Both brick and rock reached the ground at the same time. Both fell at the same rate.
2	3-lb. brick and paper clip	Both brick and paper clip reached the ground at the same time. Both fell at the same rate.
3	1-lb. rock and paper clip	Both rock and paper clip reached the ground at the same time. Both fell at the same rate.

Wanda knows that the force of gravity pulls all objects toward the surface of Earth. She now wants to determine whether heavier objects fall at a faster rate than lighter objects. To find out, Wanda decided to try experiments in which she would use a three-pound brick, a one-pound rock, and a paper clip that weighs a fraction of an ounce. In each of three experiments, Wanda dropped two objects side by side from a height of three feet and observed them as they fell. When she completed the experiments, Wanda recorded the results shown in the table.

1. From the results of her experiment, Wanda can conclude that for fairly short distances,

   (1) all heavy objects fall more quickly than light objects
   (2) metal objects fall more quickly than bricks
   (3) some heavy and light objects fall at the same rate
   (4) heavy objects fall more slowly than light objects
   (5) objects made of different substances fall at different rates

2. Suppose that Wanda now does the same experiment with a paper clip and a leaf. This time, even though the objects are about the same weight, they do not fall at the same rate: the paper clip falls much more quickly and reaches the ground much sooner.

   Which of the following can Wanda most reasonably conclude *from this observation*?

   (1) The rate at which a light object falls depends on its weight.
   (2) Very light objects fall at different rates, and these rates depend on the time of day the objects are dropped.
   (3) Man-made objects fall more quickly than objects from nature.
   (4) The rate at which a light object falls depends on how large the surface of the object is.
   (5) The rate at which a heavy object falls depends on how large the surface of the object is.

3. Noticing that a paper clip falls much more quickly than a leaf, Wanda forms a new hypothesis to explain this new discovery:

   Very light objects fall at different rates because of the effect of air resistance. Air resistance slows an object with a large surface much more than it slows an object with a small surface. Over short distances, light objects with small surfaces are not noticeably affected by air resistance.

   To test her hypothesis about very light objects, Wanda should do an experiment in which she drops

   (1) a pin and a needle
   (2) a piece of notebook paper and a book
   (3) a paper plate and a china plate
   (4) a green leaf and a brown leaf
   (5) a piece of notebook paper and a small plastic spoon

4. After doing all four experiments, Wanda had another hypothesis. She wondered whether all objects would fall at the same rate if there were no air resistance. Which of the following would be the most ideal place to test Wanda's hypothesis?

   (1) in the pressurized passenger cabin of an airplane flying at 35,000 feet
   (2) standing underwater on the bottom of a swimming pool
   (3) in the "weightless" condition of an orbiting space shuttle
   (4) on the surface of the moon, a body that has gravity but no air
   (5) in a very still room where the windows are closed and there is no air movement

ANSWERS ARE ON PAGE 306.

GED Practice
EXERCISE 12

Questions 1–4 refer to the following information.

Fernando, a psychologist, wants to determine if mice suffer from any form of anxiety or tension when they are forced to live in crowded conditions.

1. Which of the following experimental conditions will be best suited to provide evidence on which Fernando can base a conclusion?

   (1) Place a group of six mice in each of two identical small cages, each so small that the mice have only a few inches of distance between one another at all times.
   (2) Place a group of six mice in each of two identical large cages, each large enough so that the mice can have several feet of distance between one another if they so choose.
   (3) Place a single group of twelve mice in one small cage.
   (4) Place a single group of twelve mice in one large cage.
   (5) Place one group of six mice in a small cage and a second group of six mice in a large cage.

2. Suppose that the crowded mice *do* show more signs of anxiety than the uncrowded mice. How can Fernando best double-check his hypothesis that it is the crowding together that is causing these mice to experience this anxiety?

   (1) Do the experiment a second time, only this time place two mice in each cage.
   (2) Contact his friends to see if they think his hypothesis is reasonable.
   (3) Do the experiment a second time, only this time use two new groups of mice.
   (4) Do the experiment a second time, only this time do it with hamsters.
   (5) Do the experiment a second time, only this time place mice in the large cage and hamsters in the small cage.

3. Fernando believes that the findings from his mice studies might also apply to human beings. Of the following types of research, the most relevant evidence to support Fernando's belief would come from studies dealing with

   (1) the anxiety and depression levels of people living in crowded conditions in an inner-city neighborhood
   (2) the rate of teenage pregnancies in cities that have a population of one million or more
   (3) the anxiety levels of farmers struggling to exist during low-income years
   (4) the anxiety levels of people living in a small midwestern town
   (5) the rate of crime occurring in large cities where there is a high rate of drug use

4. Fernando believes that his research will show that crowding leads to anxiety, and anxiety leads to panic in an emergency. If Fernando is correct, in which location would panic most likely occur if a fire breaks out?

   (1) a nearly empty restaurant
   (2) a golf course with people waiting to play
   (3) an indoor shopping mall
   (4) a football field near a forest
   (5) a hotel lobby

ANSWERS ARE ON PAGE 306.

UNDERSTANDING SCIENCE

■ Plant and Animal Biology
■ Human Biology
■ Earth Science
■ Chemistry
■ Physics

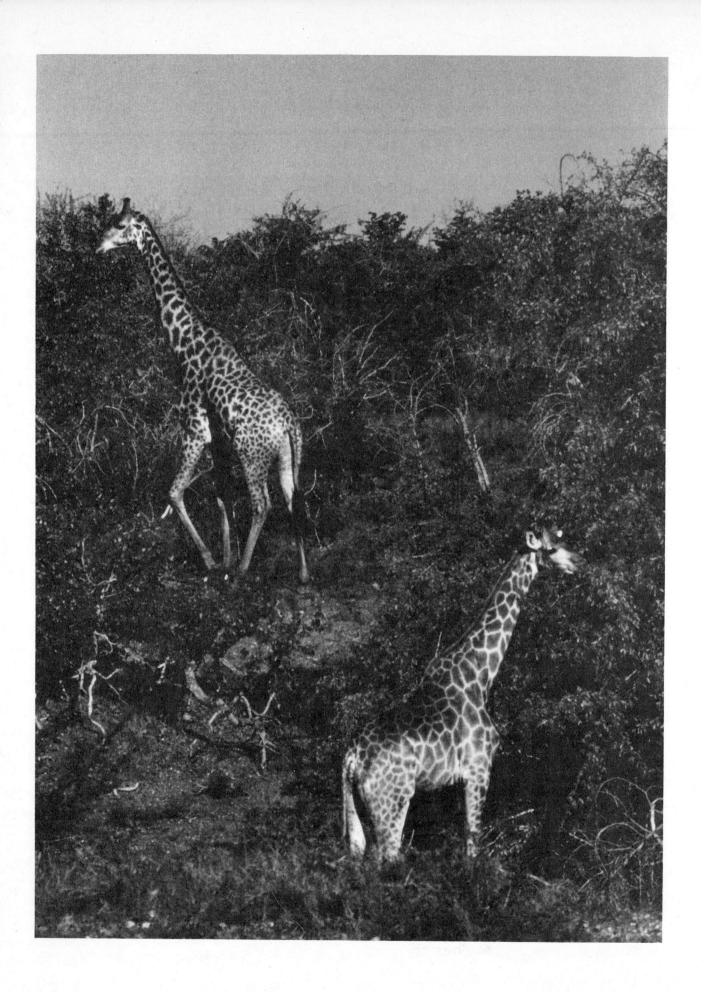

5 Plant and Animal Biology

Imagine for a moment what it's like to sleep in a meadow. Until you fall asleep, you listen to the chirping of crickets, the croaking of frogs, and the occasional buzzing of a bothersome mosquito. Unless you're used to these sounds, you're probably surprised at how much of a racket these little animals can make!

But you soon grow used to the noise, and the next thing you know you're awakening to the first rays of sunlight. Your sleeping bag and the grass around you are moist with morning dew—but at least the crickets and frogs are quiet! The only sounds you hear now are those of insects busily starting their day. Small bees hover above the flowers, looking for blossoms from which to take the sweet nectar they need for making honey. A butterfly alights on a dandelion a few feet away. Beyond the butterfly, spring buttercups slowly open their golden petals toward the morning light. And just beyond the buttercups, a robin pulls a worm from the grass and flies off to feed its young. Sitting up and starting to feel hungry yourself, you are amazed at the variety of life and activity around you.

Sleeping in a meadow is quite an educational experience. It gives you a glimpse into the world of plants and animals—some big, some small, but all living out their lives in their own ways while sharing Earth together.

Biology is the study of all these living things, from plants and animals too small to be seen by the human eye to huge redwood trees, elephants, and whales. The interests of biologists are almost as numerous as the one and one-half million types of **organisms** (living things) known to be on Earth. Much of this interest focuses on the study of plant and animal structures and on life cycles.

Of recent interest is the field of **ecology**, the study of the relationship of organisms to their environment. An **environment** is all the living and nonliving things that affect an organism's life in some way.

The study of biology really began thousands of years ago, when people first attempted to understand living things. In fact, the word *biology* comes from two Greek words: *bios*, which means "life," and *logos*, which means "study of."

Even though the study of life has been going on during all this time, one important principle—called **biogenesis**—is only about 150 years old.

According to this principle, life can come only from life. Each organism must come from the reproduction of other organisms. This idea seems obvious to us today. But, before the mid-1800s, it was widely believed that insects and worms could form from rotting soil! People also believed that frogs formed in clouds and fell to Earth during rainstorms!

Today, biologists know quite a lot about the types of organisms that inhabit Earth. Many of these have been identified and studied, and they are broadly classified into two groups: plants and animals. The study of plants is called **botany**, and the study of animals is called **zoology**. This chapter will focus on many of the characteristics of life that are of interest in both botany and zoology, characteristics that are common to all living things.

EXERCISE 1

Directions: Match each item on the left with the phrase that best describes it on the right. Write the letter of the phrase on the line before the correct number.

_____ **1.** botany

_____ **2.** ecology

_____ **3.** biology

_____ **4.** environment

_____ **5.** zoology

(a) the study of all living things

(b) the study of animals

(c) the study of the relationship of organisms to their surroundings

(d) the study of plants

(e) all things affecting an organism

ANSWERS ARE ON PAGE 306.

GED Practice
EXERCISE 2

Questions 1 and 2 are based on the information on pages 81–82.

1. Which of the following best summarizes the first two paragraphs on page 81?

  (1) A meadow is a cold damp place at night, and you'll want to take plenty of warm clothes if you camp there.

  (2) By sleeping overnight in a meadow, you can hear firsthand how much noise small animals can make.

  (3) A meadow is filled with a variety of life forms, each going about an activity that is part of its life cycle.

  (4) Some animals eat plants, while some animals eat other animals.

  (5) Many baby animals, such as small robins, depend on their mothers for food.

2. Which of the following statements is an opinion, not a fact?

  (1) Frogs eat insects, a fact that makes them more important to humans than worms are.

  (2) Certain types of animals hunt for food mainly at night, while other animals hunt mainly during the day.

  (3) The study of an organism includes the way in which it interacts with other organisms.

  (4) Many flowers respond to the sun's coming over the horizon by opening their petals.

  (5) Both plants and animals exhibit behavior that helps ensure their survival.

Questions 3–5 refer to the following passage.

In a famous experiment performed in the seventeenth century, Francesco Redi wanted to disprove the common belief that meat left to rot would turn into maggots. (Maggots are the newly hatched, crawling stage of flies that later mature to become adult flies.) Redi believed that an organism such as a maggot could result only from the reproduction of parent organisms of the same type. To prove this, Redi performed the experiment shown below. He placed a piece of meat to rot in each of two jars. The control jar was covered with a piece of cloth. Although air could pass through the cloth, the flies couldn't. The experimental jar was left open.

EXPERIMENT BEGINS

control jar   experimental jar

As the experiment begins, no maggots are on the meat in either jar. Flies can lay eggs only in the experimental jar.

SEVERAL WEEKS LATER

control jar   experimental jar

Several weeks later, maggots cover the meat in the experimental jar. No maggots have appeared on meat in the control jar.

3. For what purpose did Redi place the cloth over the control jar?

   (1) to keep dirt off the meat in the control jar
   (2) to keep the smell of rotting meat from leaving the control jar
   (3) to keep fresh air from circulating around the rotting meat in the control jar
   (4) to give the flies two places to lay their eggs, on the rotting meat and on the cloth
   (5) to prevent flies from laying eggs on the meat in the control jar

4. What is the most reasonable conclusion that can be drawn from these results?

   (1) Rotting meat will turn into maggots only when the meat is left open to fresh air.
   (2) Maggots will turn into flies only when they get their nutrients from rotting meat.
   (3) The effect of the cloth is to slow down the rotting process by about a week.
   (4) Maggots appear on rotten meat only after hatching from eggs that flies have laid on the meat.
   (5) Flies are able to reproduce only when there is a source of rotten meat on which to lay their eggs.

5. Which of the following factors should Redi have been most careful about when he began his experiment?

   (1) that both jars were exactly the same size
   (2) that both pieces of meat were free of insect eggs or larvae
   (3) that the temperature of each jar would be kept constant
   (4) that both pieces of meat were exactly the same size
   (5) that no flies would ever be allowed to enter the room in which the experiment was to be performed

ANSWERS ARE ON PAGE 306.

CHARACTERISTICS OF LIVING THINGS

KEY WORDS

cell—the basic unit of all living things

food—a substance that helps an organism grow and provides it with energy

response—a reaction, usually expressed as a change in an organism's activity

stimulus—anything that causes an organism to react

Seeing a squirrel or dog is a commonplace experience that's easily taken for granted. Too often we forget just how unique and remarkable life is. Perhaps it is a good idea from time to time to remember that of all the planets in the solar system (and possibly of all the planets in the universe), Earth is the only one that contains life. This means that Earth is a very special place. Earth has just the right combination of chemical elements and climatic conditions needed to produce and sustain an incredible variety of living things.

WHAT DOES IT MEAN TO BE A LIVING THING?

To answer this question, first notice that living things are certainly different from nonliving things. For example, you don't have much in common with a chair or a glass. However, you're also very different from a tree or a bird, and they—like you—are living things. In defining living things, scientists have found it more useful to look at how living things are similar to one another than to look at how they are different. Below are some characteristics common to all organisms, both plants and animals.

All living things go through a life cycle that can be divided into five stages: beginning, growth, maturity, decline, and death. During the beginning stage, an organism takes shape. For animals, the beginning is the time preceding birth. Growth is the period when an organism grows to its mature size and develops the ability to reproduce. During maturity, an organism uses energy mainly for the maintenance of life. During decline, an organism is not as able to keep itself in top shape, and it may become less active.

In order to go through this life cycle, living things need energy. Everyone is familiar with the feeling of hunger. This feeling is just your body's way of telling you that it needs a source of energy. You and all other organisms use energy to carry on daily activities. Green plants get energy from glucose, a food sugar that they produce by combining sunlight energy, carbon dioxide gas, and water. Animals cannot produce their own food directly, so they use the food energy produced by plants. Animals either eat the plants themselves or eat other animals that eat plants.

All living things can reproduce, or make more of their own kind. Each individual animal or plant will eventually complete the life cycle and die. Reproduction makes it possible for each type of organism to continue to exist.

All living things respond to things that happen around them. An organism will react to a stimulus, or change, in its environment. A stimulus may be something seen, heard, felt, smelled, or tasted. Living things always respond to a stimulus in a way that helps them in their constant struggle to survive. For example, when a deer hears a mountain lion growl, it bolts. The big cat's growl is the stimulus. The deer's reaction—running away—is called a response.

Finally, all living things are made up of basic units called cells. Cells carry out important life activities during each stage of an organism's life. There are tiny organisms made up of only one cell, and there are organisms, such as ourselves, that are made up of trillions of cells.

EXERCISE 3

Directions: In each blank, write the stage of development and growth (beginning, growth, maturity, decline, death) during which each of the following usually occurs in the life cycle of a human being.

_____ **1.** growth of permanent teeth

_____ **2.** great-grandchildren

_____ **3.** existence as a fetus

_____ **4.** decomposition of the body

_____ **5.** working and raising a family

GED Practice
EXERCISE 4

Questions 1–3 are based on the information on pages 84–85.

1. What name is given to the basic unit of all living things?

(1) energy
(2) environment
(3) organ
(4) response
(5) cell

2. What is most likely to be true of a mouse that responds more slowly to a cat's hissing than most other mice?

(1) It will have a slower-than-average growth rate.
(2) It will have a shorter-than-average life span.
(3) It will use less than an average amount of energy for its daily activities.
(4) It will be rejected by other mice.
(5) It will have a longer-than-average life span.

3. Nonliving things also change when their environment changes. For example, a puddle of water will freeze solid when the water temperature drops below 32° F. Which of the following statements tells the most important difference between a puddle freezing and an animal's response to freezing temperature?

(1) An animal responds more slowly to temperature change.
(2) An animal does not freeze because it is not made of pure water.
(3) An animal does not freeze as quickly as a puddle does.
(4) An animal responds to freezing temperatures in a way that best ensures its own survival.
(5) An animal freezes solid at a different temperature from that at which a puddle freezes.

ANSWERS ARE ON PAGE 306.

CHARACTERISTICS OF FLOWERING PLANTS

Besides being delicious and nutritious, what do oranges, apples, strawberries, tomatoes, avocados, grapes, and hickory nuts all have in common? One thing is that they are all produced by flowering plants. Spring flowers on these plants give way to summer fruit. Now, how about broccoli, cabbage, and cauliflower—what do they have in common? This answer may surprise you: the parts of them that we eat are flowers!

Flowering plants are only one of many types of plants, but they play a special role in our lives. They provide us with fruits, nuts, vegetables, and, of course, flowers. Because of their importance, much is now known about both the structure and the behavior of these plants.

Like all other plants, flowering plants are faced with basic survival needs. They need a source of energy, a source of water and minerals, and an efficient means of reproduction. A drawing of a flowering plant is shown below.

PARTS OF A FLOWER

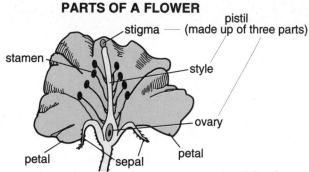

Unlike animals, which move around in search of food, most plants spend their entire life in one spot. A plant can do this because of its roots. Roots both anchor a plant in the ground and absorb water and minerals from the soil. Plants such as grass have a system of small branching roots. Most larger flowering plants have a single large root, called a *tap root* or primary root, and numerous smaller *secondary roots*.

Growing above the ground are the stem and leaves of a plant. The stem holds the leaves up to sunlight and conducts water and minerals from the roots to the leaves. Stems such as those found on small wildflowers may be shorter than an inch. The trunks of trees, which are also stems, may grow to be hundreds of feet tall. One of the most noticeable features of stems is their buds, the part where new growth takes place. On the top of the stem is a terminal bud from which the plant grows taller. Along the sides of the stem are lateral buds that develop into branches, leaves, or flowers.

It is in the leaves that plants carry on photosynthesis, the production of food from sunlight energy, water, and carbon dioxide gas. The larger a plant grows, the more leaves it will usually have. In many plants, leaves and stems form as a single structure. The prickly stem of a desert cactus is an example.

REPRODUCTION OF FLOWERING PLANTS

Flowers are the parts of plants in which reproduction occurs. Inside the petals, the large brightly colored parts of an open flower, are the stamens and the pistil. *Stamens* are the male reproductive structures, and the *pistil* is the female reproductive structure.

Flowering plants reproduce by a process called pollination. During this process, pollen—a grain that contains the male sex cell—leaves the stamen and gets deposited on a *stigma*, the top part of a pistil. From the stigma, the pollen moves through the style, a tube that connects the stigma with the ovary. The female sex cell is contained in the ovary. When male and female cells join in the ovary, they form a fertilized egg that develops into a seed. Usually, a new plant grows from the seed.

Many plants self-pollinate. This means that the plant's pollen fertilizes the same plant's eggs to produce seeds. However, not all plants are able to do this. These other plants must be fertilized by pollen from a second plant. Since plants can't go and search for mates, they must rely on nature to carry pollen to them. Pollen is carried by wind, water, and animals. Bees, butterflies, and hummingbirds are the best-known pollinators.

EXERCISE 5

Directions: Answer the questions below.

1. Name the four main parts of a flowering plant and briefly tell why each part is important.

a. _____

b. _____

c. _____

d. _____

2. Briefly describe the role that each of the following parts of a flower plays in reproduction.

a. stamen _____

b. stigma _____

c. style _____

d. ovary _____

e. pollen _____

3. Name two animals that carry pollen from one flower to another

a. _____   **b.** _____

4. Read each statement below. Circle *T* if the statement is true or *F* if the statement is false.

T   F   a. Photosynthesis is the production of food from the sun's energy.

T   F   b. A flowering plant contains only female reproductive parts.

T   F   c. A plant's stem absorbs water and minerals from the soil.

ANSWERS ARE ON PAGE 307.

WRITING ACTIVITY 1

Part of what makes each area of the world unique is its plants and trees. When we think of the desert, we imagine cactus plants; when we think of California, we picture palm trees or giant redwood trees.

Think about the variety of plants in your environment. On a sheet of paper, jot down the names of plants and trees that grow in the area where you live. Then write one paragraph describing those plants.

ANSWERS WILL VARY.

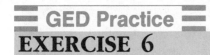

EXERCISE 6

Questions 1–5 refer to the following information.

The responses made by plants to environmental stimuli can be classified in various ways. Below are five types of responses to common stimuli.

phototropism—the bending (or growth) of a plant toward a source of light

touch response—the movement of leaves or other parts of a plant in response to being touched

positive geotropism—the downward growth of a plant root in the direction of gravity

negative geotropism—the upward growth of a plant stem, directly away from the direction of gravity

circadian rhythm—a natural pattern of plant activity that takes place in a twenty-four-hour cycle

1. When an insect enters the open leaves of a Venus's-flytrap, the plant's leaves snap shut and trap the insect. The plant's reaction is an example of

    (1) phototropism
    (2) touch response
    (3) positive geotropism
    (4) negative geotropism
    (5) circadian rhythm

2. Morning glories open their petals each morning when the sun comes up and close them each night at dusk. This daily activity is an example of

    (1) phototropism
    (2) touch response
    (3) positive geotropism
    (4) negative geotropism
    (5) circadian rhythm

3. When she planted flowers in the spring, Trinh accidentally planted her tulip bulbs upside down. Later, when she found out about her mistake, Trinh dug up a bulb and found that the root had simply sprouted from the top and was now growing downward—deeper into the soil, passing along the side of the bulb. This response of the bulb root is known as

    (1) phototropism
    (2) touch response
    (3) positive geotropism
    (4) negative geotropism
    (5) circadian rhythm

4. On clear days, the large yellow-rayed flowers of Bob's mature sunflower plants slowly follow the sun as it moves. This plant movement is a response best classified as

    (1) phototropism
    (2) touch response
    (3) positive geotropism
    (4) negative geotropism
    (5) circadian rhythm

5. A small corn plant was accidentally uprooted and buried upside down. A few days later the stem of the plant had broken through the surface of the ground and was growing upward. This response of the corn plant is known as

    (1) phototropism
    (2) touch response
    (3) positive geotropism
    (4) negative geotropism
    (5) circadian rhythm

ANSWERS ARE ON PAGE 307.

ANIMAL CHARACTERISTICS

> ### KEY WORDS
>
> ***adaptation***—the process by which an organism becomes well suited to survive in its home environment
> ***behavior***—actions or reactions of an organism in different circumstances
> ***sense organ***—a structure that reacts to stimuli and sends messages to the brain

If living things are to survive, they must be adapted to cope with the conditions of the place in which they live. A sea gull, for example, is well suited for life along the coast. A sea gull has long, angled wings that help it glide in coastal air currents as it hunts for food. These wings are also well oiled in order to deflect ocean water as the gull picks its prey from the surf. The gull's webbed feet enable it to walk on the sand and paddle on the water's surface.

As exemplified by the sea gull, traits that help an animal to survive tend to be more complex than those of plants. Since an animal has a brain and a variety of sense organs, animal traits involve not only body shape, size, and color but also patterns of behavior. In addition to the sense of touch, most animals can see, hear, taste, and smell. These senses give animals a wide range of experiences unknown to plants. Also, animals have developed means of movement that plants don't have. Animals can swim, fly, crawl, walk, dig, and burrow. Although no one animal can do all of these, many animals can do more than one.

The complex behavior patterns of most animals are concerned mainly with the constant struggle to survive and reproduce. The types of animals alive on Earth today are those that have been successful in this struggle. Although most animals die young, enough of each type survive until their reproductive years to ensure that their type does not become ***extinct*** (disappear from Earth).

The behavior exhibited by animals varies greatly. Many animals are ***predators***, hunters of other animals. Predators such as sharks and lions are powerfully built, can move rapidly, and have teeth designed to rip a prey (hunted animal) apart. The bodies of these animals are ideally suited for the type of aggressive behavior required of successful hunters. Other animals are not hunters; they are simply the hunted. For these animals, survival depends on one or more types of animal defenses.

ANIMAL DEFENSES

One type of animal defense is simply the ability to move quickly. Animals such as antelopes and gazelles rely on alertness, speed, and endurance to outrun lions or other predators that hunt them.

An animal's coloring can be a defense. One type of protective coloring is called **camouflage**—the animal's colors enable it to blend into its surroundings and not be seen by predators. For example, green-colored snakes and frogs live in green weeds. And to hide from their enemies, rabbits and weasels have earth-colored fur in the summer and white fur in the winter.

For some animals, it's an advantage to be highly visible. An animal's distinctive coloring may be a defense, warning predators of previous bad experiences with that type of animal. The black and white stripes of a skunk—warning of the horrible smell it emits when approached—may be the most familiar example.

Some animals rely on a strong or menacing outer layer for protection. The armadillo, for example, has a covering of tough, bony plates that predators cannot grasp. Clams and snails have shells that they can pull back into and hide. The North American porcupine has sharp fishhook-like quills that cover its body and, if touched, can come out and cause painful wounds. Similarly, the porcupine fish has sharp spines that stick out of its body like thorns.

For many animals, the best defense is simply to fight back. Some animals fight back by biting, kicking, or ramming. The baboon fights with sharp teeth and powerful jaws. Elk and deer fight by kicking with sharp feet and by ramming a predator with their antlers. Other animals resist their attackers with chemical weapons. Ants and bees use stingers to inject poison, while many snakes and spiders inject poison with fangs.

Finally, some animals play dead when attacked. For example, when an opossum is attacked, it closes its eyes and goes limp. Many predators will not bother with an animal that appears dead.

EXERCISE 7

Directions: Answer each question below.

1. Match each word on the left with the phrase that is the best description on the right. Write the letter of the phrase on the line before the correct number.

    _____ **1.** behavior

    _____ **2.** predator

    _____ **3.** prey

    _____ **4.** adaptation

    _____ **5.** camouflage

    (a) the process of becoming suited for an environment

    (b) the actions or reactions of a living thing

    (c) a hunted animal

    (d) a type of protective coloring

    (e) an animal that hunts other animals

2. For what purpose do animals rely on animal defenses?

    _____

    _____

    _____

ANSWERS ARE ON PAGE 307.

EXERCISE 8

Questions 1–3 refer to the following passage.

Many animals live with their own kind for the purposes of feeding, reproducing, and migrating and for mutual protection. Fish swim together in schools, elephants roam together in herds, wolves hunt together in packs, and ducks migrate together in flocks. The most complex living arrangement, though, occurs with the social insects: ants, bees, wasps, and termites. Social insects form groups in which the needs of the group are more important than the needs of any particular member. Each individual is specially adapted to perform a function for the group, not for itself. In fact, the group's survival often depends on individuals giving up their own lives!

Social insects are characterized by several kinds of group behavior. They live together, forming a colony or hive; they care for their young; they often feed each other as well as their young; and they usually all stem from the same female parent who is the lone queen of the colony or hive.

Each type of member of a social-insect group differs in both shape and function from other types. For example, a honeybee hive consists of a single queen bee, many worker bees (underdeveloped female bees), and many drones (male bees). The sole job of the queen, the largest honeybee, is to lay the eggs. A worker's job is more varied: she must gather nectar, feed and care for the queen and drones, and keep the hive clean and cool. A drone's only task is to fertilize the queen bee when she is aloft in the "marriage flight." After the drone performs this single task, he dies.

If the hive is attacked, the workers fight back and sting the aggressor. Once a worker has stung the aggressor, the worker dies. Unlike other animal associations, social-insect groups place the survival of the group at a much higher level of importance than the survival of any individual in the group, except for perhaps one—the queen.

1. Which of the following is the best summary of key points made in the passage on social insects?

    (1) Social insects work together, each member of a group playing a role to aid in the survival of the group.
    (2) Social insects form loose but cooperative group living associations.
    (3) Social-insect groups place low value on the lives of those members designated as workers.
    (4) Social-insect groups are inefficient because many members do little or no work.
    (5) Members of social-insect groups must often sacrifice their own lives.

2. Which of the following would *best* explain the presence of a lot of dead worker bees on the ground in an area around a beehive?

    (1) The hive was hit by a falling branch.
    (2) The worker bees accidentally gathered poison nectar.
    (3) The worker bees had mated with the drones.
    (4) The hive was disturbed by a bear looking for honey.
    (5) The drones killed the worker bees to make more room in the crowded hive for newly developing bees.

3. In what important way does a social-insect group differ from a human social group?

    (1) Social insects join together to better accomplish a group purpose.
    (2) Social insects share the group's labor in an orderly way.
    (3) Some members of a social-insect group give up their lives as a natural result of performing their role for the group.
    (4) Social insects care for and feed the young who are members of the group.
    (5) Each member of a social-insect group specializes in a certain type of work.

Questions 4–6 refer to the following passage.

Scientists have long felt that tool making is a skill that separates human beings from other animals. Now they've learned that chimpanzees also make and use tools, in ways that perhaps are similar to the tool making of the earliest known human cultures. Through observation, scientists have discovered that chimpanzees in the wild use broken branches to attack predators. They also use stones to crack nuts, and they have learned to make a sort of sponge from a wad of leaves to hold drinking water.

Perhaps their most clever use of a tool, though, is the use of a stick to go after ants or termites. The chimpanzee finds or makes a long thin stick by removing leaves and their stems. He or she then breaks the stick to a suitable length and inserts it into the ant or termite nest. The angry insects swarm onto the stick, only to be removed from the nest and eaten.

If a chimpanzee can find no suitable branch or stick nearby, he or she will travel for up to half a mile to find a suitable branch that can be fashioned into a probe.

Scientists point out that chimpanzees are demonstrating the remarkable skills of searching for tools, making tools, and using tools. Research continues in an effort to learn more about this remarkable primate.

4. Which of the following best summarizes the main point of the passage?

   (1) Chimpanzees are as intelligent as humans.
   (2) Chimpanzees are not strict vegetarians because they eat termites and ants.
   (3) People in primitive cultures were no more intelligent than chimpanzees.
   (4) Chimpanzees have developed a skill once thought possible only of human beings.
   (5) Chimpanzees may have many skills that we don't yet know about.

5. An unstated assumption made by the observing scientists is that the chimpanzees

   (1) are demonstrating all the tool-making skills that they have
   (2) are just performing for the scientists in hopes of being fed
   (3) are not just mimicking activities they previously saw humans do
   (4) become more intelligent as they get older
   (5) are not capable of being taught other types of skills by human beings

6. Until the 1960s, many scientists believed that animals in the wild were incapable of making or using tools. This opinion was most likely based on each of the following *except*

   (1) pride in human accomplishments
   (2) knowledge available at that time about animal intelligence
   (3) a shared view about human intellectual superiority
   (4) detailed observations of animals in captivity
   (5) detailed observations of animals in the wild

ANSWERS ARE ON PAGE 307.

GROWTH OF LIVING THINGS

CELLS: THE BUILDING BLOCKS OF LIFE

KEY WORDS

cell membrane—a membrane that holds a cell together as a single unit
chromosomes—carriers of hereditary information
nucleus—the control center of a cell
protoplasm—the complex chemical compounds that are the substance of life

---

Though the exact date of the invention of the microscope is unknown, its development was a great leap forward in the work of biologists in the seventeenth century. For the first time, they could see beyond the limits of the naked human eye. The British scientist Robert Hooke, after looking at slices of cork with the new instrument, was amazed at the tiny boxlike cavities out of which the cork was made. Because these cavities reminded him of cells (rooms) in a monastery, he gave the name *cells* to these tiny units of cork.

Today biologists know that cells are the basic units from which all living things are made. A cell is the smallest living unit that carries on the activities of the life of an organism. A cell is made up of protoplasm, complex chemical compounds that are the substance of life. Illustrated below are sample plant and animal cells.

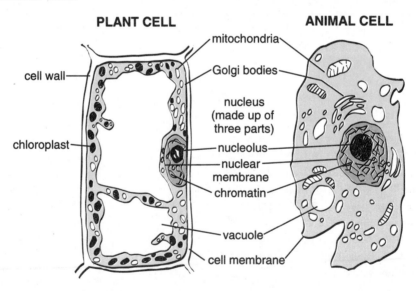

PLANT CELL   **ANIMAL CELL**

mitochondria

cell wall — Golgi bodies

nucleus
(made up of
three parts)

chloroplast — nucleolus
— nuclear
membrane
— chromatin

vacuole

cell membrane

Though cells of plants and animals differ in some ways, they do have several common characteristics.

Each cell has a cell membrane. This membrane separates the cell from other cells and holds it together as a unit. The cell membrane is not solid but is permeable, allowing needed substances to pass in and out of the cell. Food molecules, needed to provide energy, pass into the cell, while waste products produced within the cell pass out of it.

Each cell contains a single large oval or round body called the nucleus. The nucleus controls the activities of the cell. A smaller round body within the nucleus, called the **nucleolus**, is responsible for the making of protein used in new cell growth. Also within the nucleus are strands of chromatin. When a cell divides, the chromatin forms chromosomes—rod-shaped structures that carry hereditary information.

Each cell contains cytoplasm. **Cytoplasm** is the name given to all the protoplasm that is outside the nucleus. Mitochondria are the centers of respiration in a cell. These objects release the energy that provides for all of a cell's activities. Golgi bodies are involved in preparing important types of protein substances for movement out of the cell. Vacuoles are fluid-filled cavities that temporarily hold both food materials and waste products.

As the illustration shows, a plant cell has two special structures not found in an animal cell. These are the cell wall and chloroplasts. A cell wall surrounds the cell membrane of most plant cells. This wall both supports and protects the cell. In many plants, the cell wall is tough but flexible. Cell walls are what make vegetables like celery crunchy to bite and chew. In plants such as trees, cell walls are thick and rigid, which enables them to provide the tree with great strength.

Chloroplasts contain **chlorophyll**, the green pigment that is used to capture sunlight energy. The plant uses this energy from the sun to produce glucose, a food sugar that the plant itself uses as its source of energy. As mentioned on page 86, this process is called photosynthesis.

EXERCISE 9

Directions: Match each item on the left with the phrase that is the best description on the right. Write the letter of the phrase on the line before the correct number.

_____ **1.** cell wall

_____ **2.** cell nucleus

_____ **3.** mitochondria

_____ **4.** vacuole

_____ **5.** cell membrane

(a) the body in a cell that controls the cell's activity

(b) the surface layer of a cell through which certain substances can pass

(c) a cavity within a cell

(d) the outer rigid layer of a plant cell

(e) bodies that release energy used for all cell activities

ANSWERS ARE ON PAGE 307.

EXERCISE 10

Questions 1–3 are based on the information on pages 94–95.

1. Which of the following is found in plant cells but not in animal cells?

   (1) cytoplasm
   (2) nucleolus
   (3) cell membrane
   (4) Golgi bodies ·
   (5) cell wall

2. A one-celled animal reproduces by simply dividing itself into two equal parts. Which body in the nucleus of the original cell contains hereditary information that will be passed on to the two newly formed cells?

   (1) the nucleolus
   (2) the strands of chromatin
   (3) the Golgi bodies
   (4) the vacuole
   (5) the mitochondria

3. Mushrooms, like other fungi, do not carry on photosynthesis. Instead, they obtain their nutrients by absorbing them from other living or dead organisms. Knowing this, which of the following bodies would you *not* expect to find in a mushroom cell?

   (1) cytoplasm
   (2) a cell wall
   (3) chloroplasts
   (4) a nucleus
   (5) strands of chromatin

ANSWERS ARE ON PAGE 307.

THE STRUCTURE OF ORGANISMS

KEY WORDS

one-celled—consisting of only one cell
many-celled—consisting of more than one cell
cell specialization—when each cell has a specific function, as in an organism with different kinds of cells
tissue—a group of cells that are alike in structure and function
organ—a group of different kinds of tissues working together

Which do you think is the largest: a bone cell from a giraffe, a bone cell from a frog, or a stem cell from a rosebush? Because the giraffe is so large, most people would say that the bone cell of a giraffe is huge compared to the other two cells. However, that's not correct. Biologists have discovered that the cells of all organisms are about the same size, averaging a few ten-thousandths of an inch across. A giraffe is larger than a frog or rosebush simply because it is made up of many more cells. This fact is a clue that helps us understand how organisms grow.

One-Celled Organisms

In the late seventeenth century, Antonie van Leeuwenhoek—famous mainly for the improvements he made in microscope design—was looking through one of his instruments at a sample of pond water. Surprised at what he saw, he used the word *beasties* to describe the tiny creatures he watched scurrying about in the drop of water!

The beasties of van Leeuwenhoek are known today simply as one-celled organisms. The most common examples are blue-green bacteria and amoebas. Tiny as each one is, though, every one-celled organism is a complete living thing. And, although they do not grow larger, these one-celled creatures carry on all of the life activities that characterize the more familiar many-celled organisms.

Many-Celled Organisms

Many-celled organisms such as giraffes, frogs, and rosebushes are similar to one-celled organisms in that each of them begins life as a single cell. However, a many-celled organism doesn't stay a single cell. And as the organism grows, other important differences become apparent.

One difference is that specialized kinds of cells develop. As an example, a frog begins life as a single fertilized egg cell. Then, as more cells form and the frog grows, new types of cells are produced that take on special roles in the frog. These new cells include muscle cells, nerve cells, fat cells, bone cells, and brain cells, to name just a few. Groups of the same type of cell usually develop together and are called tissue. A group of muscle cells in a frog's leg is one example of a tissue. The skin of a tomato is another.

A many-celled organism also shows a high degree of organization not found in a simple one-celled organism. Not only do tissue cells work together, but groups of different types of tissue cells often work together, forming a structure called an organ. A frog's leg is an organ that is made up of muscle tissue, bone tissue, nerve tissue, fat tissue, and skin tissue. Other examples of a frog's organs are its eyes, heart, lungs, and stomach.

Several organs working together are called an **organ system**. The digestive system of a frog is an organ system that provides the frog with a way of getting energy from food sources. The digestive system includes the mouth, stomach, small and large intestines, and other organs. Other systems common to most animals are the respiratory system (used for breathing), the circulatory system (used for moving blood), the nervous system (used for transmitting messages to and from the brain), the reproductive system (used for reproduction), and the excretory system (used for the elimination of waste). Vertebrates (animals with backbones) also have a skeletal system that serves as a support structure.

EXERCISE 11

Directions: Circle *T* for each statement below that is true and *F* for each statement that is false.

T   F   **1.** Cells grow in size in proportion to the size of an organism.

T   F   **2.** One-celled organisms carry on all of the basic life activities of many-celled organisms.

T   F   **3.** Groups of organs work together in a structure called a tissue.

T   F   **4.** Both plants and animals have tissues and organs.

T   F   **5.** Each kind of cell has its own structure and performs a special function for an organism.

ANSWERS ARE ON PAGE 307.

WRITING ACTIVITY 2

Just as animals have organs such as eyes, lungs, and hearts, so do humans. Sometimes people become seriously ill when an organ such as a kidney or liver fails. Many people carry cards in their wallets that state that in the event of their accidental death, they would be willing to donate organs to people who would otherwise die or, for example, be blind.

Would you be willing to be an organ donor? Jot down all the reasons you can think of for being an organ donor and all the reasons against it. Then pick one side of the issue and write a paragraph stating your opinion.

ANSWERS WILL VARY.

GED Practice

EXERCISE 12

Choose the best answer for each statement or question below.

1. One similarity of one-celled and many-celled organisms is that

(1) each is made up of only one cell
(2) each is made up of more than one cell
(3) each contains tissue
(4) each starts life as a single cell
(5) each develops organ systems

2. Which of the following would a doctor need to know in order to determine the function of a sample of tissue taken from his patient?

(1) the weight of the tissue sample
(2) the length and width of the tissue sample
(3) the number of cells contained in the tissue sample
(4) the organ the sample was taken from
(5) the type of cells that make up the tissue

ANSWERS ARE ON PAGE 308.

THE MECHANISM OF HEREDITY

KEY WORDS

> ***genes***—hereditary units contained in a chromosome; each gene controls one hereditary trait
>
> ***heredity***—the passing of certain traits, through genes, from parents to their offspring
>
> ***species***—genetically similar organisms that can mate and produce fertile offspring
>
> ***trait***—a characteristic, or distinguishing feature, of an organism

---

How do newly produced cells know what they're supposed to do? This question puzzled biologists for a long time. As we'll see, the answer is related to the answer of a second question: why do children tend to look so much like their parents?

Research has now provided answers to both of these questions. Biologists have discovered that an organism grows by a process called ***cell division***. During cell division, known as ***mitosis***, one cell (called the ***parent cell***) divides into two new cells (called ***daughter cells***). During mitosis a set of coded instructions is passed on from the parent cell to each of the two daughter cells. Each instruction is actually a complex chemical called a gene. These instructions control the activities of both daughter cells and make sure these cells perform their proper functions.

The genes are carried in chromosomes, rod-shaped structures made of chromatin and found in a cell's nucleus. Hundreds of genes make up each chromosome.

Just before a cell divides, the chromatin forms a second set of identical chromosomes. During cell division, two daughter cells form from the parent cell, and each daughter cell receives one set of the chromosomes. In this way, each new cell has the same set of activity-controlling genes as the parent cell that formed it.

FIVE STEPS OF MITOSIS

Interphase	Prophase	Metaphase	Anaphase	Telophase

Chromatin—
Nuclear membrane
Cell membrane

Two sets of chromosomes have formed. The nuclear membrane disappears.

Chromosomes line up in spindle fiber that forms in center of nucleus.

Chromosomes separate and move apart on spindle fibers.

Two nuclei and nuclear membranes form. The cell divides and two daughter cells form.

Reproduction and Heredity

Biologists have also discovered that chromosomes play a major role in mating, while genes play an essential part in heredity. Different organisms have different numbers of chromosomes. Organisms that have the same number of chromosomes look alike and are said to be in the same species. In most cases, members of the same species can mate and produce fertile offspring (offspring capable of reproducing). When a male and a female mate, chromosomes from a male sex cell combine with the chromosomes of a female sex cell. Together, they make up the chromosomes of the fertilized egg—the one-celled first stage of the offspring. In this way, every offspring receives an equal number of chromosomes from each parent.

The genes carried in the chromosomes determine the traits of the offspring. Animals, for example, may inherit eye color, hair color, and height. Two inheritable traits in plants are flower color and leaf shape.

When male and female organisms mate, their offspring always receives two genes for each inheritable trait. One gene for each trait comes from each parent. For example, each parent in the diagram below has two eye-color genes, which we've labeled *Br* for brown and *Bl* for blue. The mother has one *Bl* gene and one *Br* gene. The father has two *Bl* genes. A child of this couple will inherit one eye-color gene from each parent. The child may receive any of the four possible combinations of genes as shown in the boxes.

(Mother)

		Br	*Bl*
(Father)	*Bl*	*Br Bl* (Child 1)	*Bl Bl* (Child 2)
	Bl	*Br Bl* (Child 3)	*Bl Bl* (Child 4)

Eye color, like every other inheritable trait, depends on the presence or absence of a ***dominant*** gene. A dominant gene is one gene in a gene pair that determines the effect of the gene pair. For example, a *Br* gene is dominant over a *Bl* gene. Because of this, a person who has either one or two *Br* genes will have brown eyes. A person will have blue eyes only if he or she has two *Bl* genes, like children 2 and 4 in the diagram above. *Bl* genes are said to be ***recessive***—that is, they have no effect if a dominant gene is present.

In the example above, the mother has brown eyes and the father has blue eyes. The child's eyes will be brown if he inherits a *Br* gene. Two of the four possible gene combinations result in the child inheriting a *Br* gene and two don't. Therefore, the child is equally likely to be born with brown eyes or blue eyes. This will also be true for any other child this couple may have in the future.

EXERCISE 13

Directions: Complete each sentence by filling in the blanks with the correct word(s).

1. _____ is the passing of traits, through genes, from parents to offspring.

2. Chromosomes are made of the _____ found in a cell's _____.

3. A _____ is an individual instruction that is transmitted from parent to offspring.

4. An offspring receives _____ gene(s) for each inheritable trait.
   (number)

5. Each member of a species has the same number of _____.

ANSWERS ARE ON PAGE 308.

 GED Practice

EXERCISE 14

Questions 1–3 are based on the information on page 100.

1. Which of the following statements best summarizes the role played by genes in heredity?

   (1) A gene may be either dominant or recessive.
   (2) An organism receives identical genes from each of its parents.
   (3) The number of an organism's genes determines which two organisms are able to mate.
   (4) Genes carry the hereditary messages that determine an organism's traits.
   (5) Genes always occur in pairs and determine how many chromosomes an organism has.

2. Which of the following pairs of animals is least likely to be genetically related?

   (1) pheasants and turkeys
   (2) gorillas and horses
   (3) bees and wasps
   (4) alligators and crocodiles
   (5) robins and sparrows

3. The best experiment to try in order to determine which personality traits are inherited and which are formed by a person's upbringing would be to compare the personalities of

   (1) identical twins who were separated at birth and raised in different families
   (2) an older sister and younger brother who were raised in the same family
   (3) two adopted children who were raised separately in two families that live in the same city
   (4) two unrelated children of the same age who were raised in different cultures
   (5) two unrelated adults who were raised in different cultures

Questions 4 and 5 refer to the following.

Each parent organism contains two genes for every inheritable trait. One or both of these genes may be the dominant gene for that particular trait. Remember, though, that during reproduction each parent passes on to its offspring only one gene from each pair of its own genes.

Below we show two parent pea plants, A and B. Plant A (*TT*) has two tall-plant genes, while plant B (*tt*) has two short-plant genes. The first-generation offspring are all *Tt*, inheriting one gene from each parent plant. (Notice that all first-generation plants will inherit a *T* from plant A and a *t* from plant B.)

Plants C and D are first-generation offspring that produce second-generation offspring.

Plant A

tall
TT

Plant B

short
tt

First-Generation Offspring

Plant C

tall
Tt

Plant D

tall
Tt

Plant E

tall
Tt

Plant F

tall
Tt

Second-Generation Offspring

tall
?

tall
?

tall
?

short
?

4. From the illustration, you can conclude that

  (1) both plants A and B have a dominant gene for tallness

  (2) neither plant A nor B has a dominant gene for tallness

  (3) each first generation offspring plant has two dominant genes

  (4) the *T* gene is dominant, while the *t* gene is recessive

  (5) the *t* gene is dominant, while the *T* gene is recessive

5. Which of the following correctly labels the gene combinations that are possible in the second generation plants produced by crossing plants C and D?

  (1) *TT, TT, TT, tt*
  (2) *TT, TT, tt, tt*
  (3) *TT, tt, tt, tt*
  (4) *TT, Tt, Tt, tt*
  (5) *Tt, Tt, Tt, Tt*

ANSWERS ARE ON PAGE 308.

COMMUNITIES OF LIVING THINGS

ECOSYSTEMS

Many different kinds of animals and plants live in and around a pond. The survival of each of these organisms depends on the others. Many animals eat plants, and plants depend on animals for waste products that provide nutrients. Along the shore, insects eat plants, frogs eat insects, snakes eat frogs, and birds eat snakes. Within the pond, small fish feed on *plankton*—tiny plant and animal life that floats in great numbers in the water. Bass, other large fish, and perhaps a few ducks eat the smaller fish. Through this interdependence, called a food chain, each organism plays a role in the total life of the pond.

A pond is just one example of a habitat, or home, of a community of living things. Other types of habitats are forests, grasslands, deserts, mountains, rivers, and oceans. A community of organisms, together with its habitat and all the other nonliving things that affect the community, is called an ecosystem. Examples of nonliving resources that are important in an ecosystem are adequate sunshine, clean water, and clean air.

There are many types of relationships among the plants and animals in an ecosystem. One is nutritional and leads to food chains. In every food chain, organisms either produce their own food or obtain food by eating other organisms. Algae and green plants, for example, make food from nutrients they find in water and soil. Mushrooms and other fungi can't make food, so they take nutrients from trees and other plants. Animals don't make their own food either and must obtain it by eating plants and other animals. The resulting food chains tend to go full circle and are called *food webs*. For example, think of a pond in which water lilies are growing. The leaves of one of the lilies are eaten by a snail who in turn is eaten by a small fish. The fish lives for a while but is then swallowed by a duck. Circling over the duck's head, though, is a hawk. Not long after the hawk eats the duck, the hawk dies near the pond, and bacteria feed on its decomposing body. The bacteria return nutrients to the soil. The nutrients in the soil are washed into the pond where they are used by water lilies to grow new leaves.

A second relationship in a community is based on competition for limited resources. For example, in a pond both bass and ducks eat small fish. The more successful the ducks are, the less food there will be for the bass. Each of these animals has other sources of food, so this competition is not likely to lead to the death of one of them. However, competition among members of the same species is much more intense. Because each has exactly the same needs and is after the exact same resources, all members of a species often directly compete, with starvation waiting for the poorest competitors. Besides food, animals might also compete for resources such as mating partners and space in which to live.

In a stable ecosystem, the population of each plant or animal stays about constant. The number of each species that die is balanced by the number of their newborn that survive.

Disruptive changes can easily upset the stability of an ecosystem. Destructive acts of nature can occur. A forest fire can destroy all plant and animal life in a forest, along a river, and around the shore of a pond. It can also pollute a pond with ash. A flood or mudslide can wipe out the side of a mountain, flood the banks of a river, and dump tons of sediment into a pond—destroying life along the shore and within the pond as well. Pollution from acts of human beings can also affect an ecosystem. A chemical spill or pesticides sprayed overhead can kill all plant and animal life with which it comes in contact. A housing development along the bank of a river or on the shore of a pond can bring both garbage and noise pollution, in addition to direct physical destruction of these habitats.

EXERCISE 15

Directions: Match each item on the left with the best example on the right. Write the letter of the example on the line before the correct number.

_____ **1.** resource

_____ **2.** population

_____ **3.** ecosystem

_____ **4.** act of nature

_____ **5.** human-caused disaster

(a) a volcanic eruption

(b) a pond and all the organisms in it

(c) clean water

(d) a chemical spill into a river

(e) the number of frogs living next to Juniper Lake

ANSWERS ARE ON PAGE 308.

EXERCISE 16

Question 1 refers to the following diagram.

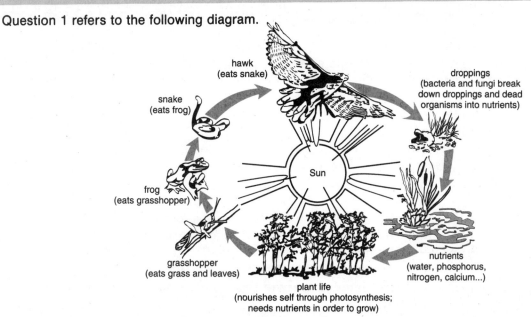

hawk
(eats snake)

snake
(eats frog)

frog
(eats grasshopper)

grasshopper
(eats grass and leaves)

Sun

droppings
(bacteria and fungi break
down droppings and dead
organisms into nutrients)

nutrients
(water, phosphorus,
nitrogen, calcium...)

plant life
(nourishes self through photosynthesis;
needs nutrients in order to grow)

1. Based on the diagram above, what most likely would happen to the animal populations after chemical spraying kills most of the region's mosquitoes and gnats, both of which are sources of food for frogs?

   (1) a decrease in both frogs and snakes
   (2) a decrease in frogs and an increase in grasshoppers
   (3) an increase in both frogs and snakes
   (4) a decrease in snakes and an increase in hawks
   (5) an increase in both snakes and hawks

2. In order for the population of an organism in a habitat to increase, which of the following must be true?

   (1) The organism's reproduction time must be short compared to the reproduction time of other organisms in the habitat.
   (2) The organism must have no predators.
   (3) The organism's birth rate must be equal to its death rate.
   (4) The organism's birth rate must be greater than its death rate.
   (5) The organism's birth rate must be less than its death rate.

3. At present there are no bass in Waldo Lake, a high-mountain fishing lake that doesn't freeze during winter. Richard, a wildlife biologist who works for the forest service, is going to start a bass population in the lake by releasing 10,000 baby bass during the warm month of June.

   Which of the following will be the *least* relevant factor in determining the eventual size of a stable bass population in Waldo Lake?

   (1) the availability of food sources in Waldo Lake for bass
   (2) the average number of fishermen who will fish for bass in Waldo Lake during the coming summers
   (3) the health of the insect populations in and around Waldo Lake during the coming years
   (4) the number of other fish that presently live in Waldo Lake
   (5) the types of plants that live on the shore of Waldo Lake

ANSWERS ARE ON PAGE 308.

CHARLES DARWIN'S DISCOVERIES

> ### KEY WORDS
>
> ***evolution***—the idea that a species may change over time, both in appearance and in inherited behavior patterns
>
> ***favorable trait***—any characteristic that gives an individual an advantage in the struggle for survival
>
> ***genetic variation***—a difference in appearance or behavior that can be inherited by offspring
>
> ***natural selection***—the idea that individuals with favorable traits are the most likely members of a species to survive and reproduce

In 1832, a twenty-four-year-old naturalist named Charles Darwin sailed from England aboard Her Majesty's Ship *Beagle*. During the next three years, Darwin explored the rain forests of South America and hiked throughout the Galapagos Islands, located off that continent's western shore. These explorations revealed things to Darwin that forever changed his ideas about the nature of life on Earth.

On the Galapagos Islands, Darwin saw creatures that existed nowhere else in the world. He saw tortoises that seemed to be the same as the small land tortoises of South America. However, the island tortoises were huge—large enough to ride! He saw small birds called finches that seemed to be like the finches found on the continent, only they weren't quite the same. The island finches had beak shapes and eating habits that were different from those of the South American variety.

Thinking about how similar the island animals were to the continent animals, Darwin concluded that each island species had originally come from the continent, perhaps thousands of years ago or more. At that distant time, each island species must have been exactly like its mainland relatives.

To account for the differences that he saw, Darwin concluded that once on the islands, each species had become isolated from the mainland. Then, because the island environment had fewer life forms and much harsher conditions than the mainland, the island species slowly changed through many generations. There were changes in both appearance and behavior. The island species that he saw now were visibly different from their South American relatives, but they were much better suited (or fit) for the island environment. Darwin used the word *evolution* to refer to this process of gradual change.

Darwin theorized that evolution is a process that probably occurs in all populations of organisms. As generation follows generation during a long period of time, adaptive changes occur. These changes appear as variations in structure and behavior, the changed organisms being much better suited for the environment in which they live. Darwin thus looked at evolution as a process that directly links today's life forms with life forms of the past.

Darwin's Theory of Evolution

Darwin's theory can be summarized as follows:

- *There are genetic variations among the members of every species.* Many of these variations, called favorable traits, may actually aid in an individual's struggle for survival. For example, a hawk that has long claws will be able to kill prey more easily than a competing hawk that has short claws.

- *An ecosystem can support only a certain number of organisms of any one species.* Competition for food, water, and a place to live limit the population growth of each species. There are also threats to life such as predators and disease.

- *Members of a species that are most likely to survive during a time of changing environmental conditions are those with favorable traits.* For example, during a time of limited prey, the hawks with long claws are much more likely to capture prey than are the hawks with short claws. By surviving, long-claw hawks will likely reproduce and pass on this favorable trait to their offspring. But short-claw hawks are not so lucky. It is likely that many of these hawks will starve to death and not produce offspring. Because of this, the unfavorable trait of short claws will slowly be eliminated in this species of hawk.

The idea that individuals with favorable traits are the most likely members of a species to survive, reproduce, and pass on those traits is known as natural selection. Natural selection, a key principle in Darwin's theory, ensures that only favorable traits are likely to be passed on to future generations. Darwin realized that natural selection, operating over thousands of years or more, would lead to just the type of world that he saw: one in which organisms were superbly adapted to the environmental conditions around them.

EXERCISE 17

Directions: Match each item on the left with the best example or definition on the right. Write the letter of the phrase on the line before the correct number.

_____ **1.** evolution

_____ **2.** genetic variation

_____ **3.** favorable trait

_____ **4.** unfavorable trait

_____ **5.** natural selection

(a) a duck, living near a polluted lake, giving birth to a duckling with only one wing

(b) better-adapted individuals having a survival advantage

(c) the structure and behavior of organisms changing over many generations

(d) the ptarmigan growing white plumage that helps it hide in the winter snow

(e) a boy having six toes on his left foot, just like his father

ANSWERS ARE ON PAGE 308.

EXERCISE 18

Questions 1–5 refer to the information on pages 106–107.

1. Which of the following best summarizes Darwin's theory of evolution?

   (1) Organisms purposely change in order to adapt to changing environmental conditions.
   (2) Organisms change over time, and those that are the most fit have the best chance of surviving and passing on their own characteristics.
   (3) Although many life forms are now extinct, living organisms have not changed since the beginning of life on Earth.
   (4) Genetic traits are passed from one generation of an organism to the next generation.
   (5) All organisms have an equal opportunity to learn to adapt to changing environmental conditions.

2. From the list below, choose the trait that would be most useful for birds on a small island that is hit periodically by severe storms that kill most of the island's land animals.

   (1) longer claws, useful for carrying twigs
   (2) a high-pitched vocal cry, useful for attracting mates
   (3) darker-colored tail feathers, useful for camouflage
   (4) a wider beak, capable of capturing insects and tiny fish swimming in water
   (5) sharper claws, useful for killing small rodents

3. The most important factor in determining what shape of beak would be the most favorable trait for a bird is

   (1) the types of food sources in the bird's habitat
   (2) the bird's average life expectancy
   (3) the type of predator that hunts the bird
   (4) the bird's nesting habits
   (5) the times during the day or night that the bird hunts

4. Which of the following observations best supports Darwin's theory of evolution?

   (1) Offspring of organisms tend to look and behave in ways that are very similar to their parents.
   (2) Dinosaurs were once the dominant life form on Earth, but now they are extinct.
   (3) If polar bears were not a protected species, they would soon become extinct because of hunters.
   (4) Certain genetic diseases such as sickle-cell anemia can be inherited.
   (5) Fossils show that many of today's organisms are similar to, but not identical to, organisms that are now extinct.

5. Which of the following is the hypothesis best supported by Darwin's theory of evolution?

   Humans and chimpanzees have many similar body features because

   (1) all primates, including humans and chimpanzees, have similar features
   (2) humans have not evolved from their original form
   (3) chimpanzees evolved from humans
   (4) humans and chimpanzees evolved from a common ancestor
   (5) neither humans nor chimpanzees have evolved from their original forms

Questions 6 and 7 refer to the following passage.

Before Darwin's ideas were published, Jean Lamarck, a French biologist, proposed a different idea of how organisms obtained favorable traits. According to Lamarck, an individual organism could acquire certain favorable traits by its own efforts. Lamarck believed that these traits would then be inherited by all of the organism's future offspring.

Lamarck's most famous example was the giraffe. He claimed that giraffes once had short legs and short necks. But then, as they strained to reach leaves higher up on trees, giraffes stretched their necks and legs, a little bit at a time. In this way the bodies of giraffes changed shape. When each "stretched" giraffe reproduced, its offspring were born with the favorable traits of long necks and long legs!

Since the time of Darwin, biologists have concluded that Lamarck was incorrect. Although organisms can adapt their own bodies to the conditions of their environment, they cannot automatically pass these acquired traits on to offspring.

6. Which of the following is the best example of an inherited trait that Lamarck would have said was acquired by a previous generation?

(1) the strength of a bullfrog's hindlegs
(2) the thickness of a sheep's wool
(3) the uselessness of a penguin's wings for flying
(4) the amount of hair on a gorilla's body
(5) the whiteness of a polar bear's fur

7. According to Lamarck's theory, which of the following factors most influenced a change in shape in giraffes?

(1) a genetic variation that proved to be favorable
(2) an abundance of vegetation close to the ground
(3) the great depth of rivers during frequent floods
(4) a scarcity of vegetation close to the ground
(5) the need to be larger than its predators

ANSWERS ARE ON PAGE 308.

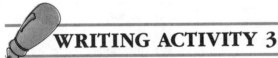

WRITING ACTIVITY 3

Botanists estimate that a considerable number of all species of organisms on Earth face extinction during the next ten to thirty years. The endangered species include unique plants and animals that could possibly provide new forms of energy or even a cure for cancer. These species may die out because their habitat—the rain forests of Latin America, Africa, and Australia—is being destroyed. Major causes of this destruction are rapid population growth, the need for land on which to raise crops, and the world's demand for timber.

Is it important to protect these plants and animals, or would our money and time be better spent on other projects? Pick one side of the issue and write a paragraph explaining your viewpoint.

ANSWERS WILL VARY.

PLANT AND ANIMAL BIOLOGY

Questions 1–4 refer to the following diagram and passage.

OPARIN'S THEORY OF THE ORIGIN OF LIFE

In 1924, a Russian scientist named Alexander Oparin proposed a theory to explain how life might have started on Earth. Oparin proposed that before life began, Earth's atmosphere contained four main gases: methane (made up of carbon and hydrogen), ammonia (made up of nitrogen and hydrogen), water vapor (made up of oxygen and hydrogen), and pure hydrogen.

According to Oparin, sunlight or lightning provided the energy needed to split these gases into the elements that make them up. Instead of recombining into the gases they had been originally, these elements recombined in new ways, creating new types of molecules called organic molecules. Organic molecules are known to be the basic building blocks of all living organisms.

Oparin believed that large numbers of these organic molecules were then washed from the atmosphere by rain. They collected in shallow "organic pools." While in organic pools, the organic molecules combined to form more complex molecules. Then, he believed, these complex molecules somehow organized and eventually became the first living cells.

1. In Oparin's theory, which of the following would have had to come first?

   (1) rocks containing carbon
   (2) a multi-cellular organism
   (3) an atmosphere containing methane
   (4) the first living cell
   (5) a pool containing organic material

2. Before life began, the main element in Earth's atmosphere was most likely

   (1) oxygen
   (2) hydrogen
   (3) carbon
   (4) iron
   (5) nitrogen

3. Oparin's theory attempts to explain each of the following *except*

   (1) the formation of the first organic molecules
   (2) how atmospheric gases might be split apart
   (3) how sunlight and lightning played a part in the development of the first living cells
   (4) differences between plant and animal cells
   (5) the formation of shallow organic pools

4. The biological principle of biogenesis asserts that a living organism can only come from another living organism. Oparin's theory

   (1) is not consistent with biogenesis
   (2) supports biogenesis
   (3) proves that biogenesis is not correct
   (4) proves that biogenesis is correct
   (5) supports the theory of evolution

Questions 5–7 refer to the following drawings and passage.

METAMORPHOSIS OF FROGS AND BUTTERFLIES

Egg Stage	Larva Stage	Growth of Adult Structures	Adult Stage

newly born tadpole

tadpole with limbs

adult frog

newly hatched caterpillar

pupa

adult butterfly

During development from egg to adult, many animals undergo a process called *metamorphosis*, the formation of radically different stages of life. Along with structural differences, each life stage may involve its own distinct habitat and feeding behavior. Most often, each stage is specialized for a particular function. One stage may be for feeding and early growth, one for habitat selection, and one for the growth of structures characteristic of the adult. The early stage is called the *larva stage*, while the reproductive stage is known as the *adult stage*.

Frogs and butterflies both go through metamorphosis. A frog starts as an egg in water and forms a tadpole as its larva stage. A tadpole feeds on plant life and, like fish, breathes through gills. Later, it absorbs its tail, grows limbs and lungs, and leaves the water to live on land as an insect eater.

A butterfly starts out as an egg and forms a caterpillar as its larva stage. During the quiet stage in which the pupa (or chrysalis) is enclosed in a cocoon, the tissues of the caterpillar change and wings develop. The familiar winged butterfly emerges from the cocoon and is now capable of reproduction.

5. Metamorphosis is best defined as

   (1) the growth of an animal from egg stage to adult stage
   (2) the difference in growth patterns characteristic of different animals
   (3) the different types of food that an animal eats as it develops
   (4) the formation of distinctly different stages of development in an animal
   (5) the development of the reproductive stage of an animal

6. Which of the following makes it possible for a frog to live out of water?

   (1) tail
   (2) large eyes
   (3) lungs
   (4) legs
   (5) gills

7. The chief difference between the metamorphosis of a frog and of a butterfly is that

   (1) the frog's life span is longer
   (2) the frog's metamorphosis is shorter
   (3) the young do not resemble the adults
   (4) caterpillars feed on plants, tadpoles do not
   (5) the butterfly's structural growth stage is inactive

ANSWERS ARE ON PAGE 308.

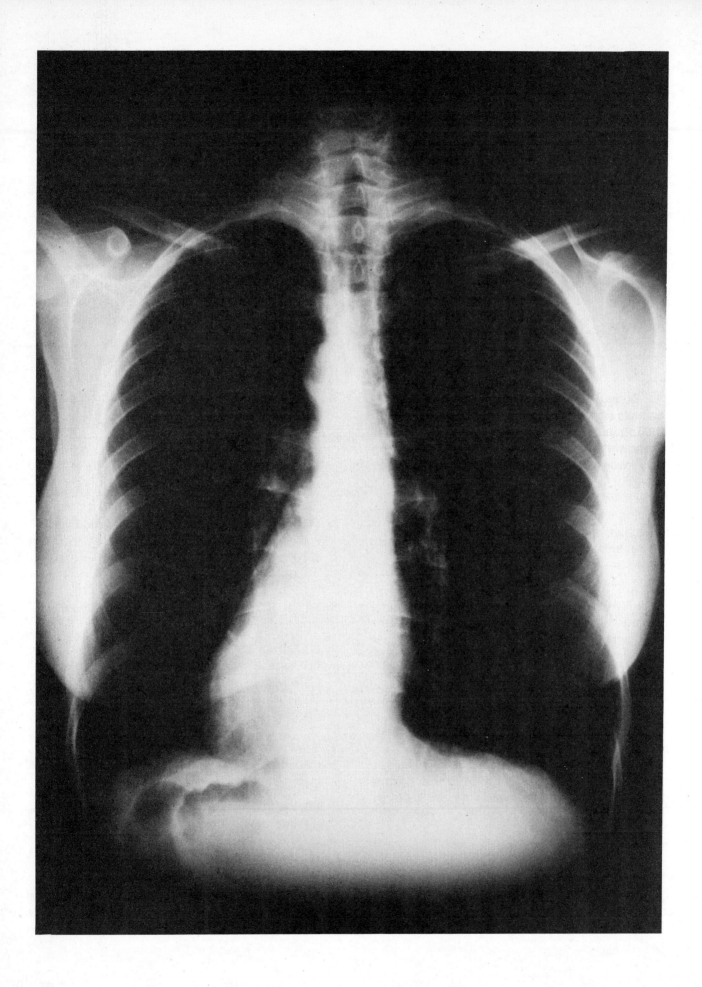

6 Human Biology

Animals, as a rule, stay in the environment for which they're best adapted for survival. You may find lots of penguins living near the coast of Antarctica, but you'd be surprised to see even one in the Sahara Desert! Likewise, while you expect to see camels in the Sahara Desert, you wouldn't expect one to live near Antarctica. Penguins and camels, like almost all other animals on Earth, show no desire or ability to venture away from their home environment. Even animals that migrate spend their lives in only two homes for which they're specially adapted.

The one exception to the rule is human beings. By nature, humans—naked and without thick skin or a coat of fur—are adapted only to life on land where the temperature is mild. Compared to most other animals, we don't seem very fit for survival even there! We aren't very strong, we can't run very fast, we can't fly, and we can't fight very well. But here we are! By inventing clothes, forms of shelter, weapons for hunting, and other survival aids, we have done things that no other animal, no matter how well adapted, has ever done. We have made homes on all the continents and islands of Earth. We have lowered ourselves to the bottom of the ocean, and we have flown to the top of the atmosphere and to the moon. Perhaps most important, we have produced a culture where the least fit have as much opportunity to survive and prosper as do the most fit. These are remarkable achievements.

What makes human beings unique? Most certainly it is the power of the human mind. Although many of our survival needs are the same as those of other animals, our means of meeting those needs are much more complex. We can anticipate and plan for the future, we learn from experience (both our own and the experiences of others), and we have free choice. Other animals have none of these abilities. While an ant can build only an anthill, we can build a skyscraper, a school, a church, or a sports stadium. While other animals spend their time in a constant search for food, we can pursue goals that help lead to fulfilling work and recreational lives. Although it's fun to think about our special talents, the study of human biology is also about the similarities that are found in all life forms. We know we differ from other animals, but in what ways are we the same?

One important discovery is that human beings may be biologically related to many different species. Similarities in body structure suggest that humans and other animals have similar genetic codes for the formation of many different organs. The arm bones of a human, for example, are very similar to the leg bones of a dog as well as to the forelimb bones of a bird.

BIRD **DOG** **HUMAN**

forelimb bones

leg bones

arm bones

Similar bone structure indicates that many different species of animals may be biologically related.

FISH **BIRD** **HUMAN**

Similarities shown in the stages of embryonic development may indicate a common biological history.

Surprising similarity also exists between organisms at the embryo stage—the early stage of development of a new individual from a fertilized egg. For example, embryos of many vertebrates (animals with backbones) are so similar that it is difficult for an untrained person to tell a fish embryo from a bird embryo or a human embryo. Many scientists think that embryonic similarity is a sign of common biological history.

Biologists have also discovered that the chemical makeup of a human is much like that of other animals. For example, the proteins in the human body differ in structure by less than 1 percent from the proteins in the body of a chimpanzee. Because of these structural and chemical similarities, biologists now think that human beings may share many more characteristics of other life forms. They hope to use this information to help understand the biological origin of human life as well as the origin of other forms of life.

Biologists classify all animals according to body structure and function. Different species that look very much alike tend to be placed in the same classification group. For example, cattle and sheep are classified in a group that does not include chickens or salmon. Human beings are classified in a large group called *mammals* and are given the biological name *Homo sapiens*. We are also placed in a small subgroup called primates. *Primates* are mammals that can walk erect on two legs. This subgroup includes human beings, apes, and monkeys.

We'll begin our study of human biology by discussing the most amazing organ of the human body, the brain.

EXERCISE 1

Directions: Answer each question below.

1. Complete each sentence by filling in the blanks with the correct word(s).

   a. Biologists classify animals according to their _____

   and _____.

   b. _____ is the biological name given to the animal species better known as human beings.

2. Name two types of evidence that suggest that human beings are biologically related to other animals.

   a. _____

   b. _____

ANSWERS ARE ON PAGE 309.

GED Practice

EXERCISE 2

Questions 1–4 are based on the information on pages 113–114.

1. The best summary of the first two paragraphs of the reading selection is that human beings are

   (1) only one of many types of animals that can change their environment significantly
   (2) the only animals that are solely adapted to life on land
   (3) biologically related to other animals
   (4) adapted by nature to life on all the land masses of the Earth
   (5) the only animals that can live in environments for which their bodies are not adapted

2. According to the reading selection, human beings are classified in a group called *primates*. Which of the following animals is also a primate?

   (1) goat
   (2) gorilla
   (3) dolphin
   (4) sparrow
   (5) horse

3. According to the reading selection, animals that show similarity in body structure may also have similar

   (1) genetic codes
   (2) interests
   (3) life spans
   (4) behavior patterns
   (5) brain sizes

4. The best example of appendages that have similar bone structures but very different uses are

   (1) the leg of an elephant and leg of a human
   (2) the wing of a falcon and the wing of a bat
   (3) the arm of a human and arm of a monkey
   (4) the leg of a human and leg of a dog
   (5) the forelimb of a bird and the arm of a human

Questions 5–7 refer to the following passage.

The publication in the last half of the nineteenth century of Charles Darwin's ideas on evolution and natural selection started a bitter controversy among biologists, religious leaders, and the general public. This controversy centered around Darwin's conclusions that both plant and animal species change over time and that new species may develop in the process. A particular point of contention was Darwin's suggestion that human beings, like other animals, evolve as a result of natural selection.

The idea of human evolution remains today as one of the most discussed and debated ideas in biology. Many people now believe that human beings did, in fact, evolve from a simpler life form, most probably an apelike primate that lived millions of years ago. According to this idea, the evolution of these prehuman primates resulted in the formation of several new species. One of these species is *Homo sapiens*, or human beings. If this conclusion is correct, human beings are related to other modern primates much more closely than scientists before Darwin's time could ever have imagined.

5. Charles Darwin noticed certain similarities between the physical features of chimpanzees and those of orangutans. Based on his beliefs, which of the following conclusions could he most likely have drawn?

   (1) Chimpanzees are not biologically related to orangutans in any way.
   (2) Either the chimpanzee or the orangutan, but not both, evolved from an apelike primate that lived millions of years ago.
   (3) Chimpanzees evolved from orangutans that lived millions of years ago.
   (4) Chimpanzees and orangutans both evolved from the same apelike primate that lived millions of years ago.
   (5) Neither chimpanzees nor orangutans evolved at all during the last few million years.

6. Which of the following discoveries would be the best evidence that human beings and modern apes may have evolved from a common ancestor?

   (1) With proper training, an ape can learn to communicate in simple sign language with human beings.
   (2) Apes can be raised from babies to adulthood by human beings.
   (3) Ancient skulls have been discovered that show both humanlike and apelike features.
   (4) Apes can walk upright on their two back legs in a way that's similar to how human beings walk.
   (5) Apes in the wild form family groups similar to the family groups formed by human beings.

7. Which of the following human activities may improve any natural human evolution that may be taking place?

   (1) educating as many people as possible
   (2) encouraging all children and adults to participate in physical exercise
   (3) providing an economic system where each person can succeed up to the level of his or her ability
   (4) using genetic engineering to cure debilitating diseases
   (5) supporting more research efforts to better understand the history of life on Earth

ANSWERS ARE ON PAGE 309.

WRITING ACTIVITY 1

In order to test new products or develop cures for diseases, scientists often experiment on such animals as rats, monkeys, dogs, and cats. For example, in order to find out if a new eye cosmetic is safe for humans, researchers might place the product in a monkey's eye even though the animal might be injured or blinded.

Do you believe that such experiments are fair and necessary? Make a list of reasons that support your point of view. When you are finished, reread the list carefully and organize the reasons from strongest to weakest.

POSSIBLE ANSWERS ARE ON PAGE 309.

THE HUMAN BRAIN

KEY WORDS

brain hemisphere—one of the two halves of the human brain
emotion—a strong feeling such as joy or sadness
intelligence—the ability to acquire and apply knowledge
intuition—problem-solving insight that is based on inner feelings
logic—careful reasoning used to solve problems
neuron—a nerve cell

The human brain is often described as the most marvelous yet mysterious organ in the human body. You use yours in everything that you do. Because of your brain, you have special qualities that make you unique among all other living organisms. From it comes the personality that is the "you" whom other people know.

As you read this page, your brain receives electrical signals from your eyes. Somehow—nobody knows how—you change these signals into the thoughts of your conscious mind. You then remember some of these thoughts and simply forget others. Yet, as familiar as these processes are to you, scientists do not yet know what the conscious mind is or how it is actually related to the brain. This mystery—often called the *mind-brain problem*—will undoubtedly remain one of the most challenging and exciting areas of brain research well into the twenty-first century. In this section we'll mention a few of the most important discoveries about the mind and brain.

Seen from above, the human brain looks much like a large gray walnut. Its typical weight is about three pounds. Although we usually think of the brain as a single unit, it is actually divided into two halves. Each half, called a hemisphere, is joined to the other half by bundles of nerve fibers. Biologists believe that these nerve fibers enable the two halves of the brain to communicate with each other.

TOP VIEW OF HUMAN BRAIN

left hemisphere   right hemisphere

The two halves of the human brain are connected in the center by bundles of nerve fibers.

If brain tissue is examined under a microscope, it is seen to consist of nerve cells called neurons. Although the exact number is unknown, each human brain is believed to contain more than ten billion neurons! These neurons form an interconnected network of cells through which electrical and chemical messages pass. Because these messages occur at all hours of day and night, scientists believe that they must be directly related to mental activities that take place both while we're awake and while we're asleep and dreaming.

Because it has so many neurons, the human brain has the capacity to store more information than is in all the libraries in the world. However, we don't use our brain power just to memorize information. We can use books and computers to do that. Instead, we use our brain power to carry out the more complex activities of intelligent living beings. The brain thinks, feels, stores memories, and interprets. It also responds to sight, sound, touch, and other body sensations and controls body movement and body growth.

TWO NEURONS IN SYNAPTIC CONTACT

dendrite — nucleus — axon — myelin sheath — synapse — cell body

A neuron consists of a cell body, nucleus, a long fiber called an *axon* through which a nerve impulse is sent, and a large number of branching fibers called *dendrites*. Messages are transmitted across a tiny synaptic gap from the ends of the axon of a neuron to the dendrites of other neurons. This "contact" is called a *synapse*. No one knows how information is coded and sent from neuron to neuron, but scientists know that both chemical and electrical processes are involved.

LOCALIZATION OF BRAIN FUNCTIONS

Each of our body sensations and movements is controlled by one of the brain hemispheres. The left hemisphere controls the right side of the body, and the right hemisphere controls the left side of the body. If one hemisphere is damaged, the opposite side of the body may be partly or completely paralyzed. This often occurs with accident and stroke victims.

Besides controlling sensations and movements, the brain provides us with intelligence and emotions. Intelligence is the ability to acquire and apply knowledge; emotions are our inner feelings. Each hemisphere appears to play a special role in the many ways in which knowledge and feelings are acquired and remembered. The left hemisphere appears to be more important for reasoning skills such as mathematics and science and for language skills. The right hemisphere is more important for spatial-relations skills, artistic skills, and imagination. This division of skills has led many researchers to comment that the two halves of the brain are much like the two ways we deal with problem solving: the left half gives us logic, while the right half gives us intuition.

number skills

$$\frac{4a^2b^3}{2ab} = 2ab^2$$

spoken language

written language

MANDARIN
Français
ESPAÑOL

right-hand control

left-hand control

music awareness

three-dimensional forms

art awareness

scientific skills

reasoning

insight

imagination

EXERCISE 3

Directions: Complete each sentence below by filling in the blanks with the correct word(s).

1. The human brain is divided into _____ hemispheres.
(number)

2. The _____ hemisphere of the brain controls the right side of the body, while the _____ hemisphere controls the left side of the body.

3. The cells that make up the human brain are called _____.

4. Enjoyment of music is a function of the _____ side of the brain.

5. The two sides of the brain are connected by _____.

6. The question of how the mind and brain are related to one another is often referred to as the _____.

≡ GED Practice ≡
EXERCISE 4

Questions 1–3 are based on the information on pages 117–119.

1. For what purpose do bundles of nerve fibers join the two brain hemispheres?

  (1) to enable dreaming during sleep
  (2) to hold the two brain halves close together
  (3) to enable the two brain halves to exchange information
  (4) to enable blood to flow from one side to the other
  (5) to separate the two brain halves

2. An elderly man who has suffered a stroke that left the right side of his body partially paralyzed has most probably experienced a decrease in blood flow to

  (1) his heart
  (2) the right half of his brain
  (3) the left side of his body
  (4) both halves of his brain
  (5) the left half of his brain

3. David has incorrectly assumed that a larger brain size indicates greater intelligence. Which two ideas can Maddie use to demonstrate that he is wrong?

  A. The brains of all human adults are about the same size.
  B. A teenager's brain is larger than a baby's brain.
  C. The brain of an elephant is larger than the brain of a human being.
  D. The brain of a human being is larger than the brain of a dog.

  (1) A and B
  (2) A and C
  (3) A and D
  (4) B and C
  (5) C and D

ANSWERS ARE ON PAGE 309.

WRITING ACTIVITY 2

Some researchers say that people are either right-brained or left-brained. A right-brained person is more artistic, imaginative, and intuitive—the right half of the brain dominates the personality. In contrast, a left-brained person is more logical and is good at dealing with numbers and language.

Do you believe this theory? Have you observed that you or your friends are particularly right-brained or left-brained? Write a paragraph stating your opinion. Be sure to give examples to support your point of view. It may be helpful to describe the personalities of people you know.

ANSWERS WILL VARY.

TAKING CARE OF YOUR BODY

A LONG AND HEALTHY LIFE

KEY WORDS

aging—changes that take place in an organism as it grows older
life expectancy—the average life span of an animal or plant
stress—tension caused by emotional, chemical, or physical factors

Have you ever wished for a magic pill or magic formula that would let you live happily forever? If you have, don't feel alone! It's a very common, natural wish that has a long history. Spanish explorers of the sixteenth century even tried to find a fountain of youth in what is now the state of Florida. The water of this legendary fountain, which no one has yet found, was believed to restore youth and good health to those who drank it.

Biologists today don't expect that anyone will find a magical fountain of youth. Growing older is a natural part of the life cycle that can't be reversed. As human beings grow older, organs such as the heart and lungs may stop functioning properly. Sight and hearing may become impaired. And the human body becomes more likely to come down with serious illnesses from which it cannot recover.

Considered together, changes that bring about the decline of an organism are called aging. Because of aging, many biologists believe that there may be a maximum age limit to which even the healthiest organisms can live. For human beings, this maximum age limit is about 110 years. Body cells seem to have an internal clock that determines the maximum life span of each species.

Perhaps the most important thing you can learn from your study of human biology is that you have a lot of control over how the aging process occurs in your own life. Having a long and healthy life and living beyond average life expectancy are not necessarily matters of luck. They can be planned for. In fact, within our control are many physical and mental factors that have much to do with aging. For example, although half the deaths each year in the United States are caused by heart and blood vessel disease, these diseases are almost unknown in many countries of the world. Why is this so? The answer is related to our lifestyle!

Recent research indicates that each of us can do many things to help prevent heart and blood vessel disease. For example, we can avoid eating a lot of fatty meat (mainly fatty beef and pork). Eating too much of these types of animal fats can lead to the clogging and hardening of blood vessels. We can cut back on smoking and try to quit entirely. We can limit the amount of alcohol we drink and the amount of sugar we eat. We can exercise regularly to strengthen the heart and other organs. And we can remember to take time out each day for ourselves, time just to relax. Exercise, recreation, and relaxation all reduce stress—inner tension that is hard on all body organs.

There is also a lot we can do to decrease our risk of getting cancer, the second leading cause of death. By not smoking, we also greatly reduce the chances of getting lung cancer. Recent evidence suggests that by eating a diet high in fiber we can reduce the chances of getting cancer of the digestive system. Good sources of fiber are fresh fruits and vegetables and foods made from whole grains.

Evidence also suggests that by keeping our weight down we can reduce our chances of getting many diseases, including heart disease and diabetes. Although eating is enjoyable to the mind, overeating is slow torture to the body.

One final thing we can do is to try to keep aware of advances made in health education. Information is often available free of charge from county health clinics or schools.

EXERCISE 5

Directions: Circle *T* for each statement below that is true and *F* for each statement that is false.

T F   **1.** Many biologists believe that each species has a natural maximum life span.

T F   **2.** There is much you can do to help prevent many diseases.

T F   **3.** Mental attitude is not a factor that is related to good health.

T F   **4.** Doctors believe that smoking increases a person's chances of getting both lung cancer and heart disease.

ANSWERS ARE ON PAGE 309.

GED Practice
EXERCISE 6

Questions 1–3 refer to the following information.

In 1900, U.S. citizens could expect to live an average of forty-seven years. Today, the average life expectancy in the United States has risen significantly—to about seventy-five years. There are several reasons for this increase. First, fewer children are dying. Laws now prohibit child labor, which caused many deaths and injuries at the turn of the century. Better nutrition and new vaccinations against disease help ensure children's health. Second, adult Americans are healthier. Workplace safety laws and advances in medicine and technology have protected more and more adults. And finally, increased education throughout the twentieth century has brought about a new public awareness of health and safety.

1. Which of the following is *not* one of the reasons given for the increase in average life expectancy in the United States during the twentieth century?

   (1) increased average income
   (2) better nutrition
   (3) improved working conditions
   (4) development of vaccines
   (5) increased education

2. Which of the following items of information would be *least* important to a researcher studying ways to increase life expectancy in the United States?

   (1) the quantities and types of food eaten by people in the United States
   (2) the smoking and drinking habits of people in the United States
   (3) the leading causes of death of people in the United States
   (4) the amount of money the average American household spends on food each year
   (5) the percent of people receiving adequate medical care

3. Approximately how many years has average life expectancy in the United States risen since 1900?

   (1) 10
   (2) 20
   (3) 30
   (4) 40
   (5) 50

Questions 4 and 5 are based on the information on pages 121–122.

4. The leading cause of death of people in the United States is

   (1) heart disease
   (2) cancer
   (3) accidents
   (4) childhood diseases
   (5) alcoholism

5. People in the United States have a higher incidence of heart disease than people in many poorer countries. This problem is *most* directly related to the fact that people in the United States

   (1) pay more for medical insurance
   (2) use more labor-saving devices and thus get less exercise
   (3) have a higher life expectancy
   (4) have more unavoidable sources of stress
   (5) eat more whole grains

Questions 6–8 refer to the following passage.

In order to observe the relation between aging and the amount of food an organism consumes, a researcher did the following experiment. He placed four mice in each of two cages and fed each group of mice the same type of food. He kept the food trays in cage 1 full at all times. The mice in cage 1 could eat any time and any amount they wanted. He placed only small portions of food in cage 2. The mice in cage 2 were purposely underfed. The results of his experiment were as follows:

- The mice in cage 1 seemed to lack energy and were sick a lot. They all died before reaching the average life expectancy of a mouse.

- The mice in cage 2 were energetic and healthy. They all lived long beyond the average life expectancy of a mouse.

6. The most reasonable conclusion that you can draw from the results reported in the passage above is that

   (1) the death of the mice in cage 1 was related to the type of food they ate
   (2) the mice in cage 2 would probably have lived beyond their life expectancy even if they hadn't been underfed
   (3) underfeeding slows the aging process in mice
   (4) overfeeding slows the aging process in mice
   (5) neither overfeeding nor underfeeding affects the aging process in mice

7. Which of the following would be the *least* important item of information that the researcher would want to know before drawing a conclusion about his experimental results?

   (1) the exact causes of death of the mice in cage 1
   (2) the time of day that the mice in cage 2 were fed
   (3) the average daily amount of food consumed by each group of mice
   (4) the daily amount consumed by a normal mouse
   (5) the life expectancy of a mouse fed an average amount

8. Suppose these research results also apply to humans. Which of the following statements *least supports* the opinion that overeating leads to poor health?

   Overeating

   (1) ensures that your body has an adequate supply of vitamins and minerals
   (2) overloads your body's ability to deal with chemical pollutants found in food
   (3) may make you uncomfortable and unable to get needed restful sleep
   (4) requires a great amount of energy for digestion, energy that could be used for better purposes
   (5) results in excess weight that causes your heart to work extra hard

ANSWERS ARE ON PAGE 310.

WRITING ACTIVITY 3

Even though aging is a natural part of the life cycle, many people worry about growing older. Some fear that they will face discrimination in a society that values youth. Other people worry that they'll be lonely or become sick.

How do you feel about growing older? Make a list of concerns that you have about aging and then think of some of the benefits of being a senior citizen.

POSSIBLE ANSWERS ARE ON PAGE 310.

NUTRITION

How does a piece of chocolate cake and a milk shake sound to you for lunch? If you're hungry, it may sound pretty good—unless, of course, you're on a diet! Then you may not want the weight gain this food will give you.

While a piece of cake and a milk shake provide lots of calories, they do not provide the nutrients your body needs. Calories are a measure of food energy. We all need calories for daily activities and during sleep, but many people eat more calories than they need. These excess calories are stored as unwanted body fat. Nutrients, on the other hand, are food substances that the body can use for tissue growth and repair as well as for energy. Without nutrients, the human body ceases to function properly, and sickness and death can result. A well-balanced diet is made up of foods that provide an adequate, but not excessive, number of calories while supplying all the nutrients needed for good health.

Nutrition is the study of the health value of food. Nutritionists have discovered that the most important nutrients found in food are carbohydrates, fats, protein, and vitamins and minerals. Many types of food are major sources of one type of nutrient but also contain smaller amounts of the other nutrients.

- Carbohydrates are our main sources of food energy. Bread, rice, potatoes, fruits, and grain cereals are some healthful sources of carbohydrates. These sources also contain important vitamins, minerals, and protein. Less-healthful sources include sugar and sugar-sweetened desserts such as cakes, cookies, doughnuts, and ice cream. Healthful sources are low in calories, while less-healthful sources are high in calories and contribute to unwanted weight gain. What's more, evidence now indicates that sugar and sugary products contribute to heart disease and diabetes as well as to tooth decay.

- Fats are another energy source. Some fats should be eaten only occasionally and in limited amounts. These fats are found in beef, pork, chicken, and many dairy products. As indicated on page 122, these fats are known to contribute to heart and blood vessel disease. For cooking, oil from vegetable sources should be used instead of oil made from animal fat. One exception is fish oil. Recent research has shown that fish oil, though an animal source, does not seem to carry the risk for heart disease as the other animal fats do.

● Protein is vital to body growth and to the repair of body tissues. The most healthful sources of animal protein are lean beef, chicken, fish, and dairy products. Good sources of protein from vegetables include grain products, potatoes, and beans.

● Vitamins and minerals are chemicals that are used by the body in small amounts. Though they contain no calories, vitamins and minerals are important for proper body growth, for body activity, and for the prevention of certain diseases. The most common sources of vitamins and minerals are fruits and vegetables. Many people also supplement their diets with vitamin-and-mineral pills.

● Water, which makes up more than two-thirds of your body weight, is also an important part of your diet. Water is used in the digestion of food, in the production of blood, and in the elimination of body waste. Water also helps regulate body temperature.

As a general rule, in a well-balanced diet 55 to 60 percent of the calories come from carbohydrates, no more than 30 percent come from fats, and 10 to 15 percent come from protein. The exact number of calories your body requires on a daily basis depends on your age, your body size, and your activity level. If you increase your activity level, you need more calories and nutrients. Information about diet and nutrition is available in bookstores, schools, and county health clinics.

EXERCISE 7

Part A

Directions: Match each word on the left with the best descriptive phrase on the right. Write the letter of the phrase on the line before the correct number.

_____ **1.** calorie

_____ **2.** water

_____ **3.** carbohydrate

_____ **4.** protein

_____ **5.** vitamins

(a) needed for cell growth and repair

(b) a measure of food energy

(c) needed by the body in small amounts

(d) an energy-providing nutrient

(e) helps regulate body temperature

Part B

Directions: Answer each question below.

6. Name two diseases that can be caused by a diet high in sugar.

_____ and _____

7. In a well-balanced diet, what percent of calories should come from

    a. protein? _____   **b.** carbohydrates? _____   **c.** fats? _____

ANSWERS ARE ON PAGE 310.

EXERCISE 8

Questions 1–6 are based on the information on pages 125–126.

1. What does the human body do with the excess food calories present in such foods as chocolate cake and milk shakes?

   (1) It stores them as muscle tissue.
   (2) It stores them as nerve tissue.
   (3) It passes them through the digestive system.
   (4) It digests them only when the body needs it.
   (5) It stores them as fat tissue.

2. Of the following, the person who probably needs the least number of calories during an average day is

   (1) a pregnant housewife
   (2) a professional football player
   (3) an accountant
   (4) a construction worker
   (5) a waitress

3. Which of the following do vegetarians (people who don't eat meat) risk getting too little of?

   (1) carbohydrates
   (2) vitamins
   (3) fat
   (4) protein
   (5) minerals

4. For which ailment is a doctor or nurse most likely to recommend that the patient drink lots of water?

   (1) chest cold
   (2) high fever
   (3) broken arm
   (4) toothache
   (5) plantar wart

5. Which of the following describes the relationship between food intake and exercise?

   (1) The more a person exercises, the less need he has for nutrients.
   (2) The more a person exercises, the fewer calories he can eat each day without gaining weight.
   (3) The amount of exercise a person gets each day has nothing to do with weight gain or weight loss.
   (4) The more a person exercises, the more calories he can eat each day without gaining weight.
   (5) The less a person exercises, the more need he has for nutrients.

6. To advise a patient about how to lose weight slowly in a healthful way, a doctor would need to know all of the following *except*

   (1) the person's present weight
   (2) the present state of the person's health
   (3) the average weight of other patients who are the same age and sex
   (4) the amount of exercise the person presently gets
   (5) the amount and types of food the person presently eats

Questions 7 and 8 refer to the following chart.

Nutritionists categorize food in four food groups. The food groups, recommended servings, and nutrients provided by each group are shown below.

THE BASIC FOOD GROUPS				
	Meat, Beans, and Nuts	Dairy	Fruits and Vegetables	Grain Products, Cereal, Bread
How many servings per day?	2 3 for teenagers	2–3 for children under 9 3–4 for children 9 through teens 3 for pregnant women 4 for nursing mothers 2 for adults	4 (include 1 dark green or deep yellow vegetable for vitamin A and 1 citrus fruit or juice for vitamin C)	3 to 4 servings per day (at least one cereal)
What do you get from this group?	Protein Fats Minerals B vitamins	Calcium Phosphorus Protein Vitamin A Riboflavin	Vitamins A and C Minerals Fiber	Starch Fiber Protein Vitamins Minerals

7. According to the chart above, the most important sources of fiber are the

(1) meat and fruits-and-vegetables groups
(2) fruits-and-vegetables and grain products groups
(3) dairy and fruits-and-vegetables groups
(4) dairy and grain products groups
(5) meat and grain products groups

8. According to the chart, which of the following people should drink the most milk on a daily basis?

(1) a child, age seven
(2) a young adult, age twenty-one
(3) a pregnant woman, age twenty-three
(4) a nursing mother, age twenty-one
(5) a retired man, age seventy-six

ANSWERS ARE ON PAGE 310.

SYSTEMS OF THE HUMAN BODY

BODY STRUCTURE AND MOVEMENT

Like the frame of a house, your skeleton gives form to your body. It also provides protection for internal organs. A typical human skeleton, shown at right, is made up of about 200 bones and numerous joints.

The shape of the skeleton allows for great freedom of movement while at the same time providing strength and protection. The skull surrounds and protects the brain, while the bones of the upper spine (backbone) support the skull and allow you to turn your head without turning your body. The ribs form an enclosed upper-body cavity that protects the most important internal organs. The numerous bones in the hands allow for many types of highly skilled thumb and finger movements, from tying shoes to assembling machines and playing musical instruments. The numerous bones of the feet help provide for balance and ease of movement while a person is in a standing posture.

Joints are formed where two bones come together. To prevent the bones from grinding against each other, the surfaces of contact are covered with ***cartilage***, a tough but flexible tissue. Cartilage is also the tissue that makes up the tough part of both your nose and ears.

THE HUMAN SKELETON

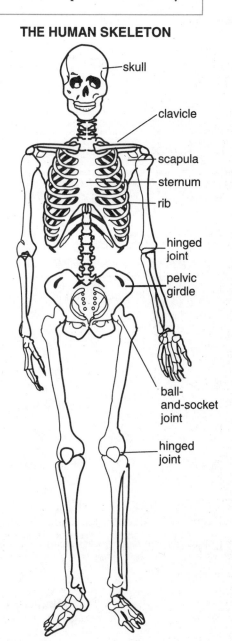

- skull
- clavicle
- scapula
- sternum
- rib
- hinged joint
- pelvic girdle
- ball-and-socket joint
- hinged joint

There are three main types of joints. Ball-and-socket joints, such as those found in the shoulders and hips, allow for wide circular motion. Hinged joints, such as those in the elbows and knees, allow for back-and-forth motion. Finally, joints such as those found in wrists and ankles allow limited motion in many directions.

Movement in the human body is made possible by muscles. A muscle is a special type of tissue that has the ability to contract (to shorten or pull together). Muscles are connected to bone by **tendons**—strong, fibrous connective tissue. Because a muscle can only contract, every joint is controlled by opposing muscles. This enables back-and-forth movement to occur. As shown below, you contract your biceps muscle to bend your arm. You contract your triceps muscle to straighten it.

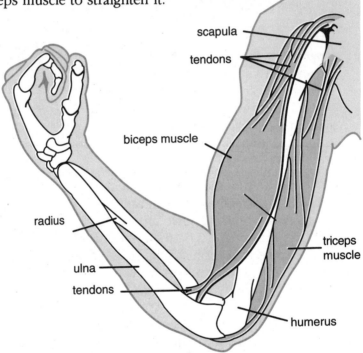

Muscles are usually spoken of as being either voluntary or involuntary. **Voluntary muscles** are those that you can consciously control. Muscles that you use to control bone movement are all voluntary muscles. When you raise your hand, you consciously use the voluntary muscles of the arm and shoulder.

Involuntary muscles are those over which you normally have no conscious control. The muscles of the lungs, stomach, intestines, heart, and blood vessels are examples of involuntary muscles.

Both voluntary and involuntary muscles produce heat as they contract and relax. This is the reason you feel so warm when you exercise. It's also the reason that people often jump up and down to keep warm while waiting in line on a cold day.

To control the working of all its muscles and to sense stimuli both inside and outside of itself, the human body contains a network of nerves that thread throughout the body. These nerves are like tiny wires that carry electrical signals called nerve impulses. Each nerve connects with the spinal cord, a large central nerve within the spine that serves as the communication link with the brain.

When you decide to move your arm, your brain sends a nerve impulse down the spinal cord and out the correct nerve. The impulse reaches the muscles involved and causes them to contract and raise your arm.

If you cut your finger, a nerve impulse is sent from the point of the cut to the brain by way of the spinal cord. It is only when this impulse reaches your brain that you feel pain. Pain and all other sensations actually occur within your brain, although the stimulus that produces each sensation may occur anywhere on your body. As you can imagine, nerve impulses are very complex and race back and forth in a fraction of a second between your brain and points on your body.

THE HUMAN NERVOUS SYSTEM

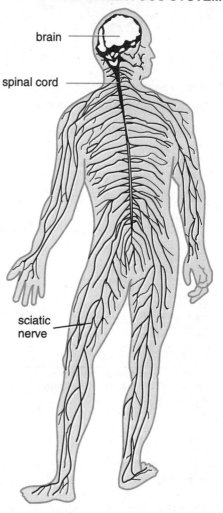

brain

spinal cord

sciatic nerve

EXERCISE 9

Directions: Circle *T* for each statement below that is true and *F* for each statement that is false.

T   F   **1.** Nerve impulses travel both to and from the brain.

T   F   **2.** Only involuntary muscles are controlled by the nervous system.

T   F   **3.** A joint is a break in a bone.

T   F   **4.** Voluntary muscles can be controlled by conscious decision making.

T   F   **5.** The bones that give protection to the internal organs within the chest are called femur bones.

ANSWERS ARE ON PAGE 310.

GED Practice
EXERCISE 10

Questions 1–6 are based on the information on pages 129–131.

1. Which of the following phrases best sums up the function of the nervous system?

    (1) communication network
    (2) support structure
    (3) waste elimination
    (4) food processing
    (5) transport and delivery

2. Which of the following is the best example of the use of voluntary muscles?

    (1) a heart beating
    (2) an eye twitching
    (3) a hand waving
    (4) an eyelid blinking
    (5) teeth chattering

3. Which of the following activities is the best example of a use of involuntary muscles?

    (1) jumping rope
    (2) driving a car
    (3) signing your name
    (4) lifting weights
    (5) breathing

4. Damage to the spinal cord can interfere with any nerve impulses that must flow through the injured point on their way to and from the brain. A person who falls and seriously injures his or her lower back might experience temporary loss of feeling

    (1) in the arms
    (2) on the right side of the body
    (3) on the left side of the body
    (4) in the legs
    (5) in the shoulders

5. A young girl quickly pulls her hand away after accidentally touching a hot burner on the stove. During this incident, four things quickly happen, although not necessarily in the following order:

    A. pain felt
    B. muscles contract to pull hand back
    C. nerve impulse sent from hand to brain
    D. nerve impulse sent from brain to hand

    The order in which these four things actually happen is:

    (1) A, C, B, D
    (2) C, A, D, B
    (3) B, A, C, D
    (4) A, D, C, B
    (5) C, D, A, B

6. Together with information given in the reading selection, which of the following facts best supports the hypothesis that the purpose of shivering is to generate heat when the body is cold?

    (1) Shivering is an involuntary action.
    (2) Shivering occurs mainly in the upper part of the body.
    (3) Shivering is movement caused by muscles that rapidly contract and relax.
    (4) Shivering interferes with normal speech.
    (5) The amount that a person shivers may depend on how long it's been since he or she has last eaten.

ANSWERS ARE ON PAGE 310.

EATING AND BREATHING

Among life's great pleasures, eating rates pretty high for most people.
However, when we talk about eating, we usually think only about tasting,
chewing, and swallowing. That's the fun part, but it's only the first step of the
process called digestion, the breaking down of food into nutrients that the
body's cells can use. As shown below, the human digestive system consists of
many more parts than just the mouth.

THE HUMAN DIGESTIVE SYSTEM

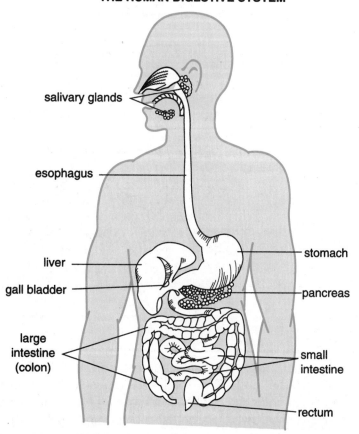

After food is chewed and swallowed, it passes down the esophagus and
into the stomach, the body's main organ of digestion. In the stomach, the food
is churned in digestive juices much like a washing machine churns clothes in
soapy water. After being in the stomach for two to five hours, the partially
digested food passes into the small intestine.

With the help of digestive juices from the liver and pancreas, the small intestine completes the digestion process. From here the digested nutrients and water pass through the walls of the intestine and into the bloodstream, where they will travel to the body's cells. Waste products continue through the small intestine and move into the large intestine, where they are prepared for passage out of the body.

Closely related to the body's need for food is its need for oxygen. Oxygen is only one of many gases found in air, but it is the gas that cells use for respiration—the process in which food sugar is broken down and energy and carbon dioxide gas are released. This energy powers all of the cell's activities, while the carbon dioxide gas is a waste product.

THE HUMAN RESPIRATORY SYSTEM

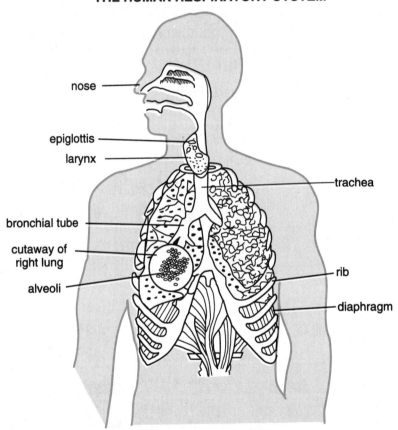

In order to get oxygen into our blood, we breathe air. As shown above, inhaled air passes through the nose and mouth, down the trachea (windpipe), and into the lungs. The epiglottis, a muscle that works like a trapdoor, allows the air to enter the trachea but closes the opening to the trachea when food or water is swallowed. Bronchial tubes branch off the trachea and carry the air into each of two lungs. In the lungs, the bronchial tubes branch into even smaller tubes that end in millions of little air sacs. It is in these tiny air sacs that blood vessels absorb the oxygen from the air. At the same time, the blood releases the waste carbon dioxide gas it has brought from the body cells.

Blood, which serves the body by transporting nutrients, water, and oxygen to all body cells, is an important part of the circulatory system shown at right.

The center of the circulatory system is the heart, a fist-sized muscle that is divided into two upper chambers and two lower chambers. The upper chambers pump blood out from the heart, through the lungs, and back again to the heart. While in the lungs, the blood absorbs oxygen gas and releases waste carbon dioxide gas that it has taken from body cells. The lower chambers of the heart then pump the oxygen-rich blood away from the heart and out through arteries to the rest of the body.

When it reaches body cells, the oxygen-rich blood gives up its oxygen and nutrients and picks up carbon dioxide gas. The blood, now rich in carbon dioxide, leaves the cells and returns to the heart through veins in the upper chambers. From there the carbon dioxide–rich blood begins the flow cycle once again.

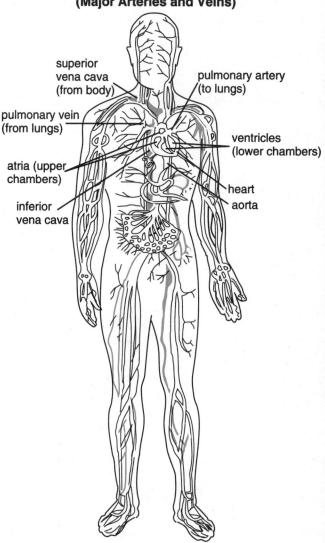

**HUMAN CIRCULATORY SYSTEM
(Major Arteries and Veins)**

superior vena cava (from body)

pulmonary artery (to lungs)

pulmonary vein (from lungs)

ventricles (lower chambers)

atria (upper chambers)

heart
aorta

inferior vena cava

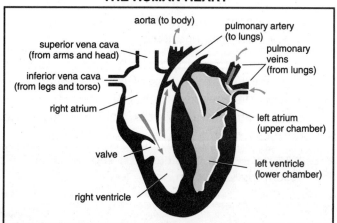

THE HUMAN HEART

aorta (to body)

superior vena cava (from arms and head)

pulmonary artery (to lungs)

pulmonary veins (from lungs)

inferior vena cava (from legs and torso)

right atrium

left atrium (upper chamber)

valve

left ventricle (lower chamber)

right ventricle

EXERCISE 11

Directions: Match each word on the left with the best definition on the right. Write the letter of the definition on the line before the correct number.

_____ **1.** heart

_____ **2.** lungs

_____ **3.** stomach

_____ **4.** arteries and veins

_____ **5.** small intestine

(a) organs in which blood takes oxygen from the air

(b) primary organ of digestion

(c) organ from which digested food enters bloodstream

(d) muscle responsible for pumping blood

(e) tubes that carry blood

ANSWERS ARE ON PAGE 311.

WRITING ACTIVITY 4

White blood cells, part of the circulatory system, help the body fight disease. The HIV virus—the virus that can lead to AIDS—infects certain white blood cells, impairing the body's ability to fight off disease. Victims of AIDS (acquired immune deficiency syndrome) are susceptible to diseases that a normal immune system could fight off easily.

The HIV virus is transmitted through body fluids. It is most often spread through sexual contact, the use of intravenous needles, and blood transfusions as well as from infected mothers to their babies during childbirth and breast-feeding.

Because sexual contact has been the most common form of HIV transmission, the medical community and AIDS activists have worked hard to spread the "safe sex" message. Billboards and TV commercials often use blunt language about condoms and sexual practices. Some public schools now give free condoms to high school students. Parents are urged to discuss sex and safety with their children.

Many Americans, however, are offended by this open discussion of sex. They feel that, regardless of health concerns, sexual practices should not be discussed so openly. Many point out that abstinence is the only *true* form of safe sex and that the words "safe sex" are misleading.

Do you agree that we should have open discussion of AIDS and of sexual practices—even with children and teenagers? Write two or three paragraphs describing your opinion.

POSSIBLE ANSWERS ARE ON PAGE 311.

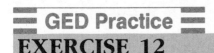

EXERCISE 12

Choose the best answer to each question below.

1. What function is performed by the epiglottis?

   (1) It prevents food from entering the trachea.
   (2) It prevents food from entering the esophagus.
   (3) It prevents air from entering the trachea.
   (4) It prevents air from entering the esophagus.
   (5) It produces the sounds of speech.

2. Which of the following phrases best sums up the function of the circulatory system?

   (1) communication network
   (2) support structure
   (3) waste elimination
   (4) food processing
   (5) transport and delivery

3. What gas does blood release into the lungs during breathing?

   (1) oxygen
   (2) nitrogen
   (3) carbon monoxide
   (4) carbon dioxide
   (5) helium

4. Which of the following statements is correct?

   (1) Arteries carry blood both away from the heart and back to the heart.
   (2) Veins carry blood both away from the heart and back to the heart.
   (3) Capillaries carry blood both away from the heart and back to the heart.
   (4) Veins carry blood away from the heart; arteries carry blood back to the heart.
   (5) Arteries carry blood away from the heart; veins carry blood back to the heart.

5. What is the most likely reason that being overweight puts an extra burden on the heart of the overweight person?

   (1) A person who is overweight often feels self-conscious.
   (2) The heart of an overweight person must pump a greater amount of blood in order to nourish the extra fat cells.
   (3) An overweight person has an increased risk of developing diabetes.
   (4) The heart of an overweight person tends to tire quickly.
   (5) An overweight person may not consume enough protein.

6. Which of the following comments about an artificial heart is most likely based on human values rather than on scientific evidence?

   (1) An artifical heart is a mechanical pump that takes the place of a seriously damaged human heart.
   (2) Implanted artificial hearts have shown a high failure rate because of unusual blood-clotting problems.
   (3) After its design is perfected, an artificial heart may give a patient a longer life expectancy than a transplanted human heart.
   (4) The decision to implant an artificial heart ought to be left solely up to the patient and his or her doctor, regardless of the risks involved.
   (5) Today's artificial heart may best be used as a temporary life-support measure that keeps a patient alive until a human heart can be obtained for transplant.

ANSWERS ARE ON PAGE 311.

REPRODUCTION AND HUMAN GENETICS

KEY WORDS

egg cell—the female sex cell
sperm cell—the male sex cell
fertilized egg cell—the one-cell first stage of a human being
fetus—the name given to the prebirth stage of a human being
amniocentesis—the examination of amniotic fluid in order to detect
    possible genetic problems in a fetus
amniotic fluid—fluid that surrounds the fetus, protecting it

The human reproductive system not only maintains your functioning as an individual but also enables you to create another person very much like yourself. And, unlike the organs of other body systems, reproductive organs are distinctly different in males and females.

Reproduction starts with the union of a male sex cell (a sperm) and a female sex cell (an egg). The combined cell, called a fertilized egg cell, develops quickly into a ball of many cells that implants itself on the inner wall of the female uterus. Here it develops into a fetus, the name given to the beginning (prebirth) stage of a human being. For the nine months that the fetus grows, it receives nourishment from the mother's circulatory system.

Inherited Traits

Reproduction results in a new individual who has many of the features (traits) of each parent. These traits are passed from parents to child by genes, chemical messengers that make up the strands of chromosomes present in each body cell. Sperm and egg cells bring hereditary information from each parent and combine it to produce the unique mixture of traits acquired by the child.

In the nucleus of each of your body cells is a set of forty-six chromosomes. These chromosomes are arranged as twenty-three pairs and contain about 100,000 genes that determine all your traits. For example, whether you have your mother's nose, your father's hands, or your grandfather's hairline are all determined by your genes.

The only human body cells that do not contain forty-six chromosomes are the female egg cell and the male sperm cell. Each of these cells has only one set of twenty-three unpaired chromosomes. However, a fertilized egg cell is also a cell with forty-six chromosomes (twenty-three pairs): twenty-three unpaired chromosomes in the egg are joined by twenty-three from the sperm. In this way, the fertilized egg receives exactly half of its genes from the male parent and half from the female parent.

In most cases, a single fertilized egg develops into a single fetus. Once in a while, though, a fertilized egg will separate into two cells that move away from each other. Each of these cells may develop into a fully formed fetus. The two children that are born are known as *identical twins*. Because they form from the same fertilized egg cell, identical twins are genetically identical. Each has exactly the same set of chromosomes and genes. *Fraternal twins*, on the other hand, develop when two egg cells are fertilized by two sperm cells during the same reproductive cycle. Although fraternal twins develop in the mother-to-be's uterus at the same time, they are no more alike than regular brothers and sisters who may be born years apart.

Prenatal Care

Protecting the health of a developing fetus is the best way to ensure that a healthy baby will be born. This care is called **prenatal care**. To provide good prenatal care, a mother-to-be needs good nutrition, healthful exercise, and periodic medical checkups.

Because substances in the mother's blood can affect the health of the developing fetus, a mother-to-be should avoid smoking, drinking alcohol, and taking any medicines or drugs of any kind except those prescribed by her doctor. She should also avoid all sources of chemical fumes such as garden sprays, oven cleansers, and other household chemicals. These fumes contain chemicals that could possibly harm the fetus.

Genetic Disorders

Once in a while a gene will change structure and cease to function properly. This changed gene can produce an inheritable trait. Such a defective gene will usually not cause any problem that affects a child's health or abilities. However, some defective genes do lead to harmful traits that result in generation after generation of illnesses or disabilities. Examples of inheritable genetic disorders are sickle-cell anemia, hemophilia, and color blindness.

Many types of genetic disorders can be detected in adults. When two people who have known defective genes decide to have children, they can get genetic counseling. In genetic counseling they can find out what their chances are of having a child with a particular genetic illness or disability.

Today, genetic defects can be detected in a fetus during the early months of pregnancy. Doctors use a procedure called amniocentesis, in which a needle and syringe are used to collect a sample of loose cells from the fetus. These cells are present in amniotic fluid that surrounds the developing fetus. By studying this fluid, doctors are able to identify certain types of defective genes. Although some diseases caused by defective genes can be treated, most can't.

EXERCISE 13

Directions: Circle *T* for each true statement and *F* for each false statement.

T F **1.** Genetic counseling is an attempt to resolve marriage problems caused by differences in inherited traits.

T F **2.** Color blindness can be inherited.

T F **3.** Except for egg and sperm cells, all cells of a human body contain twenty-three pairs of chromosomes.

T F **4.** Fraternal twins may be born years apart.

T F **5.** The health of a developing fetus depends in part on the care the mother-to-be gives to her own body.

ANSWERS ARE ON PAGE 311.

GED Practice
EXERCISE 14

Questions 1–4 are based on the information on pages 138–139.

1. Which of the following is *not* true about identical twins?

   (1) Identical twins form from two fertilized eggs.
   (2) Identical twins have the exact same genetic makeup.
   (3) Identical twins form from a single fertilized egg.
   (4) Identical twins are more alike than are fraternal twins.
   (5) Identical twins are always of the same sex.

2. The female egg cell differs from other cells in a woman's body because it has

   (1) twice as many chromosomes as all other cells
   (2) twenty-three more chromosomes than all other cells
   (3) no chromosomes
   (4) twenty-three fewer chromosomes than all other cells
   (5) chromosomes but not genes

3. Which of the following activities should a mother-to-be avoid during the months of pregnancy?

   (1) going to music concerts
   (2) taking daily walks
   (3) cooking meals at home
   (4) taking naps
   (5) painting the baby's room

4. If a woman who is a social drinker discovers she is two months pregnant, what is the best way for her to protect the health of the fetus?

   (1) to stop drinking any alcoholic drinks for at least four more months
   (2) to make sure she drinks alcohol only with meals
   (3) to slowly decrease her use of alcohol over the remainder of the pregnancy
   (4) to stop drinking alcoholic beverages until after the birth of the child
   (5) to continue social drinking as usual

Questions 5–7 refer to the following passage.

Sickle-cell anemia is an inheritable blood disease that affects about 50,000 Americans, most of them African Americans. There is no known cure for this disease. Symptoms include slowness in growth, swelling of the feet and hands, aching joints, and pain caused by clogged blood vessels. Many children die of sickle-cell anemia before they reach their teenage years.

Sickle-cell anemia affects red blood cells. A healthy red blood cell has a doughnut shape, but the red blood cell of a person who has sickle-cell anemia is shaped like a sickle; it is elongated and narrow. Sickle cells tend to clump together and clog blood vessels. This results in a lack of oxygen reaching the tissues of the body and causes the symptoms mentioned.

Sickle-cell anemia is known to be caused by a single gene that affects the shape and function of red blood cells. About 9 percent of all African Americans are carriers of a single sickle-cell gene. However, because this gene is recessive, only those who have inherited two sickle-cell genes display symptoms of the disease. Carriers of a single sickle-cell gene do not suffer symptoms of the disease. Because it is a genetic disease, sickle-cell anemia is not contagious.

It is now possible with prenatal testing to determine if a fetus has either one or two sickle-cell genes. The diagrams on page 141 illustrate how either the sickle-cell trait (one sickle-cell gene) or the sickle-cell disease (two sickle-cell genes) can be passed on to offspring.

5. Sickle-cell anemia is a disease that affects the structure of

   (1) white blood cells
   (2) blood vessels
   (3) red blood cells
   (4) arterial walls
   (5) oxygen molecules

6. Which of the following phrases does *not* correctly describe sickle-cell anemia?

(1) a blood disease
(2) an inheritable disease
(3) a contagious disease
(4) a disease caused by defective genes
(5) symptoms include clogging of blood vessels

7. Which of the following statements about sickle-cell anemia and its symptoms is true?

(1) The symptoms of sickle-cell anemia occur just before a sufferer's blood clots.
(2) The symptoms of sickle-cell anemia occur only in women.
(3) A person can have the symptoms without having a single sickle-cell gene.
(4) A person with even a single sickle-cell gene will have the symptoms.
(5) A person can carry a single sickle-cell gene and not suffer any of the symptoms.

Questions 8 and 9 refer to the following diagrams.

HOW PARENTS PASS ON SICKLE-CELL ANEMIA

Diagram A

Normal Blood
NN

Sickle-Cell Trait
NS

NN = normal blood
NS = sickle-cell trait
SS = sickle-cell disease

NN *NS* *NN* *NS*

Possible gene combinations in children

Diagram B

Sickle-Cell Trait
NS

Sickle-Cell Trait
NS

NS *NN* *NS* *SS*

Possible gene combinations in children

8. Diagram A shows the gene combinations of a child who could be born to the parents illustrated. The father is a normal blood cell (*NN*) person, and the mother is a sickle-cell trait (*NS*) person (a person with a single sickle-cell gene). What are the chances that the child will also be a carrier of the sickle-cell trait?

(1) 0 percent (no chance)
(2) 25 percent (one chance in four)
(3) 50 percent (two chances in four)
(4) 75 percent (three chances in four)
(5) 100 percent (the child will be a carrier of the sickle-cell trait)

9. Diagram B shows the gene combinations of a child who could be born to two people who each have the sickle-cell trait (*NS*). What are the chances that the child will suffer from the disease of sickle-cell anemia?

(1) 0 percent (no chance)
(2) 25 percent (one chance in four)
(3) 50 percent (two chances in four)
(4) 75 percent (three chances in four)
(5) 100 percent (the child will have it with certainty)

ANSWERS ARE ON PAGE 311.

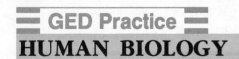

HUMAN BIOLOGY

Questions 1–3 are based on the following drawings and passage.

DEVELOPING FETUS

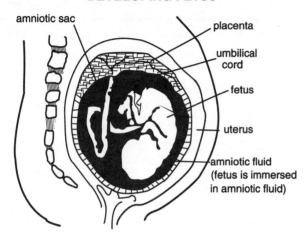

amniotic sac
placenta
umbilical cord
fetus
uterus
amniotic fluid (fetus is immersed in amniotic fluid)

AT THE START OF BIRTH

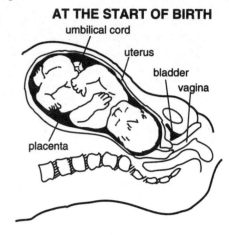

umbilical cord
uterus
bladder
vagina
placenta

A human fetus develops within the mother's uterus. During development and prior to birth, the fetus is protected by an amniotic sac, a bag within the uterus that is filled with fluid. The amniotic sac keeps the fetus at a steady temperature, protects the fetus against injury, and provides the fetal skin with moisturizing fluids.

Prior to birth, the fetus neither eats through its mouth nor breathes with its lungs. Instead, it receives nourishment and oxygen through the umbilical cord attached to its abdomen. The umbilical cord runs through the amniotic sac to the *placenta*—a special tissue that lines the inner wall of the uterus. Nourishment and oxygen from the mother's blood cross through the placenta into the blood vessels of the fetus, and fetal waste products cross through to the mother's blood for later elimination. The mother and fetus do not directly share blood.

During childbirth, the uterus undergoes a series of contractions, which push the fetus out the vaginal canal. After the baby is out, the placenta is expelled. Birth is complete when the baby begins breathing on its own. The umbilical cord is cut, and the placenta is discarded. The scar left at the point of attachment of the umbilical cord to the child is called the navel but is most often referred to as the "belly button."

1. The tissue through which fetal blood receives oxygen from the mother's blood is called the

    (1) navel
    (2) fetus
    (3) uterus
    (4) placenta
    (5) amniotic sac

2. During respiration, human body cells produce carbon dioxide gas as a waste product. This gas is carried to the lungs by blood and expelled during breathing. What most likely happens to the carbon dioxide gas produced by the body cells of a fetus?

    The carbon dioxide gas produced by a fetus

    (1) is expelled through the mother's lungs
    (2) remains in the fetus until birth
    (3) is absorbed by amniotic fluid
    (4) stays in the mother's blood
    (5) is reused by the fetus

3. Drinking alcohol and smoking cigarettes during pregnancy can harm a developing fetus. The most likely reason for this is that

    (1) mother and fetus share the same blood
    (2) the mother's long-term health is at risk
    (3) these products cost a lot of money
    (4) fetal tissue grows rapidly
    (5) substances in a mother's blood can enter the blood of the fetus

Questions 4–8 refer to the following passage.

Cholesterol is a waxlike substance made by the body cells of humans and other animals and is present in much of the food in a typical American diet. In small quantities cholesterol is important to good health. The human body uses it to help produce several hormones and bile acids, which aid in digestion. Cholesterol is not a fat, though it is often associated with fat. However, cholesterol, like fat, does not dissolve easily in water or blood.

The main sources of dietary cholesterol are animal by-products and saturated fat, which is found both in animal and plant by-products. To lower human cholesterol levels, doctors recommend that people eat less beef and pork, both of which are fatty. Fish (except shellfish) has a low cholesterol level and is recommended as a substitute for other meats. Doctors recommend that people eat more fruits, vegetables, grain products, and other plant foods—none of which contain cholesterol, and most of which contain comparatively little saturated fat. However, some plant products, such as coconut oil, palm oil, and chocolate should be eaten sparingly. These plant foods are high in saturated fat, which the body partially converts to cholesterol.

Medical researchers have discovered that excess cholesterol plays a major role in causing *atherosclerosis*—a clogging of blood arteries. When too much cholesterol gets into the blood, it settles onto artery walls, leading to a buildup of arterial plaque (a substance made up of cholesterol, fat, protein, and cellular debris). As the plaque builds up, blood flow through the arteries becomes increasingly restricted. Restricted arteries to the heart can result in a heart attack; restricted arteries to the brain can lead to a stroke.

4. Atherosclerosis can lead to

   (1) arterial plaque buildup
   (2) an excessive cholesterol level
   (3) saturated fat in the blood
   (4) a heart attack
   (5) blood flow to the heart

5. Excess cholesterol in the human body has been experimentally linked to

   (1) muscle spasms
   (2) excessive weight gain
   (3) excessive weight loss
   (4) arterial plaque buildup
   (5) heart enlargement

6. Which of the following statements is false?

   (1) Grains, fruits, and vegetables do not contain cholesterol.
   (2) Animal products are the main source of cholesterol in the typical American diet.
   (3) Cholesterol is made by the human body.
   (4) Coconut oil, palm oil, and chocolate contain cholesterol.
   (5) Low levels of cholesterol are important for human health.

7. To promote a lower cholesterol level, which of the following foods should be eaten only in small amounts?

   (1) rice
   (2) bacon
   (3) orange juice
   (4) lettuce
   (5) beans

8. The best evidence that a direct link exists between diet and atherosclerosis would be a study showing that

   (1) the first signs of atherosclerosis can be seen in children as young as age three
   (2) men tend to develop atherosclerosis at a younger age than women
   (3) people on low-fat diets have a lower than average incidence of atherosclerosis
   (4) people on high-fat diets have a higher than average incidence of obesity
   (5) many vegetarians (non-meat eaters) also develop atherosclerosis

ANSWERS ARE ON PAGE 312.

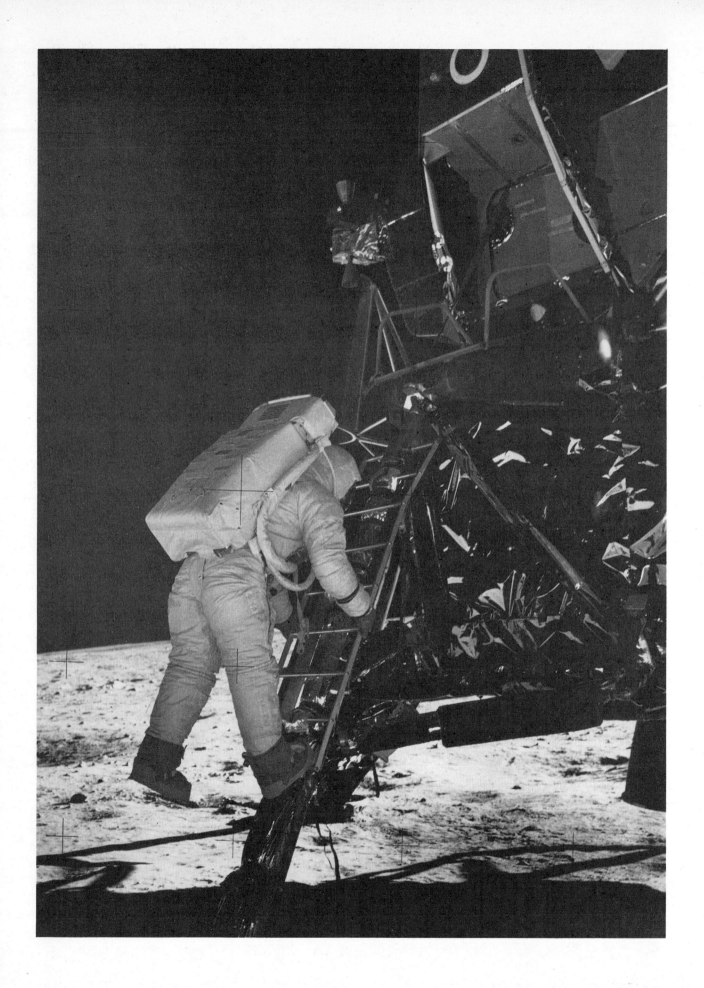

7 Earth Science

The study of the structure of Earth, the forces that change it, and Earth's location in space is known as *earth science*. Fortunately for us, but unfortunately for space travelers, Earth is believed to be the most livable of all the known planets. In this chapter, we'll look at some of the features of our evolving home planet. Topics will be chosen from the following related studies that make up the field of earth science.

Astronomy, one of the oldest sciences, is the study of the heavenly bodies in the universe. Astronomers study the structure and life cycles of stars, planets, comets, and other objects in space. From this study, astronomers hope to gain a better understanding of both the creation and the evolution of Earth. With the development of space vehicles and orbiting space stations, astronomy promises to play an even more important role in the future.

Geology is the study of the composition and structure of Earth itself. Geologists seek to understand how land and water formations develop and change over time. Many geologists study natural events, such as volcanoes and earthquakes, that often threaten human safety. Other geologists work for companies whose interests lie in the development of natural resources such as coal and oil and economically important minerals such as gold. Still other geologists work in environmental studies. Their concern is with the geological impact that human life is having on Earth and its ecosystems (plant and animal life cycles).

Oceanography is the study of Earth's oceans. Oceanographers study the movement of ocean water and its effects on weather. They also study the land formations on the bottom of the oceans. As evidenced by offshore oil rigs, the ocean bottom is proving to be a rich source of natural resources.

Meteorology is the study of Earth's atmosphere, the covering of air that surrounds our planet. Meteorologists use information about atmospheric conditions to gain an understanding of weather. Each day, using millions of temperature and air pressure readings from around the world, the United States Weather Bureau forecasts the coming weather. Weather forecasts are especially useful as an early warning of approaching storms.

Paleontology is the study of the fossils of prehistoric plants and animals. Through their work, paleontologists are able to tell us much about ancient life forms and about the geological history of our planet. Using scientific dating techniques, they have developed a geological calendar that traces simple life forms back more than two billion years.

EXERCISE 1

Directions: In each blank, write the name of the type of scientist (astronomer, geologist, oceanographer, meteorologist, or paleontologist) you would expect to find doing each of the following activities.

_____ 1. working for an oil company that is interested in drilling for oil off the California coast

_____ 2. writing an article on the nature of comets

_____ 3. trying to identify a bone chip thought to be more than 1 million years old

_____ 4. taking seismic measurements on Mount St. Helens in order to predict a possible volcanic eruption

_____ 5. working as a weatherman for a local television station

≡ GED Practice ≡

EXERCISE 2

Questions 1 and 2 refer to the following information.

While discussing the possibility of life on other planets, a group of astronomers made the following statements.

A. The winding valleys on the surface of Mars may be ancient riverbeds, carved at a time when water flowed on the Martian surface.

B. Data sent back in 1976 by the *Viking* lander from the surface of Mars did not indicate that the element carbon was present in the Martian soil.

C. Further exploration of the Martian surface should be our top priority.

D. The first astronauts will probably land on the planet Mars before the year 2025.

1. Remembering that a hypothesis is a reasonable explanation of an observed fact, which of the statements is a hypothesis?

   (1) A only
   (2) B only
   (3) C only
   (4) D only
   (5) B and D only

2. Which of the statements is most likely a fact?

   (1) A only
   (2) B only
   (3) A and C only
   (4) B and C only
   (5) B and D only

Question 3 is based on the information on page 145.

3. Which item of information below would be of most relevance to an environmental geologist working for the federal government?

   (1) the cause of the dinosaurs' extinction
   (2) the daily national weather forecast
   (3) the yearly movement of an Alaskan glacier
   (4) the life cycle of a star
   (5) the location of toxic waste dumps

ANSWERS ARE ON PAGE 312.

EARTH IN SPACE

KEY WORDS

galaxy—a group of a large number of stars
gravity—a force of attraction that exists between any two objects in the
 universe
orbit—the path followed by one body as it moves around a second body
 (Used as a verb, to *orbit* means to "travel in an orbit.")
planet—any body that moves in an orbit around a star
solar system—the sun and all the objects that are in orbits around the
 sun

Thousands of years ago, the Greeks observed the night sky with a feeling of religious wonder. As they watched from night to night, they noticed a few lights that looked like stars but seemed to move across the sky. They believed that each of these moving heavenly objects traveled around Earth in complicated loops. They named these strange objects the *planetes*, a Greek word meaning "wanderers."

The belief that the wanderers moved around Earth persisted until 1543, when Nicolaus Copernicus (1473–1543), a Polish astronomer, suggested a bold new idea. He proposed that Earth and all the other planets traveled in orbits around the sun. Together, the sun and all the bodies that orbit it are now called the solar system. The acceptance of the idea that the sun is at the center of the solar system came to be known as the Copernican theory.

GALAXIES

The Copernican theory was an important step in our present understanding of the universe. Although the size of the universe is still unknown, evidence suggests that its age may be 15 billion years or older! What's more, scientists now believe that the universe contains millions or, more likely, billions of widely separated galaxies. Each of these galaxies is a group of hundreds of millions or even hundreds of billions of stars.

Our own galaxy is called the Milky Way. The Milky Way contains the sun and about 100 billion other stars. The distance across the Milky Way is estimated to be about 100,000 light-years. The distance between the Milky Way and the nearest similar galaxy is about 2 million light-years. (A ***light-year*** is the distance that light travels in one year, about 6 trillion miles. Light travels at the incredible speed of 186,000 miles per second. Scientists believe that nothing can move faster than the speed of light.)

THE MILKY WAY GALAXY

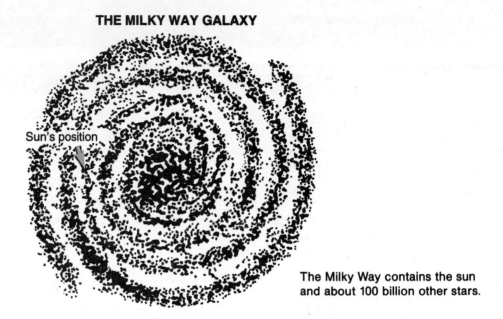

The Milky Way contains the sun and about 100 billion other stars.

THE SOLAR SYSTEM

The solar system contains the sun, nine planets, numerous comets, and a large number of asteroids—small planetlike rock fragments that orbit the sun. Many of the nine planets have one or more of their own natural moons, called satellites. For example, Earth has a single moon, while the planet Jupiter has sixteen.

The largest planets include Jupiter, Saturn, Uranus, and Neptune. Four of the smaller planets—Mercury, Venus, Earth, and Mars—are also those closest to the sun. Not much is known about the smallest planet, Pluto. It is the outermost planet, and its eccentric orbit sometimes crosses the orbit of Neptune.

OUR SOLAR SYSTEM

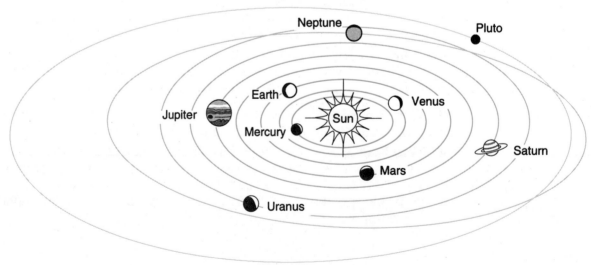

THE FORCE OF GRAVITY

The structure of both the Milky Way galaxy and our solar system results from the force of gravity. Although scientists do not know what causes gravity, they do know that it holds the objects in the universe together.

- Gravity holds stars together in galaxies.
- Gravity holds each planet in its orbit around the sun.
- Gravity holds the moon and human-made satellites in orbit around Earth.
- Gravity holds objects onto the surface of Earth.

EXERCISE 3

Directions: Answer each question in the exercise below.

1. Match each word on the left with the phrase that is the best description on the right. Write the letter of the phrase on the line before the correct number.

   ____ **1.** Milky Way

   ____ **2.** solar system

   ____ **3.** moon

   ____ **4.** galaxy

   ____ **5.** gravity

   (a) a group of millions or even billions of stars

   (b) a strong force of attraction between any two objects

   (c) the sun and the objects in orbit around it

   (d) the galaxy that contains the sun

   (e) a natural satellite in orbit around a planet

2. Complete each sentence by filling in the blanks with the correct word from the reading passage or illustrations.

   a. The closest planet to the sun is _____.

   b. Earth is the _____ closest planet to the sun.

   c. The outermost planet is named _____.

   d. One light-year is a distance of about _____ miles.

   e. The Milky Way contains about _____ stars.

   f. The speed of light is _____ miles per second.

ANSWERS ARE ON PAGE 312.

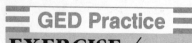

EXERCISE 4

Questions 1–3 are based on the information on pages 147–149.

1. Which statement below best expresses the idea proposed by Nicolaus Copernicus?

   (1) The sun orbits Earth and other planets.
   (2) The sun is only one of billions of stars.
   (3) Earth is at the center of a system of orbiting planets.
   (4) The sun is at the center of a system of orbiting planets.
   (5) The universe contains billions of galaxies.

2. Planets are seen as faint lights that move across the night sky. Yet, unlike stars, planets do not give off their own light. Knowing this, decide which of the following facts are needed in order to explain how we are able to see the other planets while standing on Earth.

   A. Planets that are close to the sun have higher surface temperatures than planets farther away.
   B. Five planets are at a greater distance from the sun than Earth, while only three are closer.
   C. Planets reflect part of the sunlight that strikes them.

   (1) A only
   (2) B only
   (3) C only
   (4) A and C only
   (5) B and C only

3. The ancient Greeks made the following observations:

   A. The sun appears to rise in the morning and set at night.
   B. The sun and the moon appear to be about the same size.
   C. The moon appears to change shape during different times of each month.
   D. Standing on Earth, you get the impression that Earth is motionless.

   Which of the above observations could have been used by the ancient Greeks to support their incorrect belief that the sun moved in an orbit around Earth?

   (1) A and B only
   (2) A and C only
   (3) B and C only
   (4) B and D only
   (5) A and D only

ANSWERS ARE ON PAGE 312.

WRITING ACTIVITY 1

In January of 1986, the space shuttle *Challenger* exploded after takeoff, killing the seven people on board. This accident caused many people to wonder if we should continue to send astronauts into space.

If you were in charge of the space program, would you support manned or unmanned flights? Write a paragraph explaining your decision. Be sure to give examples to support your choice.

ANSWERS WILL VARY.

SEASONS ON THE EARTH

You may not realize it, but as you're reading this sentence you are racing through space at a speed of 66,000 miles per hour! As incredible as it may seem, this is the speed at which Earth travels in its orbit around the sun. It takes 365 days (one year) to make one complete trip (revolution). During this time, the only clue you have to Earth's orbital motion is the changing of the seasons.

As it moves along its orbital path, Earth also turns (rotates) on its axis—the imaginary line running through the North Pole and South Pole. You can think of Earth as slowly spinning like a top around this axis. It makes one complete turn during each twenty-four hour period (one day). Because Earth turns from west to east, the sun appears to rise over the eastern horizon each morning and set below the western horizon each evening. Earth's rotation is what causes day and night.

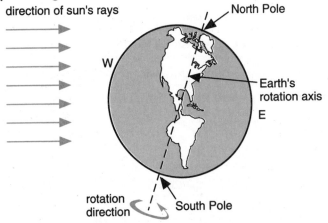

The Earth rotates from west to east on its rotation axis.
One complete turn takes twenty-four hours (one day).

As you can see from the above illustration, Earth's rotation axis is not vertical. Seasons are caused by the tilt in Earth's axis. In summer, the Northern Hemisphere is tilted toward the sun, so it receives more direct rays of sunlight. Direct rays produce more heat and light. In winter, the Northern Hemisphere is tilted away from the sun. It receives slanting rays from the sun, which are not as strong and result in colder temperatures and longer nights. The diagram on page 152 shows the position of Earth in relation to the sun at different times of year.

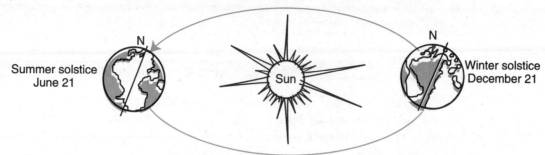

Seasons are caused by the tilt in the Earth's axis. The first day of summer and winter for countries in the Northern Hemisphere is shown above.

The situation in the Southern Hemisphere is exactly the opposite. When the northern half of the world receives more light and heat from the sun, the southern half receives less. Therefore, when it is summer in the Northern Hemisphere, it is winter in the Southern Hemisphere, and vice versa. While July is a warm month in the United States, it is a cold month in Australia.

EXERCISE 5

Directions: Answer each question below.

1. Circle *T* for each statement below that is true and *F* for each statement that is false.

   T   F   **a.** The word *rotation* refers to the turning of Earth on its axis.

   T   F   **b.** The Northern Hemisphere and the Southern Hemisphere each receive the same amount of direct sunlight in January.

   T   F   **c.** The seasons occur because of Earth's rotation.

   T   F   **d.** The sun appears to rise in the east and set in the west.

2. Complete each sentence by filling in the blanks with the correct word(s) from the reading selection.

   a. It takes Earth _____ to make one rotation.
   (time)

   b. It takes Earth _____ to make one revolution.
   (time)

   c. Day and night are caused by Earth's _____.

   d. Seasons are caused by the _____ in Earth's axis.

ANSWERS ARE ON PAGE 312.

GED Practice
EXERCISE 6

Questions 1 and 2 are based on the information on pages 151–152.

1. In which of the following months are people most likely to be sunbathing in coastal cities in southern Brazil?

   (1) February
   (2) April
   (3) July
   (4) August
   (5) September

2. In which of the following months are people most likely to be playing in the snow in Montreal, Canada?

   (1) May
   (2) July
   (3) September
   (4) January
   (5) April

Questions 3 and 4 refer to the following passage and diagram.

At any instant, people in different parts of the world see the sun in a different position in the sky. For example, while people in San Francisco are watching the sun come up, people in Moscow are watching the sun go down.

To avoid confusion in telling time, scientists have divided Earth into twenty-four time zones. As you move from west to east, you add one hour to your clock for each new time zone that you enter. For example, when it is 2:00 P.M. in San Francisco, it is 5:00 P.M. in New York City. As shown on the time zone map below, you cross into three new time zones as you go from San Francisco to New York City.

THE WORLD TIME ZONES

3. While vacationing in Paris, France, James calls his home in Seattle, Washington. If he places the call at 6:00 A.M. on Saturday, July 9, Paris time, what time and day will it be in Seattle when the call is received?

   (1) 2:00 P.M. Friday, July 8
   (2) 10:00 P.M. Friday, July 8
   (3) 2:00 P.M. Saturday, July 9
   (4) 10:00 P.M. Saturday, July 9
   (5) 2:00 A.M. Sunday, July 10

4. If an airplane leaves San Francisco at 8:00 A.M. and flies nonstop to New York, what time will the airplane arrive in New York City (New York City time), assuming that the trip takes five hours of actual flying time?

   (1) 1:00 A.M.
   (2) 10:00 A.M.
   (3) 1:00 P.M.
   (4) 4:00 P.M.
   (5) 10:00 P.M.

ANSWERS ARE ON PAGE 312.

THE STRUCTURE OF EARTH

KEY WORDS

continents—the seven large land masses on Earth
islands—small land masses that are surrounded by water
oceans—the five large bodies of salt water that cover most of Earth's surface
crustal plates—twelve to twenty rigid, separate plates that are believed to make up Earth's crust
plate tectonics—the theory that Earth's surface is made up of slowly moving crustal plates

---

Imagine for a moment that you're a sailor living in the fifteenth century. You're about to sail due west from the shore of Europe, out onto a vast unknown sea. Many of your friends say that the ocean leads to the edge of the flat Earth. Others tell of sailors who ventured out past the horizon and never returned. Still others warn of giant sea monsters swallowing up ships—like yours—that dare to sail too far from land.

Do these ideas sound funny? Sure, they do today, but you probably wouldn't be laughing if you were about to set sail with Columbus in search of a "new world"! During those adventurous days, when very little was known about Earth, it was normal to have fears about the nature of our planet.

Today we have a much better understanding of Earth. We know that its surface is mostly water (about 71 percent) divided into several large oceans. The land portion (about 29 percent) is divided into seven continents and numerous islands. The oceans and land masses are the visible part of the outer skin of Earth known as the ***crust***. The crust varies in size, being about six miles thick under the oceans and as much as forty miles thick under high mountain ranges on the continents.

Beneath the crust is a very thick layer called the ***mantle***. The mantle is about 1,800 miles thick and is made up mainly of heavy rock.

Beneath the mantle, and running to the center of the earth, is the core. The core is divided into two parts: a solid ***inner core***, made up of iron, and a liquid ***outer core*** that is composed mainly of melted iron. The inner core is shaped like a ball. The radius (distance from the center to the edge) is about 800 miles. The outer core is about 1,400 miles thick.

THE STRUCTURE OF THE EARTH

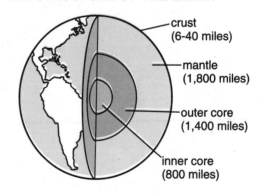

crust
(6-40 miles)

mantle
(1,800 miles)

outer core
(1,400 miles)

inner core
(800 miles)

PLATE TECTONICS

Looking at a world map, you can't help but notice that the east coasts of North and South America look like pieces of a jigsaw puzzle of which Greenland, Europe, and Africa are also a part. It appears that if you could slide the Americas over next to Europe and Africa—placing Greenland in the opening at the top—the coastlines would neatly fit next to one another. Although this fit has been noticed for centuries, it has only been in recent years that geologists have come to understand this remarkable circumstance.

There is now evidence to indicate that the continents may have actually sat side by side at one time, perhaps 200 million years ago. In fact, geologists have given the name *Pangaea* to this possible supercontinent. According to the most recent theory, called plate tectonics, Earth's crust is made up of from twelve to twenty separate rigid plates that slowly move around on the surface of the mantle. Although each crustal plate moves only about two inches per year, 200 million years would have been enough time for Pangaea to separate into today's continents.

A

200 million years ago

B

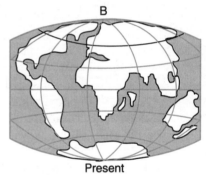

Present

The theory of plate tectonics does more than describe the possible movement of continents—often called **continental drift**. It also helps geologists understand earthquakes and volcanoes. Both of these natural phenomena occur along the boundary lines where two plates collide with each other. When slippage occurs between two plates, an enormous amount of energy is released. This energy results in one or more earthquakes, felt mostly by those around the plate boundary. For example, California experiences thousands of small quakes each year along the plate boundary known as the San Andreas fault. Volcanoes can be caused by the tremendous pressure that develops as one plate actually moves under a second plate at the collision boundary. The group of islands that now make up Japan is an example of a whole string of volcanoes formed near the boundary of two plates.

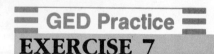

EXERCISE 7

Questions 1–5 are based on the information on pages 154–155.

1. We live on the part of Earth that scientists call the

   (1) crust
   (2) mantle
   (3) outer core
   (4) inner core
   (5) tectonic

2. Which of the following best summarizes the main idea of the theory of plate tectonics?

   (1) Earth's crust varies in thickness, being much thicker beneath mountain ranges than beneath bodies of water.
   (2) Earth's crust is made up of rigid plates that slowly move along Earth's surface.
   (3) Earth's continents are slowly being pushed apart by the movement of the oceans.
   (4) The coasts of several continents are similar in shape, giving Earth the appearance of a jigsaw puzzle.
   (5) Earth is round and not flat as was once widely believed.

3. Which of the following is a hypothesis based on the Pangaea theory?

   (1) In the fifteenth century, no one knew for sure that Earth was round.
   (2) Seismic measurements (measurement of shock waves from earthquakes) indicate that Earth's crust tends to be thicker beneath the continents than beneath the oceans.
   (3) Seventy-one percent of Earth's surface is covered by water and 29 percent by land.
   (4) Earth's continents look like a jigsaw puzzle because they were once part of a huge supercontinent that split apart.
   (5) Earth is the only planet in the solar system that looks blue when seen from space.

4. Which of the following would *not* be important to a geologist interested in predicting the possibility of a volcanic eruption from a peak in the Appalachian Mountains?

   (1) the history of volcanic activity in all parts of the eastern United States
   (2) the average amount of yearly rainfall received in the Appalachian Mountains
   (3) the location of the nearest boundary between two crustal plates
   (4) the history of any earthquake activity in or near the Appalachian Mountains
   (5) the age and structure of the Appalachian Mountains

5. Each of the following could be used as evidence that Pangaea did exist *except* the discovery

   (1) of fossils in Europe and in North America of the same extinct bird
   (2) of rare plants living in both South America and Africa
   (3) of ancient European pottery found in diggings in Mexico
   (4) that even now South America is slowly moving away from Africa
   (5) of the shape of the fault line that runs beneath the Atlantic Ocean

Questions 6 and 7 refer to the following diagram. The diagram shows how four main types of rocks can be changed into one another.

6. Granite is a form of

(1) magma
(2) sandstone
(3) igneous rock
(4) sedimentary rock
(5) metamorphic rock

7. Which of the following are needed to change sedimentary rock into metamorphic rock?

(1) cooling and chemical change
(2) heat and erosion
(3) heat and chemical change
(4) erosion and chemical change
(5) erosion and cementation

ANSWERS ARE ON PAGE 313.

WRITING ACTIVITY 2

As you know, earthquakes occur when the plates of Earth's crust shift and cause the ground to move. Should the public be told about a predicted earthquake if scientists are not certain that the earthquake will occur?

Some people say that earthquake warnings are necessary to prevent death and destruction. Others point to cases where people were needlessly evacuated from their homes on the basis of an erroneous prediction.

List two reasons why it may be wise to inform people and two problems that informing them can cause.

POSSIBLE ANSWERS ARE ON PAGE 313.

EARTH'S ATMOSPHERE

> ### KEY WORDS
>
> *air*—the mixture of gases found in the lower atmosphere
> *atmosphere*—the blanket of air that surrounds Earth
> *ozone*—a type of oxygen gas that absorbs ultraviolet sunlight

Unless it's raining or the wind is blowing, we don't usually pay much attention to the atmosphere, the blanket of air that surrounds Earth. Yet without the atmosphere, Earth would be a desolate planet with no signs of life!

The atmosphere plays several roles in helping to make life possible. First, the atmosphere provides the three gases necessary for life: oxygen, nitrogen, and carbon dioxide. All animals, including ourselves, breathe oxygen. Nitrogen and carbon dioxide are both needed for plant growth. Less important atmospheric gases include argon, neon, helium, and hydrogen.

Second, the atmosphere protects us from most of the sun's high-energy ultraviolet light rays, which are harmful to life. Although these rays are only a small part of the sunlight striking Earth, they are known to be very dangerous. However, 99 percent of all ultraviolet rays are absorbed before they reach Earth's surface. They are absorbed by an atmospheric gas called ozone, a type of oxygen gas. The ozone layer surrounds Earth but is much thinner over the North Pole and South Pole than over other regions.

The 1 percent of the ultraviolet light in the atmosphere that does reach Earth's surface is known to cause sunburn and is now believed to cause skin cancer in many people. Because of this, doctors recommend that people limit the amount of time they spend in direct sunlight. They also recommend that people who like to sunbathe wear a suntan lotion that blocks the ultraviolet rays.

Finally, the atmosphere gives us weather—both clear blue skies and storms. It acts as a huge energy machine, changing sunlight into other forms of energy such as heat and wind. As part of this role, the atmosphere regulates the temperature at Earth's surface. First, it allows only 46 percent of the sunlight striking it to pass through and actually reach Earth's surface. Second, carbon dioxide gas in the atmosphere controls the amount of sunlight warmth on Earth's surface that is allowed to radiate back into space. By these two controlling devices, the atmosphere regulates Earth's surface temperature.

LEVELS OF EARTH'S ATMOSPHERE

When meteorologists talk about the atmosphere, they usually divide it into four (or sometimes five) layers:

- The **troposphere** is the layer closest to the ground. Most of the gas in the atmosphere is in this layer. In fact, more than half of all atmospheric gas is within an altitude, or height, of 3½ miles. It is in the troposphere that almost all weather occurs. Under normal conditions, the temperature decreases about 10°F for each mile you gain in altitude in the troposphere. The carbon dioxide gas in this layer regulates Earth's surface temperature.

- The second layer is called the **stratosphere**. The temperature is about the same throughout the stratosphere; it no longer decreases with increasing altitude. The stratosphere is especially important to us because it contains the ozone gas that protects us from harmful sunlight.

- Above the stratosphere is the **mesosphere**, a layer of atmosphere in which air temperature again drops with increasing altitude.

- The top layer of atmosphere is called the **thermosphere**, a region where the temperature rises with altitude. The thermosphere, together with the upper mesosphere, is often called the **ionosphere**, a region that reflects radio waves back toward the ground. The ionosphere can be thought of as a layer of atmosphere that is made up of parts of two other layers. The ionosphere makes it possible for a radio station to broadcast over hundreds or even thousands of miles.

EXERCISE 8

Directions: Write a brief answer to each of the following questions.

1. Define what is meant by the word *atmosphere*.

   _____

2. Why is ozone an important gas in the atmosphere?

   _____

3. Which atmospheric gas controls the amount of sunlight warmth that radiates back out into space? _____

4. What percent of the energy from the sun gets through the atmosphere and actually reaches the land? _____

ANSWERS ARE ON PAGE 313.

EXERCISE 9

Questions 1–5 are based on the following information about the layers of atmosphere.

troposphere—closest layer to Earth; weather conditions occur here; height: ground level to about eight miles

stratosphere—contains ozone gas; height: about eight miles to thirty miles

mesosphere—region of decreasing temperature with increasing altitude; height: about thirty miles to fifty miles

ionosphere—region that reflects radio waves; made up of top of mesosphere and bottom of thermosphere

thermosphere—top of atmosphere; height: fifty miles and up

1. High-altitude clouds, called *cirrus clouds*, form at altitudes of between 5 and 7½ miles. In which layer of atmosphere must pilots be concerned about poor visibility due to cirrus clouds?

   (1) troposphere
   (2) stratosphere
   (3) mesosphere
   (4) ionosphere
   (5) thermosphere

2. The top layer of the atmosphere that a space shuttle must pass through as it leaves its orbit (above the atmosphere) to return to Earth is the

   (1) troposphere
   (2) stratosphere
   (3) mesosphere
   (4) ionosphere
   (5) thermosphere

3. Disturbances in the atmosphere often affect radio reception. In which layer of the atmosphere are such disturbances most likely to affect the reception in Seattle, Washington, of stations broadcasting from Tokyo, Japan?

   (1) troposphere
   (2) stratosphere
   (3) mesosphere
   (4) ionosphere
   (5) thermosphere

4. A high-altitude balloon is sent up to take measurements of the ozone layer in the atmosphere. After rising through the ozone layer, the balloon records that the temperature is falling as the balloon continues to move upward. At this point the balloon is entering the layer of atmosphere known as the

   (1) troposphere
   (2) stratosphere
   (3) mesosphere
   (4) ionosphere
   (5) thermosphere

5. In recent years, man-made chemicals called *fluorocarbons* have been banned from use as propellants in aerosol sprays such as spray paint. Scientists believe that these chemicals get into the atmosphere and wear away the layer of protective ozone gas. In which layer of atmosphere are the fluorocarbons believed to be causing the damage?

   (1) troposphere
   (2) stratosphere
   (3) mesosphere
   (4) ionosphere
   (5) thermosphere

ANSWERS ARE ON PAGE 313.

EARTH'S WEATHER

The study of weather is the study of the changes that take place in Earth's atmosphere, the layer of gases that surrounds the planet. A local weather report usually includes the following four features of the atmosphere:

- Temperature is a measure of how warm the air is.

- Humidity is a measure of how much water vapor is in the air. Humidity readings are usually given as percents. A humidity reading of 90 percent means that the air contains 90 percent of the water vapor it can possibly hold at that particular temperature.

- Wind refers to air movement and is usually given as a wind speed and a wind direction (the direction from which the wind is blowing).

- Air pressure (most often called barometric pressure) refers to the weight of the atmosphere. Air pressure depends on atmospheric temperature, humidity, and air movement. A high-pressure reading usually indicates clear, pleasant weather, while a low reading indicates wet or stormy weather.

Although the exact causes of weather changes are not completely understood, meteorologists have discovered several characteristics of weather. For instance, they know that most changes in weather are caused by movements of large masses of air. Air masses are bodies of air at a certain temperature and with a certain moisture content.

Air masses that form over the polar regions tend to be very cold and dry, while air masses that form over tropical oceans tend to be warm and moist. An air mass takes on the characteristics of the region where it originated.

The movement of air masses is caused by temperature and pressure differences. Warm air masses tend to rise over cold ones, and air tends to flow from regions of high pressure to regions of low pressure. As an air mass moves, its direction of motion is also greatly affected by Earth's rotation.

Stormy or turbulent weather conditions tend to form along a line called a *front*, the boundary line where a warm air mass collides with a cold air mass. Because the moisture in the warm air will condense into water droplets when it cools, clouds, rain, sleet, hail, or snow occurs along the front. The actual weather you get depends on the air temperatures and moisture contents of the two colliding air masses. Because weather changes take place along a front, you'll often hear a weather forecaster talk about a "front that's moving in and bringing the weather with it!"

EXERCISE 10

Directions: Answer each question below.

1. Match each item on the left with the phrase that best describes it on the right. Write the letter of the phrase on the line before the correct number.

_____ **1.** air mass

_____ **2.** front

_____ **3.** air pressure

_____ **4.** humidity

_____ **5.** wind

(a) moisture content of air

(b) movement of air

(c) weight of Earth's atmosphere

(d) body of air at equal temperature and humidity

(e) boundary line of warm air mass against a cold air mass

2. What kind of weather is indicated by each of the following barometric pressure readings?

a. a high-pressure reading _____

b. a low-pressure reading _____

3. Which of the following is not mentioned in the reading selection as a standard feature of a weather report?

(1) humidity
(2) air pollution level
(3) wind speed and direction
(4) temperature
(5) barometric pressure

ANSWERS ARE ON PAGE 313.

 WRITING ACTIVITY 3

People's moods are often affected by the weather. Three or four days of rain can cause some people to feel depressed just as a week of sun and warm temperatures can raise spirits. Have you ever noticed that your feelings, or those of someone close to you, are connected to what's going on outside?

If so, describe in one or two paragraphs how weather influences your emotions and behavior. If you don't believe that changes in the weather can cause changes in mood, explain why not.

ANSWERS WILL VARY.

Questions 1 and 2 refer to the following passage and diagram.

FORECAST

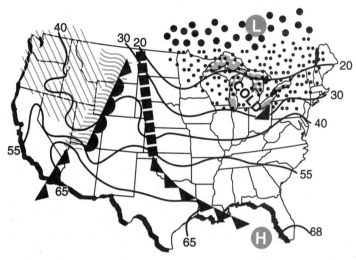

Probably the most common science diagram you'll ever see is a weather map. A weather map gives a brief summary of the weather conditions in a certain location. Most United States newspapers carry a daily weather map that shows the weather conditions over the continental United States.

Weather maps use symbols to stand for certain weather conditions. Most often, a brief definition of these symbols accompanies the map. An example of a weather map is shown above. Following the map are definitions of the map symbols.

As seen on the map, the weather in the southern states was cool (55 to 68°F) while the weather in the northern states was cold (20 to 40°F) and wet. Rain is shown over the northwestern states, while snow is shown over the northern part of the central and eastern United States.

Symbols Used On the Map

Fronts:

Rain — Cold

Snow — Warm

Showers — Occluded

Flurries — Stationary

L Low atmospheric pressure

H High atmospheric pressure

Isotherm: a line that connects points that have the same temperature

1. Cities that lie on the same isotherm could expect to have the same

   (1) weather
   (2) type of precipitation
   (3) temperature
   (4) humidity
   (5) wind speed

2. Which month is most likely represented by the weather map above?

   (1) April
   (2) June
   (3) August
   (4) October
   (5) December

ANSWERS ARE ON PAGE 313.

THE CHANGING EARTH

weathering—the natural breaking of large rocks into smaller rocks

soil—a mixture of tiny rock fragments and organic materials

erosion—the natural movement of rock fragments, soil, and sand along Earth's surface

Earth can be compared to a gigantic sculpture, slowly being shaped by the forces of nature. This comparison is especially meaningful to anyone who has seen the awe-inspiring canyons in the southwestern United States or other natural wonders such as Niagara Falls, in New York state.

The land on Earth's surface looks solid and unchanging. But while we don't notice the effects on a daily basis, changes are continually taking place in the land's features. The Grand Canyon itself was once just a highland plateau that was crossed by the Colorado River. Then, over millions of years, the river, wind, and rain combined to carve and shape this mile-deep canyon.

The two most important natural processes involved in sculpturing Earth are weathering and erosion.

Weathering

Weathering is the breaking down of large rocks into smaller pieces by natural processes. It is because of weathering that soil is produced. Soil is just a mixture of tiny rock fragments and organic materials produced by living things. Most organic materials in soil are simply the decaying remains of plants and animals.

There are several types of weathering. The most common is called *physical weathering*, also referred to as *mechanical weathering*. Physical weathering causes the rocks to break apart without changing the chemicals within the rocks. One main form of physical weathering is from the action of freezing water. Water from rain, rivers, or streams may flow over a rock and fill any small cracks in the rock's surface. Then, as the water freezes in cold weather, the ice tends to widen the cracks in the rock and split it into pieces. Nothing has been added to or taken from the rock; it has just been broken apart.

A second type of weathering is called *chemical weathering*. In this process, chemical changes cause a rock to become soft and crumble. These chemical changes occur because rock is exposed to water and atmospheric gases. For example, when iron in a rock is exposed to water, it forms rust. Rust is created from the combination of the iron in the rock and the oxygen gas that is present in water.

Sometimes plants and animals can cause physical and chemical weathering. For example, the roots of plants may grow in small cracks in rocks. As the plants increase in size, they push the rocks apart and cause them to split. Chemicals present in the plant root may help dissolve the rock. Burrowing animals such as gophers and worms also add to the weathering process. Their tunnels allow water and atmospheric gases to penetrate more easily into surface soil.

Erosion

Erosion is defined as the natural movement of rock fragments over the surface of Earth. The three main causes of erosion are gravity, wind, and water.

Because of the force of gravity, rock fragments always fall to the lowest point they can. This effect is called ***gravity erosion***. If small rock pieces break off from solid rock high on a cliff, they will fall until other rocks stop them. Hillsides covered with loose rock are often the result of the gravity erosion of rocks higher up.

Wind erosion acts mainly on small rock fragments such as loose soil and sand. An important part of wind erosion occurs when fine, hard rock particles are carried in a strong wind. This stream of particles can act like a sandblaster when they strike other rock formations. Thus, wind erosion can add to the effects of both weathering and gravity erosion.

The most powerful of all types of erosion is caused by running water. In ***water erosion***, a river tends to move rock fragments along the direction of its flow. Arizona's Grand Canyon, a magnificent natural wonder, was created by erosion caused by the Colorado River.

EXERCISE 12

Directions: Write the answer to each question below.

1. What is soil made from? _____ and _____

2. In what way do small ground animals play a part in the process of weathering?

_____

_____

3. After a new concrete slab is poured for a driveway, what tends to occur first, weathering or erosion? _____

ANSWERS ARE ON PAGE 313.

GED Practice

EXERCISE 13

Questions 1–6 refer to the following definitions:

physical weathering—weathering (the breaking up of rocks) that does not involve chemical change

chemical weathering—weathering that involves chemical change

wind erosion—rock movement caused by wind

water erosion—rock movement caused by water

gravity erosion—rock movement caused by gravity

1. When ocean waves move sand from the north end of a beach to the south end, what process is occurring?

   (1) physical weathering
   (2) chemical weathering
   (3) wind erosion
   (4) water erosion
   (5) gravity erosion

2. In a landslide, tons of rocks slide from the top of a cliff down to the bottom. This is an example of

   (1) physical weathering
   (2) chemical weathering
   (3) wind erosion
   (4) water erosion
   (5) gravity erosion

3. Trapped carbon dioxide gas in a mineral reacts with water washing over the mineral and forms an acid that causes the mineral to crumble. This is an example of

   (1) physical weathering
   (2) chemical weathering
   (3) wind erosion
   (4) water erosion
   (5) gravity erosion

4. Rainwater seeps into a crack in a piece of granite, and the granite breaks apart when the water later freezes. Which of the following processes has happened to the granite?

(1) physical weathering
(2) chemical weathering
(3) wind erosion
(4) water erosion
(5) gravity erosion

5. Which of the following processes is most important in the continually changing shape of land features now characteristic of the Sahara Desert?

(1) physical weathering
(2) chemical weathering
(3) wind erosion
(4) water erosion
(5) gravity erosion

6. An underwater mountain chain is affected by each type of weathering and erosion process *except*

(1) physical weathering
(2) chemical weathering
(3) gravity erosion
(4) water erosion
(5) wind erosion

Question 7 is based on the following information.

When a river goes round a bend, the river tends to erode the outside curve more than the inside curve. Because of this, a river that contains a slight bend can actually create a small lake that ends up cut off from the river. The small lake that is formed is called an *oxbow lake* because its *U* shape resembles the shape of an oxbow. In the illustration below, the four steps in the formation of an oxbow lake are not arranged in order.

7. In what order should the drawings above be placed to show how an oxbow lake might develop from a bend in a river?

(1) A, C, B, D
(2) C, B, A, D
(3) B, A, C, D
(4) D, A, B, C
(5) C, A, B, D

ANSWERS ARE ON PAGE 313.

WRITING ACTIVITY 4

Think about the land features of the area where you live. If you live in a city, you might be able to see the effects of weathering and erosion on sidewalks, buildings, and small patches of grass or dirt. People who live in rural areas might see some of these effects on roads, hillsides, rivers, and fields.

Choose one instance of weathering or erosion in your environment and write a paragraph describing it. If you can determine the cause, include that as well.

ANSWERS WILL VARY.

EARTH'S PAST

KEY WORD

fossil—preserved remains of traces of ancient life forms

If the history of Earth could be compressed into the span of one year's time, the story of the human race would be written as the last two hours of the final day! This fact gives you an idea of just how old Earth is. Its age is estimated to be between four and five billion years. Although there is no written record to tell us about the geological past, Earth itself has left a record in the form of fossils.

The Fossil Record

A fossil is the preserved remains or traces of an ancient living thing. Fossils are most often found buried in rock, but they may also be found in caves, ancient tar beds, and the solid ice that covers Earth's polar regions. In all these places, fossils are protected from the damaging effects of weathering and erosion.

Usually only the hard parts of a dead plant or animal are preserved. These can include bones, shells, and woody tissues. The soft parts, like flesh, either decay or are eaten by animals before they can be preserved. One exception is when an organism is subjected to extreme cold. Then the entire body may be preserved in ice. For example, the frozen bodies of extinct woolly mammoths have been found in Siberia.

Sometimes the remains of an organism are preserved after having been changed into a completely different form. For instance, coal deposits are actually the fossil remains of plants. When plants decompose, eventually only deposits of carbon remain. When the carbon is under extreme pressure for a long period of time, it is slowly transformed into coal. Coal is called a *fossil fuel* because of the way it is created.

Another type of fossil contains only the traces of an organism, not its remains. One common example is footprints left in mud that later hardened into solid rock. Geologists have found dinosaur footprints that are over 100 million years old.

Fossils can help geologists learn about how animal and plant species have changed over time. Since geologists can date the rocks that the fossils are in, they can also tell during what time period in the past a species lived. For example, on the geologic calendar on page 169, you can see that fish first appear in the era labeled *Paleozoic*. This means that the oldest rocks discovered to contain fish fossils are between 225 million and 600 million years old. We can assume that fish existed in the world at least 225 million years ago.

Fossils are also used to study extinct species. For example, there are no longer any living woolly mammoths on Earth, but we can know what a woolly mammoth looked like by studying the frozen bodies found in Siberia.

Eras	Years Before Present	Life Forms
Cenozoic		
	70,000,000	
Mesozoic		
	225,000,000	
Paleozoic		
	600,000,000	
Precambrian		

EXERCISE 14

Directions: Write the answer to each question below.

1. What is the estimated age of Earth? _____

2. Name three places where fossils may be found: _____,

   _____, and _____.

3. According to the geologic calendar, during what era did human beings appear on

   Earth? _____

ANSWERS ARE ON PAGE 314.

EXERCISE 15

Questions 1–3 refer to the following passage.

Many fossil specimens are completely altered by chemical change before they are discovered. Mineral substances near the fossils replace the organic substances out of which the organism was originally made. This process is called *petrification*.

When a fossil petrifies, it does not turn to stone as many people think. Instead, minerals slowly replace the original cell material in the fossil. Scientists believe that this process takes place molecule by molecule over a long period of time. The most common petrifying minerals are silica (a glassy mineral most commonly seen as sand), calcite (a mineral found in both limestone and marble), and pyrite (a mineral made up of iron and sulfur).

When a fossil petrifies, the petrified remains may look almost identical to the original fossil. The detailed cell structure of the original tissues may even be apparent. Perhaps the most familiar petrified fossil is petrified wood. This hard, glassy mineral substance clearly shows the growth rings and other tissue features of the ancient tree from which it was produced.

1. Petrification is a process in which minerals

   (1) surround and preserve a fossil
   (2) cause a fossil's remains to harden into a rocklike substance
   (3) replace a fossil's original cell materials
   (4) change the size of a fossil
   (5) change the shape of a fossil

2. During petrification, information about each of the fossil's original features is lost *except* information about the fossil's original

   (1) weight
   (2) color
   (3) origin
   (4) shape
   (5) chemical composition

3. What might a person be able to determine by looking at a petrified tree trunk?

   (1) the height of the tree when it died
   (2) the age of the tree when it died
   (3) the location of the tree when it died
   (4) the date that the tree died
   (5) the length of time that petrification took

Questions 4–7 refer to the following passage and diagram.

When you look at the side of a cliff, you notice something very interesting. The cliff is made up of many individual layers of rock. Often, each layer is a different type of rock from the layers above and below it. The lower layers are the oldest ones, and the upper layers are newer. As you might guess, the very top layer is the most recent.

Rock layers are a clue to the past climate and land surface conditions of a region. For example, limestone, a rock made of the compressed remains of aquatic animals and plants, is almost always formed at the bottom of an ocean. Therefore, a layer of limestone indicates that an ocean probably once covered the land. A layer of sandstone, a rock made of fine sand grains cemented together, often indicates that the region was once a windswept desert. A layer of coal, a rock made of the compressed remains of dense vegetation, indicates that the region was once a lush forest. When several rock layers appear on top of one another, it is likely that the region has undergone many changes of climate.

4. Which two layers of rock indicate the possibility that a lush tropical forest was covered by a rising ocean?

   (1) the granite layer and the coal layer
   (2) the sandstone layer and upper limestone layer
   (3) the coal layer and the lower limestone layer
   (4) the lower limestone layer and the sandstone layer
   (5) the granite layer and the upper limestone layer

5. Which of the following fossils would most likely be found in the upper limestone layer?

   (1) a dinosaur footprint
   (2) a woolly mammoth
   (3) the leaf of an ancient redwood tree
   (4) a thorn from an extinct desert cactus
   (5) an impression of a small sea worm

CLIFF LAYERS

6. Which of the following fossils would most likely be found in the sandstone layer?

   (1) an impression of a fin of an ancient fish
   (2) a bone fragment from the wing of an extinct type of penguin
   (3) a leg bone from an extinct type of camel
   (4) a jawbone from an extinct animal, similar to a gorilla, that ate mainly vegetables and fruit
   (5) a wing print from an extinct flying tropical insect

7. By looking at the order of rock layers in the diagram, it is possible to form a hypothesis about the history of this location. It seems likely that this region

   (1) was a desert that later was covered by a tropical forest
   (2) has experienced many changes of climate
   (3) has always been a hot, dry desert
   (4) has mainly been under an ocean
   (5) has been under ice for much of its past

ANSWERS ARE ON PAGE 314.

GED Practice
EARTH SCIENCE

Questions 1–3 refer to the following diagrams and passage.

VOLCANO

GEYSER

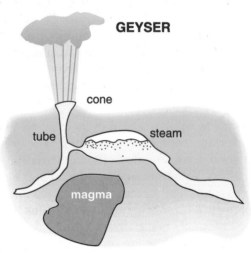

Active volcanoes and geysers both are characterized by the sudden eruption of hot liquid up through Earth's surface.

In an explosive volcanic eruption, hot molten rock called *magma* flows upward from deep inside Earth through a *tube*, a tubular crack in Earth's surface. The magma, together with hot gas and steam, is under high pressure and can blow a hole, called a *vent*, in the surface. The magma can break through the surface with enough force to blast a large part of a mountain out of its way. Magma that emerges from below the surface is called *lava*. An explosive eruption forms a cinder *cone*, made of fragments of the ejected rocks and lava.

Though volcanic eruptions aren't predictable, scientists have discovered that many eruptions are preceded by small earthquakes, apparently caused by an increased movement of magma.

A geyser eruption, on the other hand, is produced by groundwater that's heated by magma. The groundwater sits in underground chambers and slowly builds up tremendous pressure until it explosively expands and is jetted through a tube to the surface. Around the geyser's vent hole, a cone slowly builds from minerals dissolved in the hot geyser water.

After an eruption, groundwater again collects in the underground chambers. The time period between eruptions is determined by the supply of

groundwater, the speed with which the water heats, and the size and shape of the geyser's tube and chambers. These factors don't change very much, and a geyser's eruption cycle is usually predictable.

1. Scientists think that around many potential volcanoes an eruption may be preceded by

   (1) a change in the weather pattern
   (2) weak earthquakes
   (3) decreased magma flow
   (4) increased geyser activity
   (5) decreased geyser activity

2. Which of the following is most likely to cause a decrease in the length of time between two eruptions of the same geyser?

   (1) a decrease in local wind speed
   (2) an increase in local air temperature
   (3) a decrease in local air temperature
   (4) a decrease in the temperature of the magma heating the geyser's water
   (5) an increase in the temperature of the magma heating the geyser's water

3. A geyser and a volcano have each of the following in common *except* a

   (1) heat source of hot magma
   (2) flow of liquid through Earth's surface
   (3) cone that forms near the top of a flow tube
   (4) high-pressure region of hot gases
   (5) fairly predictable eruption schedule

Questions 4–7 refer to the following information.

EARTHQUAKE VIBRATION WAVES

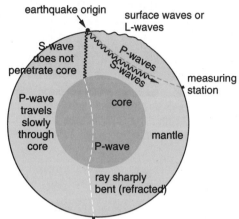

RICHTER SCALE OF EARTHQUAKE MAGNITUDE	
Magnitude	*Earthquake Effects*
0	Smallest measurable quake
2.5–3	Not felt, but measurable
4.5	Minor property damage
6.0	Considerable destruction in populated areas
7.0	Major damage to buildings, bridges, and other structures
7.9	1906 San Francisco quake
8.0 or more	Total destruction of nearby population centers

When an earthquake occurs, three types of vibration waves move out from the quake site:

Primary waves, or P-waves, result from the back-and-forth vibration of rock in each direction the P-waves travel. The P-waves travel through the body of Earth and move at a greater speed than do the other two types of waves. P-waves travel in all directions from the point of the quake.

Secondary waves, or S-waves, result from an up-and-down (or side-to-side) vibration of rock at a right angle to the direction each S-wave travels. The S-waves travel through Earth's mantle but not through its core.

Surface waves, or L-waves, result from vibration of rock on Earth's surface. L-waves are felt strongly near the quake site and travel over the surface in widening circles, like ripples made when a rock is thrown into a pond. Weaker L-waves form at distant points wherever either P-waves or S-waves reach the surface. L-waves travel more slowly than either P-waves or S-waves.

The strength of an earthquake is measured by the Richter magnitude scale shown above.

4. According to the drawing,

   (1) P-waves don't penetrate Earth's core
   (2) S-waves penetrate Earth's core
   (3) L-waves penetrate Earth's core
   (4) P-waves penetrate Earth's core
   (5) P-waves don't penetrate Earth's mantle

5. Which will be the first type of wave(s) to reach a town located 500 miles from an earthquake site?

   (1) L-wave
   (2) P-wave
   (3) S-wave
   (4) P-wave and S-wave at the same time
   (5) L-wave and P-wave at the same time

6. An earthquake of Richter magnitude 8 occurs in Japan. What magnitude of P-wave will most likely be recorded by instruments but not felt by the general population later in Brazil?

   (1) less than 0
   (2) between 0 and 3
   (3) between 4.5 and 6
   (4) between 6 and 7
   (5) between 7 and 8

7. A geologist wants to determine the location of a strong earthquake. Each of the following could be used to help him determine this location *except*

   (1) the time his instruments first started recording the arrival of the P-wave
   (2) the speed a P-wave travels
   (3) the time the earthquake occurred
   (4) the magnitude of the P-wave that his instruments record
   (5) the direction from which the P-wave is traveling

ANSWERS ARE ON PAGE 314.

8 Chemistry

Have you ever wished that you could take a piece of iron—say, an old nail—and turn it into gold? What an idea! Think of how different your life would be! Untold riches would be as close as the nearest old scrap pile. Can you believe that anyone would ever take this idea seriously? Well, early chemists once did, and the idea persisted for 1,100 years!

The idea of turning iron into gold was more than just a fanciful wish to alchemists, the chemists of the Middle Ages (A.D. 500–1600). These early scientists searched for a way to change metal into gold and tried to create a medicine that would keep people from aging. Unfortunately for all of us, the alchemists did not achieve their goals. However, their experiments revealed a lot about the metals and other substances they worked with.

Modern chemistry has come a long way since the days of alchemy. Today's chemists seek to understand the structure, composition, and properties of all matter. *Matter* is anything that has weight and takes up space. Matter can be a solid like gold, a liquid like water, or a gas like oxygen.

By learning about the properties of matter, chemists have been able to improve traditional medical remedies. A well-known example is the development of aspirin. During the seventeenth and eighteenth centuries, Native Americans used the bark of willow trees as a treatment for fever. Later, chemists discovered that the salicylic acid in the bark was the chemical responsible for the pain-relieving effect. They began to produce this acid in their laboratories. The drug proved to be helpful in easing pain, but it had unpleasant side effects, including stomach irritation. Chemists were able to reduce this irritation by adding another element to salicylic acid. The resulting drug, acetylsalicylic acid, is what we know today as aspirin.

In addition to improving traditional remedies, chemists are also developing new products at an ever-increasing rate. In fact, more than 90 percent of all the medicinal drugs now being used were not available in any form before World War II.

Chemists have also been able to create materials not found in nature. One example is plastic. Plastic has proven to be one of the most durable, inexpensive, and versatile materials known. Milk jugs, telephones, automobile parts, and clothes are just some of the products that can now be made of plastic. Yet, only a few decades ago, plastic was mainly a novelty material used to make children's toys.

Our study of chemistry in this chapter will involve three major topics: the structure of matter, the behavior of matter, and the chemistry of life.

EXERCISE 1

Directions: Match each item on the left with the phrase that best describes it on the right. Write the letter of the phrase on the line before the correct number.

_____ **1.** alchemy

_____ **2.** plastic

_____ **3.** willow bark

_____ **4.** matter

_____ **5.** aspirin

(a) anything that has weight and takes up space

(b) a natural source of salicylic acid

(c) a medicinal drug

(d) chemistry of the Middle Ages

(e) a material not found in nature

 GED Practice

EXERCISE 2

Question 1 refers to the information on page 175.

1. According to the fourth paragraph, aspirin owes its beginnings to the

(1) plastics industry
(2) American Eskimos
(3) Native Americans
(4) alchemists
(5) early American pioneers

Questions 2 and 3 refer to the information below.

Chemistry is the study of the structure, composition, and properties of matter. In a classroom discussion, students made the following statements about the study of chemistry.

A. Chemistry is the most difficult science to learn.

B. There are many practical applications of chemistry.

C. Much of the knowledge gained from chemistry is also useful in both geology and biology.

2. Which of the statements is (are) most likely fact and not opinion?

(1) A only
(2) B only
(3) C only
(4) A and B only
(5) B and C only

3. Which of the statements is an opinion?

(1) A only
(2) B only
(3) C only
(4) A and B only
(5) B and C only

ANSWERS ARE ON PAGE 314.

THE STRUCTURE OF MATTER
THE ATOMIC THEORY OF MATTER

KEY WORDS

element—a pure substance that cannot be broken down into other
substances
atom—the smallest unit of an element having the properties of that
element
nucleus—the core of an atom
mass—amount of matter

Long before scientists were able to prove it, the ancient Greek
philosophers had an idea of what an atom was. They believed that any
substance could be divided only so far before you reached the smallest
possible piece of that substance. Democritus (460–370 B.C.) called this smallest
particle an atom, from the Greek word meaning "indivisible." He believed in
the existence of only four types of atoms or elements. Each type accounted for
the properties of earth, air, water, and fire. Today our understanding of both
elements and atoms is very different from that of Democritus.

We now know that all matter in the world is formed from one or more of
ninety-two naturally occurring chemical elements. Each element is a pure
substance that cannot be broken down further. You can think of elements as
the building blocks of matter. Elements combine to form all known substances
in the same way that the letters of the alphabet combine to form words.

Surprisingly, most of the natural elements are very rare. Only fifteen
elements make up more than 99 percent of all matter on Earth. You may
already know some of these common elements, which include the gases
oxygen, hydrogen, and nitrogen, and the metals aluminum, iron, and nickel.

If we divided a gold coin into the smallest unit that still had the properties
of gold, we would end up with a single atom of gold. That atom, like the atoms
of all other elements, is made up of three types of particles: protons, neutrons,
and electrons.

Protons are particles with a positive electric charge, while ***neutrons***
have no electric charge. The protons and neutrons make up the nucleus, the
core of the atom. They are almost exactly the same size, and each is more than
1,800 times as massive as an electron. Because of this size difference, almost
all the mass (amount of matter) of an atom is concentrated in the nucleus.

In their natural state, all atoms have the same number of electrons as protons. The negatively charged ***electrons*** move in orbits around the nucleus. Although the exact path followed by an electron is not known, it is often illustrated as shown in the diagram of a helium atom below.

THE HELIUM ATOM

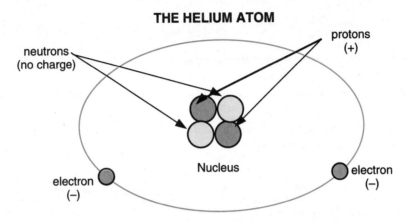

EXERCISE 3

Directions: Answer each question below.

1. Complete each sentence by filling in the blanks with the correct word from the reading passage.

   a. Oxygen and iron are examples of _____.

   b. The only three particles that are found in atoms are _____, _____, and _____.

   c. The _____ is the only uncharged particle found in an atom.

2. The statements below refer to the atomic theory of matter. Circle *T* for each statement that is true and *F* for each statement that is false.

   T F   **a.** Almost the entire mass of an atom comes from its electrons and protons.

   T F   **b.** Electrons, protons, and neutrons are found in an atom's nucleus.

   T F   **c.** More than 99 percent of all matter on Earth is made up of only fifteen out of ninety-two naturally occurring elements.

   T F   **d.** Electrons are the only negatively charged particles found in an atom.

ANSWERS ARE ON PAGE 314.

EXERCISE 4

Questions 1 and 2 refer to the following tables.

ELEMENTAL COMPOSITION OF THE HUMAN BODY	
Element	Weight (to the nearest percent)
Oxygen	65
Carbon	18
Hydrogen	10
Nitrogen	3
Calcium	2
Phosphorus	1
Traces of other elements	1

ELEMENTAL COMPOSITION OF EARTH'S CRUST, SEAWATER, AND ATMOSPHERE	
Element	Weight (to the nearest percent)
Oxygen	49
Silicon	26
Aluminum	8
Iron	5
Calcium	3
Sodium	3
Potassium	2
Magnesium	2
Hydrogen	1
Traces of other elements	1

1. According to the first table, which two elements together make up almost exactly 75 percent of the weight of a human body?

    (1) oxygen and carbon
    (2) oxygen and hydrogen
    (3) carbon and hydrogen
    (4) carbon and nitrogen
    (5) oxygen and nitrogen

2. Which conclusion below can be correctly drawn from the data shown in the two tables?

    (1) Although sodium is present on Earth, the human body contains no sodium at all.
    (2) The largest single source of oxygen on or near Earth is the atmosphere.
    (3) Iron is very important in a healthy diet.
    (4) Carbon is an element that is found in all forms of life that exist on Earth.
    (5) Although carbon is the second most abundant element in our bodies, there is little carbon on or near the surface of Earth.

ANSWERS ARE ON PAGE 315.

WRITING ACTIVITY 1

In December 1984, in Bhopal, India, more than 2,500 people died when a toxic cloud of methyl isocyanate gas leaked from a Union Carbide plant.

In one or two paragraphs, explain what you think a chemical company should do in response to such a serious accident.

ANSWERS WILL VARY.

THE PERIODIC TABLE

KEY WORDS

mass number—total of protons and neutrons in the nucleus
atomic number—total of protons in the nucleus
shells—energy levels holding a certain number of electrons

Do you ever wonder what makes one element different from another? Why, for example, is helium different from gold? Helium is a colorless, odorless gas used to fill balloons. But gold is another story! This shiny yellowish metal is valuable in jewelry and in dentistry, and it is the basis of much of the world's money. Who hasn't seen a movie about the California gold rush, which took place in the mid-1800s? Can you imagine anyone getting excited about a "Helium Rush"?

Gold in a ring or a tooth differs from helium in a balloon because the atomic structure of gold differs from that of helium. A gold atom has more electrons, protons, and neutrons than a helium atom.

Every element has a unique atomic structure. In other words, no two elements have exactly the same combination of protons, neutrons, and electrons. We can use this uniqueness to identify an element by its mass number and its atomic number.

The mass number is the sum of the protons and neutrons in the nucleus. Aluminum, shown below, has a mass number of 27: it has 13 protons and 14 neutrons. The atomic number is the number of protons in an atom. A neutral atom has an equal number of protons and electrons. Later in this chapter, you'll learn about what happens when an atom is not neutral.

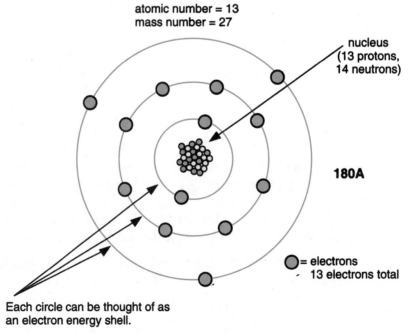

ALUMINUM

atomic number = 13
mass number = 27

nucleus
(13 protons,
14 neutrons)

180A

◯ = electrons
13 electrons total

Each circle can be thought of as
an electron energy shell.

In each atom, the electrons orbit in energy levels called shells. Each shell can hold only a set number of electrons. Atoms with larger atomic numbers have electrons in several energy shells. In the drawing on page 180, each circle represents a particular energy shell. The two electrons in the circle closest to the nucleus are in the lowest energy shell. The next higher energy shell contains eight electrons. The outer (highest) energy shell of aluminum contains only three electrons.

Reading the Periodic Table

Differing shell structure is the basis of the design of the periodic table shown on page 182. Each row (read from left to right and called a ***period***) contains elements that have the same number of shells that are at least partially filled with electrons. Each column (read from top to bottom and called a ***group***) lists elements that have the same number of electrons in their outermost shell.

Group
(same number of electrons in outermost shells)
↓

	③ **Li** Lithium 7	④ **Be** Beryllium 9	
2			
3	⑪ **Na** Sodium 23	⑫ **Mg** Magnesium 24	
4	⑲ **K** Potassium 39	⑳ **Ca** Calcium 40	㉑ **Sc** Scandium 45
5	㊲ **Rb** Rubidium 85	㊳ **Sr** Strontium 88	㊴ **Y** Yttrium 89

Period
(same number of electron shells) →

Reading from left to right, elements are listed in order of atomic number. Each element in the table is shown with its name, symbol, atomic number, and mass number.

Periodic Table of the Elements

Key:

6 — Atomic Number
C — Symbol *man made
Carbon — Name
12 — Mass Number (number of protons and neutrons)

Period																	
1	(1) **H** Hydrogen 1																(2) **He** Helium 4
2	(3) **Li** Lithium 7	(4) **Be** Beryllium 9									(5) **B** Boron 11	(6) **C** Carbon 12	(7) **N** Nitrogen 14	(8) **O** Oxygen 16	(9) **F** Fluorine 19	(10) **Ne** Neon 20
3	(11) **Na** Sodium 23	(12) **Mg** Magnesium 24										(13) **Al** Aluminum 27	(14) **Si** Silicon 28	(15) **P** Phosphorus 31	(16) **S** Sulfur 32	(17) **Cl** Chlorine 35	(18) **Ar** Argon 40
4	(19) **K** Potassium 39	(20) **Ca** Calcium 40	(21) **Sc** Scandium 45	(22) **Ti** Titanium 48	(23) **V** Vanadium 51	(24) **Cr** Chromium 52	(25) **Mn** Manganese 55	(26) **Fe** Iron 56	(27) **Co** Cobalt 59	(28) **Ni** Nickel 59	(29) **Cu** Copper 64	(30) **Zn** Zinc 65	(31) **Ga** Gallium 70	(32) **Ge** Germanium 73	(33) **As** Arsenic 75	(34) **Se** Selenium 79	(35) **Br** Bromine 80	(36) **Kr** Krypton 84
5	(37) **Rb** Rubidium 85	(38) **Sr** Strontium 88	(39) **Y** Yttrium 89	(40) **Zr** Zirconium 91	(41) **Nb** Niobium 93	(42) **Mo** Molybdenum 96	(43) **Tc*** Technetium 98	(44) **Ru** Ruthenium 101	(45) **Rh** Rhodium 103	(46) **Pd** Palladium 106	(47) **Ag** Silver 108	(48) **Cd** Cadmium 112	(49) **In** Indium 115	(50) **Sn** Tin 119	(51) **Sb** Antimony 122	(52) **Te** Tellurium 128	(53) **I** Iodine 127	(54) **Xe** Xenon 131
6	(55) **Cs** Cesium 133	(56) **Ba** Barium 137	(57) **La** Lanthanum 139	(72) **Hf** Hafnium 178	(73) **Ta** Tantalum 181	(74) **W** Tungsten 184	(75) **Re** Rhenium 186	(76) **Os** Osmium 190	(77) **Ir** Iridium 192	(78) **Pt** Platinum 195	(79) **Au** Gold 197	(80) **Hg** Mercury 201	(81) **Ti** Thallium 204	(82) **Pb** Lead 207	(83) **Bi** Bismuth 209	(84) **Po** Polonium 209	(85) **At** Astatine 210	(86) **Rn** Radon 222
7	(87) **Fr** Francium 223	(88) **Ra** Radium 226	(89) **Ac** Actinium 227	(104) **Rf*** Rutherfordium 261	(105) **Ha*** Hahnium 262	(106) **Unh*** Unnilhexium 263	(107) **Uns*** Unnilseptium 262	(108) **Uno*** Unniloctium	(109) **Une*** Unnilennium	(110) **Uun*** Unununium								

Rare Earth Elements

Lanthanide Series	(58) **Ce** Cerium 140	(59) **Pr** Praseodymium 141	(60) **Nd** Neodymium 144	(61) **Pm*** Promethium 145	(62) **Sm** Samarium 150	(63) **Eu** Europium 152	(64) **Gd** Gadolinium 157	(65) **Tb** Terbium 159	(66) **Dy** Dysprosium 163	(67) **Ho** Holmium 165	(68) **Er** Erbium 167	(69) **Tm** Thulium 169	(70) **Yb** Ytterbium 173	(71) **Lu** Lutetium 175
Actinide Series	(90) **Th** Thorium 232	(91) **Pa** Protactinium 231	(92) **U** Uranium 238	(93) **Np*** Neptunium 237	(94) **Pu*** Plutonium 244	(95) **Am*** Americium 243	(96) **Cm*** Curium 247	(97) **Bk*** Berkelium 247	(98) **Cf*** Californium 251	(99) **Es*** Einsteinium 252	(100) **Fm*** Fermium 257	(101) **Md*** Mendelevium 258	(102) **No*** Nobelium 259	(103) **Lr*** Lawrencium 260

EXERCISE 5

Directions: Answer each of the questions below.

1. Complete each sentence by filling in the blanks with the correct word(s) from the reading passage.

  a. The number of protons in an atom is known as that atom's

  _____.

  b. An atom's mass number is the sum of the number of that atom's

  _____ and _____.

2. Sodium (atomic number 11) has a mass number of 23.

  a. How many protons does sodium have in its nucleus? _____

  b. How many neutrons does sodium have in its nucleus? _____

  c. How many electrons does a neutral sodium atom have? _____

≡ GED Practice ≡

EXERCISE 6

Questions 1–4 refer to the information on pages 180–181 and the periodic table.

1. The elements are listed in the periodic table according to

  (1) the number of neutrons in an atom
  (2) the alphabetical order of the atoms' symbols
  (3) the number of protons in an atom
  (4) the sum of the number of neutrons and protons in an atom
  (5) the difference between the number of neutrons and protons in an atom

2. Calcium (atomic number 20) has two electrons in its outermost electron shell. Which of the following elements also has two electrons in its outermost shell?

  (1) potassium (K)
  (2) carbon (C)
  (3) magnesium (Mg)
  (4) helium (He)
  (5) scandium (Sc)

3. Which of the following has the same number of shells as oxygen (atomic number 8)?

  (1) sulfur (S)
  (2) lithium (Li)
  (3) phosphorus (P)
  (4) selenium (Se)
  (5) helium (He)

4. Which of the following describes the nucleus of iron (Fe)?

  (1) 26 protons, 30 neutrons
  (2) 26 protons, 56 neutrons
  (3) 56 protons, 56 neutrons
  (4) 56 protons, 82 neutrons
  (5) 82 protons, 56 neutrons

ANSWERS ARE ON PAGE 315.

ELEMENTS IN COMBINATION

molecule—formed by the combination of two or more atoms
chemical formula—an expression used to indicate the kind and number of atoms in a molecule

Look around you and notice the variety of things in your everyday life. You might see chairs, tables, curtains, windows, water, people, and much, much more. It's hard to believe that this incredible variety is made up almost entirely of combinations of fifteen elements.

When two or more atoms combine, a molecule is formed. For example, a molecule of water is formed when one atom of oxygen combines with two atoms of hydrogen. As this example shows, two elements can combine to form a completely new substance. The newly created substance—in this case, water—is called a *compound*.

CHEMICAL FORMULAS

To show which elements are contained in a molecule, chemists write a chemical formula. They use symbols to show which elements (from the periodic table) are present. They use small numbers to show how many atoms there are of each molecule.

For example, H_2O is the chemical formula for water. The subscript *2* (small number 2) tells us there are two atoms of hydrogen in one molecule of water. The *O*, written without a subscript, tells us that one atom of oxygen is in each molecule of water.

Similarly, in the formula for the gas fuel propane, C_3H_8, each propane molecule contains three atoms of carbon and eight atoms of hydrogen.

When a number is written in front of a formula, it indicates that more than one molecule is represented. The formula $4H_2O$ represents four molecules of water. Notice that four molecules of water contain eight atoms of hydrogen ($4 \times 2 = 8$) and four atoms of oxygen ($4 \times 1 = 4$).

As another example, the formula $6CaCO_3$ represents 6 molecules of $CaCO_3$, known as calcium carbonate. Each $CaCO_3$ molecule contains 1 atom of calcium (Ca), 1 atom of carbon (C), and 3 atoms of oxygen (O). Therefore, $6CaCO_3$ contains 6 atoms of calcium, 6 atoms of carbon, and 18 atoms of oxygen ($6 \times 3 = 18$).

EXERCISE 7

Directions: Answer each of the following questions.

1. **a.** In the formula Al_2O_3, how many atoms of aluminum are represented? _____

   b. In the formula $5C_3H_8$, how many molecules of propane are represented? _____

   c. In the formula $3H_2O$, how many atoms of hydrogen are represented? _____

Isobutane Molecule

```
  H—H—H
   \ | /
  H—C—H
   |  |
H—C—C—C—H
   |  |
  H—H—H
```

2. The drawing above shows the molecular structure of isobutane. The molecular structure represents the actual arrangement of atoms in space. Each *H* stands for a hydrogen atom, and each *C* stands for a carbon atom. Write a formula to represent this molecule. Write carbon as the first element shown in the formula.

≡ GED Practice ≡
EXERCISE 8

Questions 1 and 2 are based on the information on page 184.

1. One molecule of the iron oxide commonly called *rust* contains two atoms of iron (Fe) and three atoms of oxygen (O). The formula that represents two molecules of rust is written

   (1) Fe_2O_32
   (2) $2Fe_3O_2$
   (3) Fe_4O_6
   (4) $2Fe_2 2O_3$
   (5) $2Fe_2O_3$

2. Glucose is a sugar that is made by green plant cells. From its chemical formula, $C_6H_{12}O_6$, you can tell that one molecule of glucose contains

   (1) six atoms of hydrogen and twelve atoms of oxygen
   (2) six atoms of carbon, twelve atoms of hydrogen, and six atoms of oxygen
   (3) six atoms of carbon, twelve atoms of oxygen, and six atoms of hydrogen
   (4) one atom of carbon, six atoms of hydrogen, and twelve atoms of oxygen
   (5) six atoms of carbon, twelve atoms of helium, and six atoms of oxygen

ANSWERS ARE ON PAGE 315.

CHEMICAL BONDING

KEY WORD

ion—an atom that has either gained or lost an electron

The combining of atoms is a process called ***chemical bonding***. Chemical bonding results from either the transfer or the sharing of electrons between atoms.

Ionic Bonds

An ***ionic bond*** is formed when an electron in the outermost energy shell of one atom transfers to the outermost shell of a second atom. Ordinary table salt, sodium chloride, is a compound formed by the ionic bonding of sodium atoms to chlorine atoms. As illustrated below, a sodium atom has one electron in its outer shell, while a chlorine atom has seven electrons in its outer shell. The smaller inner circle represents the nucleus of each atom, while the outer circle represents an electron energy shell.

SODIUM AND CHLORINE ATOMS

(Only the electrons in the outermost energy shells are shown.)

When the two atoms combine, the outer electron of the sodium atom transfers to the chlorine atom. After the transfer, neither atom is electrically neutral any longer. Each is an ion, an atom that has either lost or gained an electron.

SODIUM CHLORIDE

The Na electron has transferred over to the Cl atom.

Having lost an electron, the sodium atom now has a positive charge, while the chlorine atom has a negative charge because it has gained an electron. Since unlike charges attract, the positive sodium ion is bonded to (attracted by and held close to) the negative chlorine atom.

Covalent Bonds

In a ***covalent bond***, electrons are not transferred from one atom to another. Instead, electrons are shared by the bonded atoms.

This is how a molecule of water is formed: by the covalent bonding of two hydrogen atoms to one oxygen atom. As illustrated below on the left, an oxygen atom has six electrons in its outermost shell. As shown in the diagram below, each hydrogen atom in a water molecule shares its one electron with the oxygen atom and also shares one of the oxygen atom's electrons. This means that four electrons are shared in a water molecule, two in each of the covalent bonds.

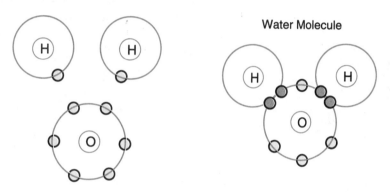

= electrons shared by hydrogen and oxygen atoms

EXERCISE 9

Directions: Answer each question below.

1. Match each item on the left with a phrase that is the best description on the right. Write the letter of the phrase on the line before the correct number.

    _____ **1.** chemical bonding

    _____ **2.** water

    _____ **3.** ion

    _____ **4.** sodium chloride

    (a) an atom that has either a positive or negative charge

    (b) a compound formed by ionic bonding

    (c) the chemical combining of two or more atoms

    (d) a compound formed by covalent bonding

2. Write a brief definition for each of the two types of chemical bonds:

    ionic bond: _____

    covalent bond: _____

ANSWERS ARE ON PAGE 315.

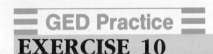
EXERCISE 10

Questions 1–4 refer to the following passage.

Two different elements may combine in more than one way and form compounds with very different properties. For example, the elements carbon and oxygen can combine to form carbon monoxide, CO, or carbon dioxide, CO_2.

Carbon monoxide is an odorless gas given off by automobile engines. Breathing concentrated carbon monoxide can quickly lead to unconsciousness and death. Many people have died from carbon monoxide poisoning after falling asleep while parked in the garage with their car engine running.

Carbon dioxide gas, on the other hand, is very much part of the life process. It is given off when people breathe, and it is used by plants during photosynthesis.

1. Which of the following is an effect of breathing carbon monoxide gas?

   (1) respiration
   (2) unconsciousness
   (3) photosynthesis
   (4) breathing
   (5) running

2. What is the most important safety consideration in an automobile repair shop?

   (1) a separate lunch room away from the working area
   (2) CPR training for all employees
   (3) properly designed tools
   (4) a safe level of ventilation
   (5) up-to-date repair manuals

3. Assume your car is parked in your garage on a freezing morning and that you can enter your garage from a door in the kitchen. Now read the following four steps, which are not in any particular order:

   A. Let the car warm up.
   B. Start the car.
   C. Drive out onto the driveway.
   D. Open the garage door.

   If you plan to go for a drive, what is the safest order of steps to follow after entering the garage and shutting the kitchen door?

   (1) B, A, D, C
   (2) D, B, C, A
   (3) B, A, C, D
   (4) C, A, B, D
   (5) D, B, A, C

4. Runners often complain of feeling light-headed or dizzy while running on or near busy city streets. A possible cause of the dizziness is that, near busy streets, there tends to be a high level of

   (1) carbon dioxide
   (2) oxygen
   (3) carbon monoxide
   (4) traffic noise
   (5) very dry air

ANSWERS ARE ON PAGE 315.

WRITING ACTIVITY 2

Why do you think the United Nations has tried to forbid the use of chemical weapons but has not banned guns or nuclear weapons? Think about how chemical weapons are different from guns or tanks. Explain and support your opinions in one or two paragraphs.

POSSIBLE ANSWERS ARE ON PAGE 315.

BEHAVIOR OF MATTER
PHASES OF MATTER

KEY WORDS

solid—matter that has definite shape and definite volume
liquid—matter that has definite volume but not definite shape
gas—matter that has neither definite shape nor definite volume

A chemical formula tells us a lot about a substance, but it doesn't tell us everything. For example, when you see the formula H_2O, you know that it stands for a water molecule. But what form of water: ice, liquid water, or steam? If you say, "All three," you're right! The formula H_2O identifies a water molecule, and it can be water in any of its three forms: solid water (ice), liquid water, or water vapor (steam).

These three forms of substances—solid, liquid, and gas—are called the three *phases of matter*. To understand the properties of each phase, you need only examine some common, everyday objects.

- *Solids:* Pick up a piece of wood or a metal spoon. Though they don't look at all alike, they do share the two common properties of solids: all solids have definite size and shape. Place a spoon in a dish, and the spoon will be unchanged in size or shape.

- *Liquids:* Pour a glass of water into a dish. Notice how the water takes the shape of the dish. Also notice that the volume of the dish that is filled is equal to the volume of the glass that was filled. This simple experiment indicates that liquids have a definite volume but not a definite shape. A liquid will take the shape of any container that holds it.

- *Gases:* Add a little more air to a soft, but not flat, football. Observe that the ball does not change shape. The entering gas easily takes the shape of the ball and crowds in as necessary without noticeably affecting the ball's shape. From this, we can see that gases, such as those in air, have neither definite shape nor definite volume. A gas will spread out or contract as needed to fill uniformly any container that encloses it.

The three phases of water: ice, liquid, and steam.

Changing from One Phase to Another

All substances change from one phase to another when their temperature is raised or lowered to certain points. Raise the temperature of ice (a solid) to its melting-point temperature, and the ice turns into liquid water. With enough heat, even solid iron can be made to liquefy.

In a similar way, a liquid can be changed to a gas. If the temperature of water is raised to its boiling point, water becomes steam, or vapor—the gaseous phase of a substance that's normally a liquid.

A gas becomes liquid when its temperature is lowered to its condensation point. Steam from a shower immediately condenses as water droplets on cool mirrors and cold-water pipes. Similarly, when the temperature of a liquid drops to its freezing point, a liquid hardens into a solid. Droplets of water, placed in a freezer, quickly turn to ice.

For many common substances, the melting point is the same as the freezing point, and the boiling point is the same as the condensation point. Because they appear so often in science, it's useful to remember these values for water at sea level. The freezing point of water (melting point of ice) is 32°F (Fahrenheit), or 0°C (Celsius). The boiling point of water (condensation point of steam) is 212°F, or 100°C.

EXERCISE 11

Directions: Complete each sentence by filling in the blanks with the correct word(s) from the reading selection.

1. The temperature at which a liquid turns into a gas is called the liquid's

_____.

2. The temperature at which a liquid turns into a solid is called the liquid's

_____.

3. The freezing point of water is _____°F or _____°C, and the boiling point

of water is _____°F or _____°C.

ANSWERS ARE ON PAGE 315.

EXERCISE 12

Questions 1–4 refer to the following passage and graph.

Antifreeze is added to a car's cooling system to protect the engine from the effects of very cold weather. Without antifreeze, a car's cooling system would contain only water. The water would freeze solid when the air temperature dropped below 32°F, the freezing point of water, and the car was not running. As many car owners have discovered, frozen coolant can crack the block of an engine.

Mixing antifreeze with the radiator water lowers the freezing temperature of the coolant below 32°F. With the proper amount of antifreeze, you can reduce the coolant freezing temperature to well below any temperature the outside air may reach.

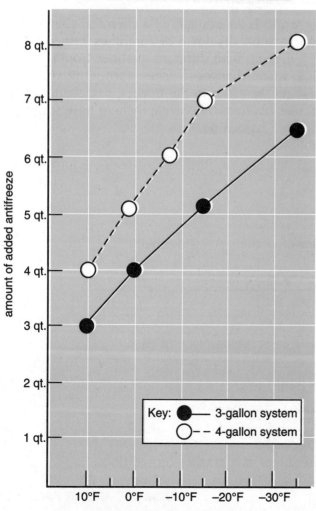

FREEZING POINT TEMPERATURE OF COOLANT WITH ANTIFREEZE

amount of added antifreeze

Key: ● — 3-gallon system
○ - - 4-gallon system

freezing temperature of coolant

1. For a car with a three-gallon cooling system, how many quarts of antifreeze are needed to protect the engine down to a temperature of −15°F?

    (1) three
    (2) four
    (3) five
    (4) six
    (5) seven

2. Assume you have a car with a four-gallon cooling system that is now protected to about 0°F. How many more quarts of antifreeze should you buy to add enough to lower the protection temperature to about −20°F?

    (1) one
    (2) two
    (3) three
    (4) four
    (5) five

3. The graph provides no information about antifreeze for temperatures

    (1) between 10°F and −35°F
    (2) below 10°F
    (3) above −35°F
    (4) above −10°F and below 10°F
    (5) above 10°F and below −35°F

4. From the information presented in the graph, you can conclude that a car with a larger cooling system

    (1) requires more antifreeze than a car with a smaller system
    (2) requires less antifreeze than a car with a smaller system
    (3) requires the same amount of antifreeze as a car with a smaller system
    (4) does not require antifreeze for temperatures above 10°F
    (5) does not require antifreeze for temperatures below −35°F

ANSWERS ARE ON PAGE 316.

PHYSICAL AND CHEMICAL CHANGES

> **KEY WORDS**
>
> *physical change*—a change that does not produce a new substance
> *chemical change*—a change in which a new substance is created

In nature, change is continually taking place. We don't usually pay attention to changes like the evaporation of water into steam. Some changes, like babies growing, we welcome; while others, like cars rusting, we don't. But all changes in nature, welcome or not, are interesting to chemists.

When ice cream melts, it changes from a solid to a liquid. Yet we still recognize it as ice cream. We know it by its color and taste, even though it may not be as cold as we'd like. What's more, by simply putting the melted ice cream in the freezer, we can change it back to its more solid texture.

Melting ice cream is an example of a physical change. During a physical change, a substance may change shape, size, or state, but the qualities by which you identify that substance don't change. In other words, the substance may look different, but it has not turned into a new substance. Melting, boiling, freezing, condensing, and cutting are all examples of physical changes.

On the other hand, burning wood is an example of a chemical change. During a chemical change, a substance breaks down or combines with another substance to become something different, with different qualities from the original substance. While burning, wood changes to ashes, carbon dioxide gas, and water. No simple act, like placing the ashes in the freezer, can change the ashes back to wood. Other examples of chemical change include milk souring, iron rusting, paint oxidizing, and glue hardening.

EXERCISE 13

Directions: Answer each question below.

1. Write a brief definition for each of the two types of change, stressing their differences:

physical change: _____

chemical change: _____

2. Write the type of change (physical or chemical) that is taking place in each action described below.

_____ **a.** An iron nail, left in the rain, rusts.

_____ **b.** A board is sawed into three smaller pieces.

_____ **c.** Gasoline burns in a car's engine.

_____ **d.** A glass vase drops and shatters as it crashes on the floor.

ANSWERS ARE ON PAGE 316.

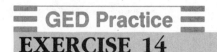
EXERCISE 14

Questions 1–6 are based on the information on page 192.

1. Each of the following is a physical property of a cube of sugar *except* its

   (1) size
   (2) weight
   (3) whiteness
   (4) feel when touched
   (5) smell when burned

2. Suppose that a quart of frozen ice cream is taken out of the freezer and left at room temperature for thirty minutes. Which of the following would be most important in determining whether all the ice cream melts?

   (1) the type of ice cream
   (2) the room temperature
   (3) the outdoor temperature
   (4) the size of the freezer
   (5) the shape of the ice cream container

3. Which of the following actions will lead to a chemical change in a piece of iron?

   (1) placing it in a warm, dry place
   (2) heating it until it turns liquid
   (3) placing it in a cool, wet place
   (4) placing it in a cool, dry place
   (5) running electricity through it

4. Which of the following is the best evidence that leaves undergo a chemical change when they change colors and drop from deciduous trees in the fall?

   (1) Leaves separate from the trees and drop to the ground.
   (2) The shape of the leaves doesn't change.
   (3) The leaves don't drop until days become shorter and weather becomes colder.
   (4) The leaves lose weight because the water content of the leaf decreases.
   (5) The leaf no longer contains active chlorophyll, used to produce sugar.

5. Melting a cube of ice and sanding a rough board are both examples of physical changes. Thinking about these two examples, which of the following statements is (are) true?

   A. A physical change in a substance can always be reversed, and the substance returned to its original form.
   B. A physical change in a substance can never be reversed.
   C. Some types of physical changes are reversible, while other types are not.
   D. Both a change of phase and a change of shape are examples of physical changes.

   (1) A only
   (2) B only
   (3) C only
   (4) A and D only
   (5) C and D only

6. Lighting a match and exposing an epoxy (a type of glue or paint) to air so that it can harden are both examples of chemical changes. Based on these two examples, which of the following statements is (are) true.

   A. A chemical change in a substance can always be reversed, and the substance returned to its original form.
   B. A chemical change in a substance can never be reversed.
   C. A chemical change changes more than just the outward appearance of a substance.
   D. A chemical change is always destructive.

   (1) A only
   (2) B only
   (3) B and C only
   (4) B and D only
   (5) C and D only

ANSWERS ARE ON PAGE 316.

CHEMICAL REACTIONS

> ## KEY WORDS
>
> ***chemical reaction***—the combining of two or more substances to form a new substance
> ***chemical equation***—expression used to show a chemical reaction
> ***reactants***—substances that combine in a chemical reaction
> ***products***—substances formed by chemical reactions

Chemists spend most of their time investigating chemical changes. In a chemical change, two or more substances combine to form one or more new substances. This process is called a chemical reaction.

To describe what happens in a chemical reaction, chemists use a kind of shorthand known as a chemical equation. The equation shows the formulas of the reactants (the substances combining) and the products (the new substances formed). An arrow shows the direction in which the reaction proceeds.

For example, the equation for the formation of a water molecule is written as follows:

$$2H_2 + O_2 \longrightarrow 2H_2O$$

Reading from left to right, the equation says that two molecules of hydrogen combine with one molecule of oxygen to form two molecules of water. The formulas $2H_2$ and O_2 indicate that both hydrogen and oxygen molecules are made up of two atoms.

A second example of a chemical reaction is the formation of ammonia, $2NH_3$. Ammonia is formed when nitrogen (N) reacts with hydrogen. The chemical equation for the ammonia reaction is as follows:

$$N_2 + 3H_2 \longrightarrow 2NH_3$$

In words, one molecule of nitrogen combines with three molecules of hydrogen to produce two molecules of ammonia.

The Law of Conservation of Matter

In studying chemical reactions, chemists have observed that new atoms neither appear nor disappear during a chemical reaction. If there are two atoms of nitrogen on the left side of the equation, there must be two atoms of nitrogen on the right side of the equation. And, if there are six atoms of hydrogen on the left side, there must be six atoms of hydrogen on the right side. The Law of Conservation of Matter says that matter is neither created nor destroyed during a chemical reaction.

EXERCISE 15

Directions: Answer each question below.

1. Complete each sentence by filling in the blanks with the correct word(s).

   a. A _____ is used to describe a chemical reaction.

   b. The _____ are the substances that combine during a chemical

   reaction, and the _____ are the substances that are formed.

2. Respiration takes place in your body's cells to provide the energy necessary for all of your activities. During respiration, glucose reacts with oxygen obtained from your breathing. The products of the reaction are carbon dioxide gas, water, and energy. The chemical equation for respiration can be written as follows:

$$C_6H_{12}O_6 + 6O_2 \longrightarrow 6CO_2 + 6H_2O$$

The following questions refer to the equation for respiration:

   a. How many molecules of glucose are represented in the equation? ____

   b. How many total molecules result when one molecule of glucose combines with six molecules of oxygen? ____

   c. How many atoms of hydrogen appear on each side of the equation? ____

GED Practice

EXERCISE 16

Questions 1 and 2 refer to the following passage.

Iron (Fe), one of the most abundant elements on Earth, is usually obtained for commercial purposes from the iron ore hematite (Fe_2O_3). To remove the iron from the ore, hematite is combined with carbon monoxide gas (CO). The chemical equation for this reaction is:

$$Fe_2O_3 + 3CO \longrightarrow 2Fe + 3CO_2$$

1. In the chemical equation for extracting iron (Fe) from hematite (Fe_2O_3), how many molecules of carbon dioxide gas (CO_2) are formed?

   (1) one
   (2) two
   (3) three
   (4) four
   (5) five

2. In the chemical equation for extracting iron (Fe) from hematite (Fe_2O_3), how many atoms of oxygen are present?

   (1) two
   (2) three
   (3) four
   (4) five
   (5) six

ANSWERS ARE ON PAGE 316.

Questions 1–5 refer to the following passage.

Chemical changes involve chemical reactions. In each chemical reaction, atoms or molecules of one or more substances combine in new ways to form new substances. Because chemical bonds are broken and new bonds are made, energy is both used and given up during these reactions. In some chemical reactions, called *exothermic reactions*, more heat energy is produced than is used, and energy is released as the reaction takes place. For example, when wood burns, both heat and light energy are given off.

Other chemical reactions, called *endothermic reactions*, use more energy than they produce. Endothermic reactions require heat energy from an outside source in order to take place. The chemical change that takes place in bread while it's cooking is a good example.

Even many exothermic reactions require that heat energy be supplied before the reactions can start. This energy is called the *activation energy* of the reaction. As an example, heat must be added to cause a firecracker to explode, an exothermic reaction that gives off energy in the form of heat, sound, and light.

1. In an exothermic reaction, heat energy is

   (1) required for the reaction to stop
   (2) required for the reaction to proceed
   (3) given off during the reaction
   (4) a form of activation energy
   (5) shared by the reacting substances

2. Activation energy is best described as energy

   (1) shared by reacting substances
   (2) required to complete a reaction
   (3) given off during a reaction
   (4) given off before a reaction starts
   (5) needed to start a reaction

3. Which of the following is an example of an endothermic reaction?

   (1) burning natural gas
   (2) drying glue in a warm room
   (3) exploding dynamite
   (4) having a fever while you're ill
   (5) burning wood in a fireplace

4. The chemical equation for the fermentation of alcohol is as follows:

   $$C_6H_{12}O_6 \longrightarrow 2C_2H_5OH + 2CO_2 + heat$$

   This equation is best described as an

   (1) endothermic reaction in which carbon dioxide gas (CO_2) is produced
   (2) endothermic reaction in which carbon dioxide gas (CO_2) is used up
   (3) exothermic reaction in which carbon dioxide gas (CO_2) is produced
   (4) exothermic reaction in which carbon dioxide gas (CO_2) is used up
   (5) neither an exothermic nor an endothermic reaction

5. Physical changes can also be classified as exothermic or endothermic. Which of the following is an example of an *exothermic physical change*—a physical change that gives off energy as it proceeds?

   A. evaporating water
   B. melting ice
   C. freezing water to make ice
   D. boiling water to make steam

   (1) A only
   (2) B only
   (3) C only
   (4) D only
   (5) A and C only

Questions 6–10 refer to the following passage.

Photosynthesis is a chemical reaction that naturally takes place in plant cells when they're exposed to sunlight. During photosynthesis, carbon dioxide gas reacts with water to produce glucose, oxygen gas, and water. The chemical equation for photosynthesis can be written as follows:

$$6CO_2 + 12H_2O \longrightarrow C_6H_{12}O_6 + 6O_2 + 6H_2O$$

This reaction is needed for a plant to live and grow. If photosynthesis does not occur, a plant will die.

6. In the equation for photosynthesis, how many molecules of water are produced in the formation of one molecule of glucose?

    (1) one
    (2) six
    (3) seven
    (4) twelve
    (5) eighteen

7. In the equation for photosynthesis, how many atoms of hydrogen (H) appear on each side of the equation?

    (1) four
    (2) eight
    (3) twelve
    (4) twenty-four
    (5) thirty-six

8. What is the best evidence that photosynthesis is an endothermic reaction?

    (1) Sugar is produced during photosynthesis.
    (2) Water is needed for photosynthesis to occur.
    (3) Photosynthesis occurs only in plants that contain chlorophyll.
    (4) Photosynthesis only occurs in the presence of sunlight.
    (5) Without photosynthesis, a green plant will wither and die.

9. For commercial purposes, great numbers of flowers are grown in sunlit buildings, called *greenhouses*, that have clear plastic or glass walls and roofs. Using controlled ventilation and watering, the greenhouse temperature and humidity are kept at levels that provide the best growing climate for the enclosed plants.

    If the attendant forgets to water a row of flowers during a hot summer month, the flowers might die. Without water, the flowers could not

    (1) keep their temperature at a safe level
    (2) produce the glucose they use as a source of life energy.
    (3) get oxygen from the soil
    (4) reflect harmful sunlight that damages glucose.
    (5) produce the carbon dioxide needed to capture the sun's energy.

10. Many greenhouse operators believe that burning natural gas year-round in their greenhouses will shorten the growing time needed for plants to mature.

    Which of the following facts about natural gas best supports what these growers believe?

    (1) Burning natural gas produces heat.
    (2) Burning natural gas places chemical impurities in the air.
    (3) Burning natural gas produces light.
    (4) Burning natural gas uses up oxygen gas.
    (5) Burning natural gas produces carbon dioxide gas.

ANSWERS ARE ON PAGE 316.

SOLUTIONS

KEY WORDS

solution—uniform mixing of one substance with another
solute—substance that is dissolved in a solution
solvent—substance that dissolves the solute

If we had to choose a single word to describe the mix of elements that appear on and within Earth, that word would be *solution*. Solutions are everywhere in nature. The air we breathe is a solution of gases. The water in the ocean is a solution of salt and other minerals, as anyone who's tasted it unhappily realizes. Earth's fiery liquid interior is believed to be one gigantic solution, a molten sea of elements and compounds.

To understand what a solution is, think of what happens when you drop a cube of sugar into a glass of water. While you watch, the sugar disappears. But is it really gone? If you taste the water, you'll find that it has a sweet taste. This lets you know that the sugar is still there, even if you don't see it.

When the sugar disappears in the water, we say that the sugar has dissolved. As it dissolves, the molecules of sugar become evenly distributed among the molecules of water. Because of this, the water is equally sweet everywhere. This even mixing of one substance with another is what defines a solution.

Two words used to describe a solution are *solvent* and *solute*. The substance that is dissolved is called the solute. The solvent is the substance that dissolves the solute. In a sugar solution, sugar is the solute and water is the solvent: the water dissolves the sugar.

Though solutions are very common, not every mixture forms a solution. For example, when sand is mixed with water, it appears at first to go into solution. But if you wait a few minutes, the sand will settle to the bottom. Sand does not dissolve in water.

EXERCISE 18

Directions: Match each word on the left with the phrase that is the best description on the right. Write the letter of the phrase on the line before the correct number.

_____ **1.** solution

_____ **2.** solute

_____ **3.** solvent

_____ **4.** air

(a) a solution made up of numerous gases

(b) a dissolving agent

(c) a dissolved substance

(d) an even mixture of one or more substances

ANSWERS ARE ON PAGE 317.

GED Practice
EXERCISE 19

Questions 1–5 refer to the following passage.

We usually think of a solution as a solid dissolved in a liquid or as a liquid dissolved in a liquid, but other kinds of solutions are also common. For example, air is a solution of gases that includes nitrogen, oxygen, hydrogen, and helium.

Gases can also be dissolved in a liquid. In carbonated soft drinks, carbon dioxide gas is dissolved in the water along with sugar and flavor additives.

Finally, solids can also be dissolved in solids. For example, metal alloys are made by dissolving one metal in another. To form an alloy, both metals are melted and then mixed as liquids. The solution of liquid metal is then cooled back to a solid. As an example, brass is an alloy made by dissolving zinc in copper. As an alloy, brass has qualities that are a mixture of the qualities of zinc and copper. Because of the presence of zinc, brass is much stronger than copper but it is less flexible.

1. Cola drinks are examples of carbonated soft drinks. What type of solution do they represent?

   (1) liquid dissolved in liquid
   (2) solid dissolved in liquid
   (3) gas dissolved in gas
   (4) gas dissolved in liquid
   (5) solid dissolved in solid

2. Paint thinner is added to paint in order to make the paint easier to work with. Water is a common paint thinner that is used in latex house paints. Which type of solution is represented by paint thinner and paint?

   (1) liquid dissolved in liquid
   (2) solid dissolved in liquid
   (3) gas dissolved in gas
   (4) gas dissolved in liquid
   (5) solid dissolved in solid

3. Many people make punch at home by adding powdered punch mix to water. How would you classify this punch mixture?

   (1) liquid dissolved in liquid
   (2) solid dissolved in liquid
   (3) gas dissolved in gas
   (4) gas dissolved in liquid
   (5) solid dissolved in solid

4. One open bottle of carbonated cola sat in a refrigerator for two hours. A second open bottle of the cola sat on a countertop at room temperature for two hours. After this time, the warm cola tasted flat, while the cold cola didn't. What's the best explanation of this discovery?

   (1) Lowering the temperature decreases the amount of carbon dioxide gas that a liquid can hold.
   (2) Raising the temperature decreases the amount of carbon dioxide gas that a liquid can hold.
   (3) Changing the temperature does not affect the amount of carbon dioxide gas a liquid can hold.
   (4) The warm cola was exposed to fresh air while cold cola was not.
   (5) Dissolved carbon dioxide gas escapes more quickly from a bottle of cola when it is shaken than when it is warmed.

5. A tablespoon of sugar is added to each of two glasses. One glass contains warm water, while the other contains cold water. The sugar dissolves most quickly in the glass of warm water. What's the best explanation of this fact?

   The rate at which a solid dissolves in a liquid

   (1) increases with increasing temperature
   (2) decreases with increasing temperature
   (3) is not dependent on temperature
   (4) increases with stirring
   (5) decreases with stirring

ANSWERS ARE ON PAGE 317.

THE CHEMISTRY OF LIFE

PROPERTIES OF CARBON

> ### KEY WORD
>
> ***organic***—produced by a living thing

On the morning of July 20, 1976, the *Viking I* lander slowly drifted, with parachutes open, down to the dusty, red surface of the plain of Chryse. The *Viking* would soon begin its mission to look for life on Mars, the planet that would now be its home. To aid in this search, *Viking II* would touch down on the Martian plain of Utopia on September 3. Disappointingly, neither landing craft was able to find any organic molecules, the fingerprints of life, on the windy, rust-colored surface.

Organic, from the word *organism*, refers to compounds produced by living things. All organic compounds contain the element carbon. Organic molecules form easily in environments that are rich in carbon and water. Scientists knew that water was present on Mars (in its polar ice caps) and that the Martian atmosphere consisted mostly of carbon dioxide gas, so it seemed likely that organic molecules could be found there. But no sign of life has yet been found on our distant neighbor.

Carbon is now thought to be so important to the life process that chemists have named the study of carbon ***organic chemistry*** and refer to it as the "chemistry of life." Several properties of carbon make it such an important element.

Carbon atoms can form covalent bonds with four other atoms at the same time. One or more of these other atoms can be another carbon atom. By linking with one another, carbon atoms can form closed rings or can stretch out in long chains. Each carbon atom in line can then combine with atoms of other elements. In this way, very large organic molecules can form. Below is an example of both a carbon chain molecule and a carbon ring molecule.

ORGANIC MOLECULES

Butane

Benzene

carbon ring

EXERCISE 20

Directions: Write the answer to each question below.

1. a. What two substances are present on Mars that gave scientists hope that there

might be life on Mars? _____ and _____

b. What element do all organic compounds contain? _____

2. What is the proper name for that branch of chemistry that is often referred to as

the "chemistry of life"? _____

═ GED Practice ═
EXERCISE 21

Questions 1–3 refer to the following passage and graph.

Fats are organic compounds made up of carbon, hydrogen, and oxygen. Fats are a large part of most people's diets. However, eating too much fat can cause heart disease and other ailments. Recent research in nutrition and health has led the American Heart Association to conclude that the average American diet is too high in *saturated fat* (a type of fat found mainly in animal products) and too low in *unsaturated fat* (a type of fat found mainly in vegetable oils). The graph compares the amounts of saturated and unsaturated fats found in several commonly eaten animal and vegetable products.

1. Which product would give you approximately equal amounts of saturated fats and unsaturated fats in one serving?

(1) safflower oil
(2) olive oil
(3) beef fat
(4) salmon fat
(5) a mixture of safflower and olive oils

2. Which of the following statements is true?

(1) Beef fat is lower in both saturated fat and unsaturated fat than olive oil.
(2) Safflower oil is higher in both saturated fat and unsaturated fat than olive oil.
(3) Salmon fat is lower in both saturated and unsaturated fat than beef fat.
(4) Olive oil is lower in both saturated fat and unsaturated fat than salmon fat.
(5) Salmon fat and beef fat contain approximately the same amount of saturated fats.

3. In order to lower consumption of saturated fat, a person could substitute

A. olive oil for safflower oil
B. safflower oil for olive oil
C. beef for salmon
D. salmon for beef

(1) A and C only
(2) A and D only
(3) B and C only
(4) B and D only
(5) B, C, and D only

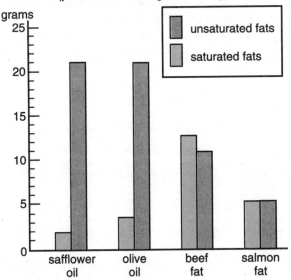

SATURATED AND UNSATURATED FAT CONTENT OF SELECTED OILS AND FATS
(present in one 25-gram serving)

ANSWERS ARE ON PAGE 317.

HYDROCARBONS

KEY WORDS

hydrocarbon—compound made only of carbon and hydrogen
polymer—hydrocarbon containing a long chain of atoms

Carbon atoms link so easily that there is almost no limit to the number of different molecules that may be possible. At present, over 3 million carbon compounds are known. Most of these are hydrocarbons, compounds composed of only carbon and hydrogen.

The main sources of hydrocarbons found in nature are coal, natural gas, and petroleum (oil). Natural gas fuels you may be familiar with are methane (CH_4) and propane (C_3H_8). Distillation of petroleum gives us other fuels such as kerosene ($C_{12}H_{26}$) and gasoline, a mixture of hydrocarbons. From petroleum we also get hydrocarbon compounds that are used to make perfumes, pesticides, medicines, and many other consumer products.

The word *polymer* is commonly used to refer to any long-chain hydrocarbon, a hydrocarbon containing a large number of carbon atoms. Most of the modern-day synthetic polymers have been made within the last fifty years. An example is polyethylene, a type of plastic. Polyethylene is a polymer that often contains between 2,500 and 25,000 carbon atoms in each molecule. Polyethylene and other synthetic polymers are used to produce textiles, shoes, toys, plastics, construction materials, medical supplies, cooking utensils, recreational equipment, and synthetic rubber and leather.

EXERCISE 22

Directions: Briefly define each of the following words:

1. hydrocarbon:_____

2. polymer: _____

ANSWERS ARE ON PAGE 317.

EXERCISE 23

Questions 1 and 2 refer to the information on page 202.

1. Which one of the following is *not* a common property of the fuels methane, propane, and kerosene?

   (1) Each fuel contains only carbon and hydrogen atoms.
   (2) In each fuel, every carbon atom links together with more than one hydrogen atom.
   (3) Each fuel is an example of a polymer.
   (4) Each fuel has more hydrogen atoms than carbon atoms.
   (5) Each fuel is in the class of compounds called hydrocarbons.

2. Based on the diagram of the atoms on page 202, you can say that in *alkane polymers* such as propane and kerosene the number of hydrogen atoms is equal to

   (1) half the number of carbon atoms
   (2) the number of carbon atoms
   (3) twice the number of carbon atoms
   (4) twice the number of carbon atoms minus two
   (5) twice the number of carbon atoms plus two

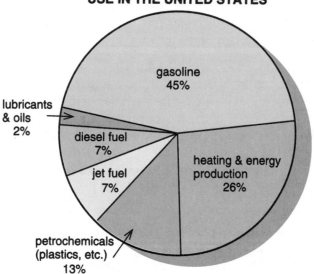

PERCENT BREAKDOWN OF PETROLEUM USE IN THE UNITED STATES

gasoline 45%

lubricants & oils 2%

diesel fuel 7%

jet fuel 7%

heating & energy production 26%

petrochemicals (plastics, etc.) 13%

3. According to the graph above, what is the main petroleum product used in the United States?

   (1) petrochemicals
   (2) diesel fuel
   (3) heating and energy production
   (4) gasoline
   (5) jet fuel

4. What total percentage of petroleum is used for the production of transportation fuels?

   (1) 7 percent
   (2) 14 percent
   (3) 59 percent
   (4) 72 percent
   (5) 98 percent

ANSWERS ARE ON PAGE 317.

PLASTIC TRASH, AN ENVIRONMENTAL CONCERN

KEY WORD

plastic—a commonly used polymer

With the invention of polymers, chemists gave us plastic, an almost ideal material. As a consumer product, plastic is strong, versatile, and durable. It can hold up under heat and pressure and can be subjected to total submersion in water (even ocean water) and not be affected. You can even leave it outside and it remains almost as good as new, despite the weather. Unlike most other materials, plastic doesn't naturally decay.

For useful consumer products, this remarkable durability is a blessing. Plastic bottles are light and unbreakable; plastic bags don't leak or tear as easily as paper bags do. But when these items are ready for the garbage, it's an environmental nightmare! Millions of tons of plastic garbage litter our highways and beaches.

Plastic trash even affects marine life in the oceans. According to the National Academy of Sciences, more than 600,000 plastic containers and bags are tossed into the oceans every day. Fishermen lose or discard an estimated 150,000 tons of plastic fishing gear each year. At least forty-two species of seabirds are known to snack on plastic, a habit that is often fatal. In addition, tens of thousands of seals, sea lions, and turtles die each year after becoming entangled in bits of fish netting.

What should we do with the hundreds of millions of tons of plastic and other polymer products that end up in the garbage each year? We could burn it. However, that creates a thick, black smoke that is not only intolerable but is also a dangerous form of air pollution. We could bury it, but solid-waste dumps pose their own pollution problems. Too often, trash in the dumps is not buried for a long period of time and becomes a health hazard for birds and other land animals, including nearby human residents. What's more, highly populated countries with limited space may find that land is far too valuable to use as a dump site.

Obviously, a large-scale solution to the plastic trash problem is not yet in sight. However, individuals can help by keeping some of that plastic out of the garbage for as long as possible. For example, people who get plastic bags from the grocery store could save them and reuse them. Some people may choose not to buy plastic products when the same item is available in paper or glass. Of course, these are only small steps, but they could eventually be part of a larger solution.

EXERCISE 24

Directions: Answer each question below.

1. Name three properties of plastic that make it such a useful consumer product.

_____ , _____ , and _____

2. Name three types of animals that are known to be harmed by plastic trash.

_____ _____ _____

ANSWERS ARE ON PAGE 317.

GED Practice

EXERCISE 25

Questions 1 and 2 are based on the information on page 204.

1. Following are four methods of disposing of polymer trash:

  A. dumping it in the ocean miles from shore
  B. recycling (reusing) polymer consumer products
  C. burning polymer trash on disposal ships far out at sea
  D. burying polymer trash in a properly designed and carefully regulated solid-waste dump

Which of the above methods are environmentally unsound?

(1) B and C only
(2) C and D only
(3) A and C only
(4) A, B, and D only
(5) A, C, and D only

2. What is the main property of plastic that makes it such an environmental concern?

(1) the ease with which it can be broken
(2) its use in such a wide range of consumer products
(3) that it can be manufactured anywhere in the world
(4) its resistance to weathering or to decay
(5) its light weight compared to steel

ANSWERS ARE ON PAGE 318.

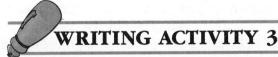

WRITING ACTIVITY 3

    One possible solution to the plastic trash problem is recycling. In the past decade, communities across the United States have begun recycling plastic, glass, newspaper, and some metal waste. Do you think that recycling can help solve our garbage problems? Write a paragraph or two explaining your opinion.

ANSWERS WILL VARY.

THE GREENHOUSE EFFECT

> **KEY WORD**
>
> ***greenhouse effect***—a warming of Earth's atmosphere as a result of pollution

Life on Earth is made possible by a delicate balance of many biological and chemical factors. If this balance is upset, the results can be disastrous. You already know how the disposal of garbage can affect the lives of many land and marine animals. In this section, we'll discuss how another form of pollution can affect all life on Earth simply by causing a slow increase in the temperature of our planet.

Our close neighbor, the planet Venus, has experienced such a temperature increase. Because it is the closest planet to Earth and appears to be made up of the same minerals, you might think that Venus is a place where living organisms could develop and grow. Not so. In fact, the surface temperature of Venus is about 900°F—so hot that no form of life could possibly exist there.

The reason that Venus is so hot is that its atmosphere contains a large amount of carbon dioxide. Because of this gas, Venus can't cool the way other planets cool—by sending heat energy back out into space. Instead, the heat energy is absorbed by the carbon dioxide.

This natural heating of the atmosphere of Venus is commonly called the greenhouse effect. The greenhouse effect gets its name from the glass-sided and glass-roofed buildings that you see in plant nurseries. In a nursery greenhouse, sunlight freely passes through the glass and warms the soil, plants, and air inside. The glass prevents the heat from leaving. The result is that the greenhouse stays warm enough for plant growth even though the temperature outside may be below freezing. On Venus, the dense carbon dioxide atmosphere traps heat and keeps surface heat energy from escaping back into space. Unfortunately, unlike a real greenhouse, the high temperature on Venus can't be controlled simply by opening a few windows!

On Earth, the current level of carbon dioxide gas in the atmosphere keeps the temperature in the range it is in now. However, the burning of wood, coal, oil, and other hydrocarbons is adding an abnormal amount of carbon dioxide to the atmosphere. The result is that the level of this gas has been slowly increasing since at least 1958, when scientists started to follow carefully the atmospheric levels of carbon dioxide. Earth's temperature has been gradually going up as well. Most probably, the increases have taken place since the beginning of the Industrial Revolution in the late eighteenth century.

CONSTANT CO$_2$ IN ATMOSPHERE

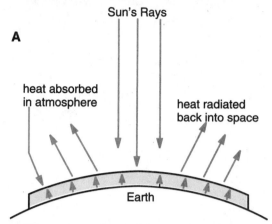

With a constant level of carbon dioxide in the atmosphere, Earth cools by radiating excess heat back into space.

INCREASED CO$_2$ IN ATMOSPHERE

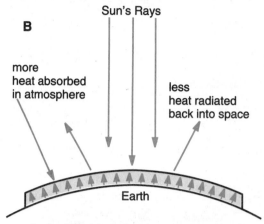

As the high level of carbon dioxide in the atmosphere increases, Earth's average temperature also increases.

Consequences of the Greenhouse Effect

No one is sure just what the consequences of the greenhouse effect will be in the long run. However, many scientists feel that if the addition of carbon dioxide to the atmosphere continues unchecked, several things could eventually happen:

- The average surface temperature of Earth will increase, perhaps by as much as 6°F to 10°F in the next fifty years.

- The warming effect will cause a lot of glacial ice to melt. This will result in the oceans rising by a couple of feet during the same fifty years. Over a period of a couple of hundred years, ocean levels could rise by as much as twenty or more feet. Cities like San Francisco and New York would find themselves under water!

- A rising surface temperature will also probably change world rainfall patterns. The United States, now the breadbasket of the world, could become an arid, parched wasteland.

Though no one is sure just how serious these effects may be and how soon they may occur, one thing is certain: everyone on Earth lives together under a single shared atmosphere. People are now beginning to realize that proper care of this atmosphere is a must if Earth's environment is to remain capable of sustaining human life.

EXERCISE 26

Directions: Write an answer to each question below.

1. What name is given to the glass-sided, glass-roofed buildings you see in plant

   nurseries? _____

2. What role does carbon dioxide gas play in the greenhouse effect? _____

   _____

GED Practice
EXERCISE 27

Questions 1–4 are based on the information on pages 206–207.

1. Which of the following is most similar to the heating that takes place inside a nursery greenhouse?

   (1) warming yourself by standing in front of a fireplace in a closed room
   (2) being warmed by sunlight while sitting inside a car with all the windows closed
   (3) becoming suntanned while lying on the beach on a warm summer day
   (4) warming yourself after a shower by standing under a sunlamp
   (5) keeping warm on a cold day by wearing a wool sweater and a heavy overcoat

2. Which of the following is given as the cause of the greenhouse effect that's starting to occur on Earth?

   (1) the increasing average temperature of Earth
   (2) the success of the Industrial Revolution
   (3) the fact that a single atmosphere covers the whole planet
   (4) the slow rising of the ocean levels
   (5) the increasing levels of carbon dioxide in the atmosphere

3. Which of the following items would be of *least* importance to someone studying the greenhouse effect?

   (1) any change in the average thickness of the ice covering the polar ice caps
   (2) any change in the average air temperature off the coast of Alaska
   (3) the success of efforts designed to protect Arctic polar bears from extinction
   (4) a comparison of summer and winter conditions on the planet Venus
   (5) any change in the average levels of high and low tides in San Francisco Bay

4. Which of the following would be the *most* effective solution for the problem known as the greenhouse effect?

   (1) reducing our dependence on all forms of hydrocarbon fuels
   (2) placing restrictions on the use of wood stoves
   (3) developing new cars that get extremely high mileage
   (4) carefully managing forests in order to prevent lightning fires
   (5) placing high taxes on all hydrocarbon fuels

ANSWERS ARE ON PAGE 318.

EXERCISE 28

Questions 1–4 refer to the following passage.

A TV commercial for a new type of synthetic car oil makes these four claims:

A. Tri-State Oil will improve your gas mileage by two to three miles per gallon.

B. Tri-State Oil can be used in engines that run on diesel fuel.

C. Tri-State Oil will reduce the emission of carbon monoxide and other greenhouse gases produced by your car's engine.

D. Tri-State Oil contains no lead products.

1. Which claim(s) could be checked only by doing a chemical analysis of Tri-State Oil?

   (1) A only
   (2) B only
   (3) C only
   (4) D only
   (5) A and D only

2. Which two claims could be proved only by doing tests on your car?

   (1) A and B
   (2) A and C
   (3) A and D
   (4) B and C
   (5) C and D

3. Which claim(s) could be checked only by doing a chemical analysis of the exhaust emitted from a car engine that's using Tri-State Oil?

   (1) A only
   (2) B only
   (3) C only
   (4) D only
   (5) B and C only

4. Scientists have discovered that carbon monoxide gas (CO) does in fact contribute to the greenhouse effect. Carbon monoxide is present in the exhaust gas of car engines. To which of the following values is the TV advertisement appealing in claim C above?

   (1) pride in reducing maintenance costs
   (2) pride in car ownership
   (3) concern about reducing United States dependence on foreign oil
   (4) concern about driving less to help reduce traffic congestion
   (5) concern about the environment

ANSWERS ARE ON PAGE 318.

WRITING ACTIVITY 4

Many scientists believe that a global campaign to reduce chemical pollution is the only way to stop the greenhouse effect.

In view of the urgency of the problem, is it likely that the countries of the world will ever agree to cut down on chemical pollution? What might be some of the objections raised by developing countries? Who should pay for cleaning up Earth's atmosphere?

Write two or three paragraphs describing the positive and negative aspects of a worldwide campaign to stop the greenhouse effect.

ANSWERS WILL VARY.

≡ GED Practice ≡
CHEMISTRY

Questions 1–6 refer to the following passage.

The three phases of matter are solid, liquid, and gas. While kept at one atmosphere of air pressure, many common substances change from one phase to another when they are heated or cooled. Each change of phase usually takes place by one of the five processes described below.

freezing—the process of a liquid changing into a solid as its temperature is lowered

melting—the process of a solid changing into a liquid as its temperature is raised

evaporation—the process of a liquid slowly changing into a gas due to the slow escape of molecules from the liquid surface

boiling—the process of a liquid rapidly changing into a gas as its temperature is raised to the point where vapor bubbles form in the liquid

condensation—the process of a gas changing into a liquid as its temperature is lowered

1. During an unusually dry year, the water level in Lake Tahoe dropped two feet below normal. If no rivers drain this lake, the water level most likely decreased in part by

   (1) freezing
   (2) melting
   (3) evaporation
   (4) boiling
   (5) condensation

2. On a cool morning, water droplets of dew often cover the grass and flowers outside. Dew forms by

   (1) freezing
   (2) melting
   (3) evaporation
   (4) boiling
   (5) condensation

3. In a blast furnace, the temperature of liquid iron may reach 3,000°F. If the temperature of the liquid drops below 2,795°F, the iron begins to solidify. This is known as

   (1) freezing
   (2) melting
   (3) evaporation
   (4) boiling
   (5) condensation

4. Below −38°F, the element mercury is a solid. As its temperature is raised to −38°F, mercury turns into a liquid metal. This is known as

   (1) freezing
   (2) melting
   (3) evaporation
   (4) boiling
   (5) condensation

5. Liquid oxygen is used as a fuel for space shuttles. As long as its temperature remains below −297°F, oxygen remains a liquid. But when its temperature reaches −297°F, liquid oxygen starts bubbling and changing back to a gas by

   (1) freezing
   (2) melting
   (3) evaporation
   (4) boiling
   (5) condensation

6. An important factor that determines which phase a substance is in is its

   (1) volume
   (2) weight
   (3) temperature
   (4) color
   (5) shape

Questions 7–10 refer to the following passage and scale.

An *acid* is a substance that releases hydrogen when mixed with water. An acid is sour to the taste. *Organic acids* are not harmful and are found in foods; for example, citric acid is found in oranges, grapefruits, and lemons. Acetic acid is found in vinegars.

Inorganic acids, on the other hand, are both strong and dangerous and can cause severe skin burns. Sulfuric acid, for example, is used in batteries, and hydrochloric acid is used as a metal cleanser.

A *base* is a substance that combines with an acid and neutralizes its effect. Together, an acid and a base form a salt and water. Some weak bases, such as baking soda, have use both as a cleanser and as a mild stomach antacid. Stronger bases such as ammonia, soap, and bleach are used as household cleansers.

Chemists measure the strength of an acid or a base by the use of a pH scale. The pH scale ranges from 0 to 14, with the value 7 representing neutrality. Acids have a pH value of less than 7, while bases have a pH value of more than 7. Pure water is neither an acid nor a base and has a pH value of 7. Common pH values are shown in the scale.

pH VALUES OF COMMON SUBSTANCES

Substance	pH	
Battery acid	0.2	
Normal stomach acid	2.0	
Lemon juice	2.3	
Vinegar	2.8	
Soft drinks	3.0	
Apple juice	3.1	more
Orange juice	3.5	acidic
Banana	4.6	
Bread	5.5	
Potatoes	5.8	
Rainwater	6.2	
Milk	6.5	
Pure water	7.0	neutral
Eggs	7.8	
Hair shampoo	8.7	more
Milk of magnesia	10.6	basic
Household bleach	12.8	

7. If a small amount of sodium bicarbonate (baking soda) is added to a glass of orange juice, the juice would taste

(1) more acidic
(2) unchanged
(3) more basic
(4) less acidic
(5) colder

8. What is the most likely pH value of acid rain?

(1) greater than 12.8
(2) between 7 and 12.8
(3) exactly 7
(4) exactly 6.2
(5) less than 6

9. The needles of evergreen trees are acidic, and lawn grass does not grow well in acidic soil. If gardeners often place lime on lawns near evergreen trees, you can deduce that lime is a

(1) weak base
(2) weak acid
(3) strong base
(4) strong acid
(5) neutral substance

10. Eaten together, which two foods will best settle an acidic stomach?

(1) a coke and a piece of bread
(2) a glass of apple juice and a banana
(3) a glass of water and a hard-boiled egg
(4) a glass of orange juice and a banana
(5) a glass of milk and a potato

ANSWERS ARE ON PAGE 318.

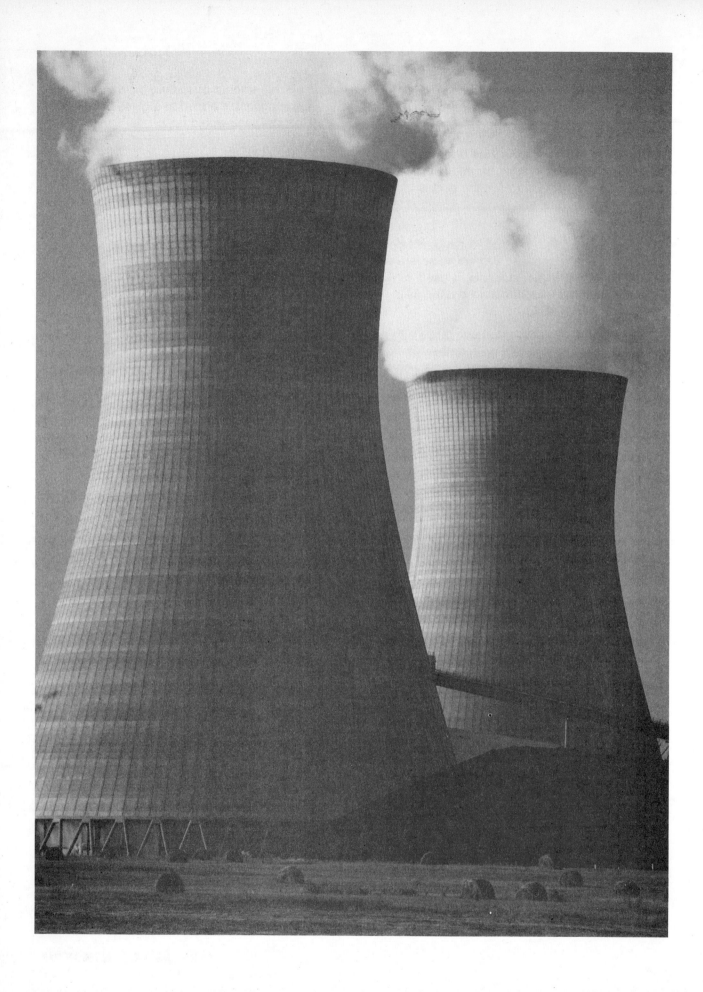

9 Physics

Imagine that you wake up tomorrow and nothing seems to work. There's no hot water, so you can't shower. The stove doesn't work, so you can't cook a hot breakfast. The refrigerator is off, and your TV won't turn on! Sound like a world gone crazy? Maybe so. But that's what life would be like if the world ran out of energy.

Because the world's population is increasing and worldwide standards of living are rising, more people can now afford energy-consuming products such as cars, stereos, and air conditioners. Since 1940, the total amount of energy used in the world has doubled almost every 20 years. Many people are worried that we are headed for a serious energy shortage, a situation in which there would not be enough energy for everyone who needed it. The challenge currently facing physics is to develop new sources of safe energy.

THE SCIENCE OF ENERGY

When most people think about energy, they think about the gasoline that powers their cars and the electricity or natural gas that heats their homes. Besides these, though, there are many other important forms of energy. Sound and light are two examples. Energy carried by water and wind are two more.

Physicists study how energy is produced and how it can be used most efficiently. They try to learn as much as possible about each form of energy. The results of their research often lead to the development of new types of consumer products. For example, physicists have helped develop and improve entertainment products such as television, video recorders, and cameras; kitchen appliances such as microwave ovens and electronic dishwashers; and medical equipment such as digital thermometers, CAT scanners (used to see inside the human body), and ultrasonic sound monitors (used to observe a growing fetus).

Processes that involve energy also play important roles in other areas of science. Because of this, several new fields have developed in recent years that link physics directly with these other sciences. For example, *biophysicists* apply the techniques and results of physics research to questions in biology. *Astrophysicists* study the birth and death of stars and planets. *Physical chemists* try to determine the atom-by-atom details of the structure of molecules.

Physics, more than any other science, uses the language of mathematics to describe its theories and experiments. However, many of the concepts of physics can be understood without the aid of either algebra or geometry. These are the concepts that appear on the GED Science Test. Topics in this chapter will include properties of motion, properties of waves, electricity and magnetism, and nuclear physics.

EXERCISE 1

Part A

Directions: Match each word on the left with the phrase that is the best description on the right. Write the letter of the phrase on the line before the correct number.

_____ **1.** biophysics

_____ **2.** physical chemistry

_____ **3.** physics

_____ **4.** astrophysics

(a) the application of physics to problems in chemistry

(b) often called "the science of energy"

(c) the application of physics to research in astronomy

(d) the application of physics to research in biology

Part B

Directions: Choose the best answer to each question.

5. Which of the following is given in the reading selection as a cause of the worldwide increase in energy use this century?

   (1) the possibility of serious energy shortage
   (2) the production of alternate energy sources
   (3) worldwide rising standards of living
   (4) the decreasing cost of energy production
   (5) the rise of the environmental movement

6. From the text you can conclude that physicists

   (1) rely on observation but not on mathematics
   (2) are involved in work that often has practical applications
   (3) support worldwide family planning efforts
   (4) do little work in biology or chemistry
   (5) work mainly in universities

7. Applying physics to questions about organisms is a study called

   (1) physical geology
   (2) physical chemistry
   (3) astrophysics
   (4) biochemistry
   (5) biophysics

ANSWERS ARE ON PAGE 318.

EXERCISE 2

Questions 1–3 refer to the circle graph below.

**ENERGY PRODUCTION IN THE
UNITED STATES (1990)**

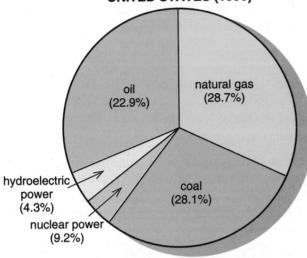

oil
(22.9%)

natural gas
(28.7%)

hydroelectric
power
(4.3%)

nuclear power
(9.2%)

coal
(28.1%)

1. Which growing form of energy production is so limited at the present time that it is not included on the graph?

   (1) coal
   (2) nuclear power
   (3) solar
   (4) oil
   (5) natural gas

2. According to the graph, approximately what total percent of the energy produced in the United States comes from fossil fuels (coal, oil, and natural gas)?

   (1) 30 percent
   (2) 50 percent
   (3) 75 percent
   (4) 80 percent
   (5) 90 percent

3. Approximately how much more energy in the United States is produced from natural gas than from nuclear power?

   (1) about two times as much
   (2) about three times as much
   (3) about four times as much
   (4) about five times as much
   (5) about six times as much

ANSWERS ARE ON PAGE 319.

WRITING ACTIVITY 1

Applications of physics have produced the technology to create many machines and consumer products, including computers. In some respects, computers have made our lives much easier, enabling us to do things we wouldn't even dream of trying if we didn't have a machine to organize the information for us. However, sometimes computers cause inconveniences.

Write two to three paragraphs explaining how computers have affected our daily lives. You may want to focus on either the positive aspects or the negative aspects. Be sure to use examples to support your point of view.

ANSWERS WILL VARY.

PROPERTIES OF MOTION

NEWTON'S LAWS OF MOTION

> ### KEY WORDS
>
> **force**—any push or pull that can affect the motion of an object
> **inertia**—natural resistance to change in motion
> **acceleration**—increase of speed

How would you answer the following two questions? (1) How many angels does it take to keep the moon moving around Earth? (2) Why does an arrow, when shot into the sky, return to Earth looking for a natural resting place?

If these questions seem a little odd to you, it's not surprising. These questions aren't often asked today! But such matters were taken very seriously in the time of Sir Isaac Newton (1642–1727), an English mathematician and philosopher. Newton spent his life looking for an explanation of motion that didn't require angels' help or natural resting places.

Newton began his study by wondering what happens to an object like a ball when a force acts upon it. (As used by Newton, a force is any push or pull that can affect an object either in motion or at rest.) By doing careful experiments, Newton made several discoveries that today are written as three laws of motion that still bear his name. Newton's Laws of Motion are now known to apply to all types of objects and all types of forces.

Newton's First Law: The Law of Inertia

Newton realized that unless some force stopped it, a rolling ball would roll forever. He also realized that without a force to start it rolling, a ball that was not moving would sit forever.

With these two ideas in mind, Newton wrote his first law: *If no force is applied, an object at rest will remain at rest, and an object in motion will continue to move in a straight line at the same speed.* You've seen this principle in action if you've ever watched children slide along an icy sidewalk. Because there is only a very slight force to slow them down, they are able to slide a long distance.

This property of matter, a natural resistance to any change in motion, is called inertia. Every object, whether sitting or moving, has inertia.

Newton's Second Law: The Law of Acceleration

Newton's second law, most easily written in two parts, is based on two observations that he made. First, Newton noticed that a ball can be thrown faster and farther simply by throwing it harder (applying more force). In other words, *an object's speed will increase in proportion to the amount of force applied.*

Second, Newton noticed that using as much force as your muscles can apply, you can throw a one-pound ball much faster and farther than you can throw a ten-pound ball. From this second observation Newton noted that *for the same amount of applied force, a lighter object will accelerate—change its speed—at a greater rate than a heavier object.* To see how this works, think of how much easier it is to throw a baseball across a yard than it would be to throw a bowling ball the same distance.

Newton's Third Law: The Law of Interaction

Finally, Newton thought about what happens when one object exerts a force on a second object. For example, imagine what happens when a child kicks a door shut. At the instant the foot strikes the door, it exerts a force that slams the door. At the same instant, though, the foot feels a reaction force from the door.

Newton stated his third law as follows: *For every action, there is an equal and opposite reaction.* When one object exerts a force on a second object, the second object exerts an equal and opposite force on the first object.

A reaction force can also act on an object that is not moving. As an example, think about a telephone sitting on a desk. Due to gravity, the phone exerts a force (its weight) on the desk. At the same time, the desk exerts an upward reaction force on the phone. To explain why the phone remains motionless, Newton would simply say that the reaction force pushing the phone up exactly balances the force of gravity pulling the phone down.

BALLOON ROCKET

The balloon rocket demonstrates Newton's third law. When released, the contracting balloon expels air from the opening, while the air pushes back and causes the balloon to move forward.

EXERCISE 3

Directions: Answer each question below.

1. Briefly define each of the words below:

a. force: _____

b. inertia: _____

2. Each of the four facts below demonstrates one of Newton's laws of motion. On the line preceding each fact, write *1*, *2*, or *3* to indicate which law is being demonstrated.

1—The law of inertia: an object's motion will not change unless a force acts on the object.

2—The law of acceleration: an object's speed increases when more force is applied.

3—The law of interaction: for every action, there is an equal and opposite reaction.

_____ **a.** When a gun is fired, the exploding gunpowder forces the bullet through the barrel and pushes the gun back against the shooter.

_____ **b.** Because the force of gravity is less on the moon than on Earth, a rock dropped on the moon would fall more slowly than an equal-size rock dropped on Earth.

_____ **c.** A fast-moving barrel, rolling on a level floor, will roll until a force is applied to stop it.

_____ **d.** Using equal amounts of force, a track athlete can toss a twelve-pound shot farther than she can toss a sixteen-pound shot.

ANSWERS ARE ON PAGE 319.

EXERCISE 4

Questions 1 and 2 refer to the information on pages 216–217.

1. The property of inertia accounts for the fact that

(1) a car without brakes is difficult to stop
(2) a telephone on a desk is acted upon by a reaction force
(3) a basketball rebounds off a backboard
(4) light reflects off a glass
(5) the effect of air friction is to slow a moving vehicle

2. The law of interaction accounts for the fact that a hunting rifle

(1) recoils when fired
(2) has weight
(3) makes noise when fired
(4) smokes when fired
(5) has moving parts

Questions 3–5 refer to the drawing below.

water escapes

head rotates

The head of the sprinkler rotates as a reaction to the force of escaping water.

3. The sprinkler head moves because of force exerted by

(1) the sprinkler head
(2) the garden hose
(3) the escaping water
(4) the action of gravity
(5) air pressure

4. The action of the sprinkler illustrates

(1) Newton's first law of motion, the law of inertia
(2) Newton's second law of motion, the law of acceleration
(3) Newton's third law of motion, the law of interaction
(4) an exception to Newton's laws of motion
(5) Newton's law of gravity

5. Which of the three actions listed below would cause the sprinkler to rotate more quickly?

A. Oil the sprinkler parts to enable the sprinkler to turn more easily.
B. Hang one-ounce weights at the end of each sprinkler nozzle.
C. Increase the amount of water flowing through the hose.

(1) A only
(2) B only
(3) C only
(4) A and B only
(5) A and C only

Question 6 refers to the line graph below.

6. The graph below shows the rate at which an object's speed increases as it falls due to the force of gravity. For example, if an object is dropped from a tall building, it reaches a speed of 96 feet per second after falling for three seconds.

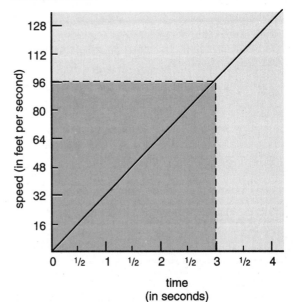

Under the action of gravity, how much does an object's speed increase each second it falls?

(1) 10 feet per second
(2) 16 feet per second
(3) 32 feet per second
(4) 64 feet per second
(5) 100 feet per second

ANSWERS ARE ON PAGE 319.

THE LAW OF CONSERVATION OF ENERGY

kinetic energy—energy of motion
potential energy—stored energy
friction—a force that tends to slow down a moving object

You can't actually see the process, but every time you turn on a lamp, energy changes from one form to another. Electrical energy flows through the light bulb and is changed into light energy and heat energy: the bulb glows brightly and gets very hot.

By studying how energy changes from one form to another, physicists discovered the ***Law of Conservation of Energy***. This law says that although energy changes from one form to another, no energy is lost. The total amount of energy present remains constant.

Kinetic Energy and Potential Energy

Two basic types of energy that an object may have are kinetic energy and potential energy. Kinetic energy is energy of motion, such as the energy that a bowling ball has while rolling down a lane. Potential energy can be thought of as stored energy, energy capable of being changed into another form. A book sitting on the edge of a table has potential energy. If the book is pushed off, its potential energy is changed to kinetic energy as the book falls to the floor. The energy changes form but is not lost.

Now think about what happens when a little girl is swinging. At the highest point of her swing, she stops moving for an instant as she reverses direction. At this point, all her energy is potential (stored) energy. A few seconds later, when she reaches the lowest point of her swing, all her energy is kinetic (motion) energy. As she swings from the highest point to the lowest point, her potential energy is changed to kinetic energy. Then, as she swings back up, her kinetic energy changes once again to potential energy. At all points between the highest and lowest points, her energy is partly potential and partly kinetic.

point where
metal supports
of swing rub
together

high point
of motion
(kinetic energy
is 0 at the
high point)

low point
of motion
(potential energy
is 0 at the low point)

The Force of Friction

Friction is a force that opposes the motion of one object rubbing against a second object. Friction tends to slow down a moving object. If it weren't for friction acting on the swing, the girl could swing back and forth effortlessly, each time reaching the same height as before. But because there is friction, the swing will slowly lose energy and come to a stop unless it is pushed.

Friction slowly changes the kinetic energy of the swing to heat energy. Heat energy is produced mainly where the metal supports of the swing rub together. You can observe a similar warming effect when you rub your hands together.

In addition, a small amount of heat is produced in the air because the girl's motion is opposed by air friction, commonly called air resistance. You can most easily feel air resistance when you're traveling down a highway and stick your hand out of the car window.

The heat produced by friction must be taken into account in the conservation of energy law. The girl stops moving, but her kinetic energy is not lost; instead, it has been changed into heat energy—heat that warms the metal supports of the swing and heat that is in the air.

EXERCISE 5

Directions: Complete each sentence by filling in the blanks with the correct word(s) from the reading passage.

1. According to the Law of Conservation of Energy, the amount of energy in any

   given situation is ———————————.

2. Energy of motion is called ———————————, while stored energy is called

   ———————————.

3. ——————————— is a force that opposes the motion of any object that is rubbing against a second object.

EXERCISE 6

Questions 1–3 refer to the following paragraph and illustration.

A pendulum consists of a suspended object that can swing freely back and forth. A wrecking ball swung by a crane is an example of a practical use of a pendulum. The wrecking ball illustrated below rises to its high point, A, before swinging back through its low point, C, and then over to the right side as indicated.

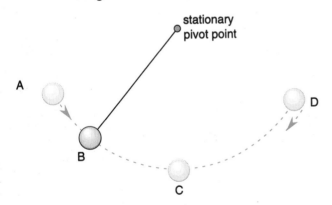

1. At which point is the energy of the wrecking ball partly kinetic and partly potential?

   (1) point A only
   (2) point B only
   (3) point C only
   (4) points A and B only
   (5) points B and C only

2. A crane operator must position a wrecking ball to strike a building. In which position will the wrecking ball have the greatest amount of impact energy?

   (1) point A
   (2) point B
   (3) point C
   (4) point D
   (5) point A or point B

3. After impact, the wrecking ball hangs motionless, having lost the total kinetic and potential energy it had while swinging.

   Which conclusion below is supported by the above observation and is consistent with the Law of Conservation of Energy (which states that energy is never lost)?

   (1) The lost energy will be recovered when the crane operator swings the ball up again.
   (2) The lost energy cannot be recovered.
   (3) Because it was being swung by the crane, the ball never did have its own energy.
   (4) The ball will continue moving on its own after a short time.
   (5) The lost energy has been changed into the energy used to break apart the building.

ANSWERS ARE ON PAGE 319.

THE NATURE OF HEAT

Ruben lives in a third-floor apartment in the city. In the summer, his apartment is stiflingly hot, even when he keeps the windows open all the time. In the winter, the landlord keeps the heat turned down, and Ruben freezes!

A physicist might describe Ruben's predicament in terms of heat energy. Heat energy is the motion of atoms. When the atoms in an object move faster, the object gets hotter; when the atoms move more slowly, the object gets colder. So when Ruben is suffering in the heat, the atoms in the air are moving very fast. When his teeth are chattering from the cold, the atoms in the air are moving more slowly.

Temperature is a measure of heat energy. When an object absorbs heat, its temperature rises. For example, room-temperature water in a pan on a lighted range will quickly come to a boil when you turn up the flame. Similarly, when an object gives off heat, its temperature falls. When put in a freezer, room-temperature water loses heat and rapidly falls to its freezing point.

When two objects of different temperature are brought together, heat energy flows from the warmer object to the cooler object. This heat flow continues until both objects reach the same temperature. When you put a package of frozen food in a sink full of hot water, the food will warm up and start to thaw. At the same time, the water will become cooler, until both the food and the water are the same temperature. The heat flows from the hot water to the package of frozen food.

EXPANSION AND CONTRACTION

As an object is heated, it expands. When the object gets hotter, its atoms move faster and are farther apart. You may have noticed that doors sometimes stick in the summer. This is because the door expands more than the door frame. Most objects expand so little that you hardly notice it. For instance, a pan heated on a stove expands a small fraction of an inch.

As objects cool, they lose heat energy. The atoms slow down, and the object contracts. For example, after you take a cake out of the oven, you need to let it cool for a while before taking it out of the pan. As it cools, the cake will contract and come farther away from the sides of the pan.

For an equal amount of heating, a gas will expand more than a liquid, and a liquid will expand more than a solid. For instance, when the outdoor temperature rises, the liquid mercury inside a thermometer expands more than the glass—a solid—containing it.

These properties of expansion and contraction hold true for solids (like doors), liquids (like water), and gases (like air).

EXERCISE 7

Directions: Each statement below refers to the effect of heat on matter. Circle *T* for each statement that is true and *F* for each statement that is false.

T   F   **1.** If a penny is placed in the sunshine, it will expand as it becomes warmer.

T   F   **2.** If a helium-filled weather balloon is released at ground level, it will expand when it reaches the cold upper atmosphere.

T   F   **3.** If car tires are filled with air at the beginning of a day-long drive, the pressure in the tires will increase during the heat of the afternoon.

T   F   **4.** As the hot water in a bathtub cools, the water expands and may flow over the sides of the tub.

ANSWERS ARE ON PAGE 319.

EXERCISE 8

Questions 1 and 2 are based on the information on pages 223–224.

1. When a piece of hot iron (temperature 380°F) is thrown into a barrel of cold water (temperature 50°F), which of the following will occur?

   (1) Heat will flow from the water to the iron until both are the same temperature.
   (2) Heat will flow from the iron to the water until both are the same temperature.
   (3) The water will be heated to 380°F.
   (4) The iron will be cooled to 50°F.
   (5) Nothing, because heat can't flow from iron to water.

2. When engineers design bridges and overpasses, they purposely place gaps between the points where large metal beams are to meet end to end. The purpose of these gaps is to

   (1) allow for water drainage during rainstorms
   (2) provide room for the beams to contract in cold weather
   (3) prevent rust from forming at the point where the beams might rub together
   (4) allow for errors in measurement during construction
   (5) provide room for the beams to expand in hot weather

Questions 3–5 are based on the following reading selection and diagram.

Your body temperature is a measure of the heat produced within your body. Most of the time, your temperature is regulated and remains about the same. However, during illness your temperature goes up as your body attempts to fight off infection or disease.

One of the first signs of illness in a child is an unusual increase in body temperature. A temperature rise can be a symptom of a cold, the flu, or even a much more serious illness such as meningitis, a disease that requires immediate medical attention. Also, extreme fever itself can be very harmful. A fever higher than 105.8°F (41°C) can cause permanent damage to a person's nervous system.

3. According to the diagram, what is the normal human body temperature?

(1) 33°C or 91.4°F
(2) 37°C or 98.6°F
(3) 39°C or 102.2°F
(4) 40°C or 104°F
(5) 44°C or 111.2°F

4. According to the diagram, which temperature below represents a slight fever?

(1) 96°F
(2) 37°C
(3) 98.6°F
(4) 38°C
(5) 106°F

5. What is the best parental response to a child's waking in the middle of the night with a 104°F fever?

(1) Tell the child to go to sleep and see how the fever is in the morning.
(2) Cool the child with a damp cloth, call the after-hours number at your doctor's office or hospital, report the child's symptoms, and get medical advice.
(3) Wait for a few hours and see if the temperature goes down by itself.
(4) Don't worry, because high temperatures in children are common.
(5) Call a friend with children and ask for advice.

ANSWERS ARE ON PAGE 320.

PROPERTIES OF WAVES

> ### KEY WORDS
>
> ***waves***—the form in which water, light, and sound travel
> ***wavelength***—the length of one wave

During the afternoon of April 1, 1946, huge ocean waves pounded the shores of the Hawaiian Islands and left 173 people dead or missing, 163 people injured, and millions of dollars worth of property damage.

Where did the ocean along the normally peaceful Hawaiian shores get all the energy to cause such extensive damage? Believe it or not, this tremendous energy came from an earthquake only five hours earlier in the Aleutian Trench, a gorge in Earth's crust that lies on the bottom of the Pacific Ocean off the shore of Alaska.

How could the ocean have moved so far so quickly? It didn't! The energy was simply carried to Hawaii by the wave motion on the ocean's surface.

The ocean is an example of the action of water waves, one of many common types of waves. Three types of waves we'll discuss on the next few pages are water waves, sound waves, and light waves.

WATER WAVES

If you look at water waves, you can see many of the properties common to all waves. For example, Picture A below shows what happens when you drop a stone into a pond. The waves move directly away in a circular pattern from the place where the stone was dropped. Like all other types of waves, water waves travel in a straight line away from their source.

Picture B is a cutaway drawing of the wave pattern. It illustrates the position of crests and troughs along the wave's surface. The distance between two crests (or two troughs) is called the wavelength.

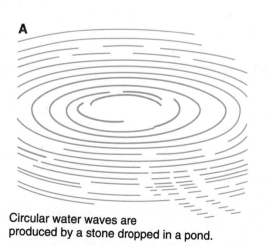

A

Circular water waves are produced by a stone dropped in a pond.

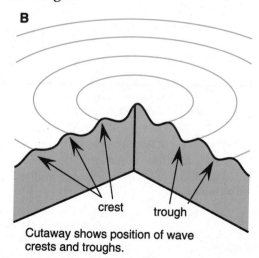

B

crest   trough

Cutaway shows position of wave crests and troughs.

When a wave hits a smooth surface, it **_reflects_**, or bounces off the surface. In Picture C, one series of waves spreads out away from the center. As the waves hit the barrier, they are reflected, causing the rainbow-shaped pattern.

As a wave crosses a boundary, it **_refracts_**, or bends, continuing its course but moving in a slightly different direction. A straight water wave refracts as it crosses from an area of deep water to an area of shallow water. Water waves tend to refract as they approach a beach.

barrier
A circular water wave reflects as it strikes a solid barrier.

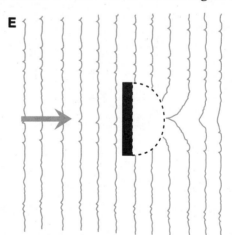

A straight water wave refracts as it moves across a boundary between deep and shallow water.

Finally, all waves **_diffract_**—they spread out into a region behind or around a barrier. You can see water waves diffracting in Picture E below.

Waves diffract as they move around a barrier. A water wave diffracts, or spreads out, as it goes by an object.

SOUND WAVES

What does a cricket's shrill have in common with a rock concert? Your answer will depend upon your interest in rock music! One similarity between them is that both are forms of sound, a type of energy that travels to our ears as a wave.

Sound can be produced by any vibrating object. For example, when a vibrating guitar string moves to the right, it compresses the air molecules to the immediate right. As the string moves to the left, the air molecules just to the right of the string become spaced farther apart. The result of the string's vibrating back and forth is a sound wave.

Like other waves, sound travels in a straight line and will reflect off a smooth surface. Reflection is most easily demonstrated by honking a car horn in a tunnel or by shouting in a canyon. The echoes that you hear are simply reflected sound waves.

Sound waves also diffract. When you stand in one room and speak with a person in another room, it is the diffraction of sound that allows you to hear the second person. Sound waves easily spread around corners and through doorways.

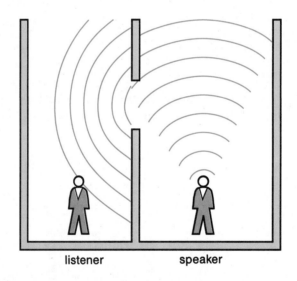

listener   speaker

EXERCISE 9

Directions: Read each statement below. Circle *T* if the statement is true and *F* if the statement is false.

T F 1. Sound waves carry energy, but water waves do not.

T F 2. The distance between two crests of a wave is called a wavelength.

T F 3. Water waves on the ocean move along the ocean's surface.

T F 4. Sound waves move in a straight line away from their source.

ANSWERS ARE ON PAGE 320.

EXERCISE 10

Questions 1–5 refer to the following paragraph and table.

The frequency of sound is the number of complete waves produced each second. Frequency determines pitch. A high-frequency sound like the high note on the piano is said to have a high pitch. A low-frequency sound like a bass drum has a low pitch. Each type of animal life on Earth has one frequency range in which it can hear and another frequency range in which it can speak or make sound. Several common frequency ranges are listed by cycles per second in the table at the right. A cycle is one complete performance of a vibration.

COMMON FREQUENCY RANGES		
Animal	Hearing*	Making Sound or Speaking*
Human	20–20,000	85–1,100
Dog	15–50,000	450–1,080
Cat	60–65,000	760–1,520
Grasshopper	100–15,000	7,000–100,000
Dolphin	150–150,000	7,000–120,000
Robin	250–21,000	2,000–13,000
Bat	1,000–120,000	10,000–120,000

*in cycles per second (cps)

1. What is the frequency range in which dogs bark?

   (1) 85–1,100 cycles per second
   (2) 15–50,000 cycles per second
   (3) 450–1,080 cycles per second
   (4) 60–65,000 cycles per second
   (5) 250–21,000 cycles per second

2. Which of the animals listed has the greatest hearing range?

   (1) human
   (2) dog
   (3) cat
   (4) dolphin
   (5) bat

3. Of the animals listed in the table, which is the only animal that can hear sounds of a lower frequency than human beings can hear?

   (1) dolphin
   (2) dog
   (3) cat
   (4) bat
   (5) grasshopper

4. Of the animals listed in the table, which is the only animal that can "speak" at frequencies far greater than the highest frequencies it can hear?

   (1) dog
   (2) dolphin
   (3) grasshopper
   (4) robin
   (5) cat

5. Which of the following conclusions is best supported by the information given in the table?

   (1) In most cases, the smaller an animal is, the more sound frequencies it can hear.
   (2) Human beings can speak at higher frequencies than other animals can "speak."
   (3) The hearing range of most animals includes both lower and higher frequencies than their speaking range.
   (4) Human beings can hear at higher frequencies than other animals can.
   (5) Four-legged mammals such as dogs and cats can hear sounds of much higher frequencies than are heard by birds or sea animals.

ANSWERS ARE ON PAGE 320.

LIGHT WAVES

KEY WORDS

vacuum—space that contains no matter
prism—a triangular piece of glass

When you look into the sky on a clear, moonless night, the stars appear as little pinholes of light shining through a black canvas. Yet, seen through a telescope, starlight reveals distant galaxies—worlds that have existed billions of years longer than our own. Today, scientists look at this starlight with the hope of discovering how stars and planets are created.

Light is a special form of wave called an ***electromagnetic wave***. Unlike other waves, electromagnetic waves can travel through a vacuum, space that contains no matter. In fact, all the light we receive from the sun, moon, and stars travels to us through the vacuum of space. This light moves in a straight line on its long journey to us. It is only because sunlight moves in a straight line that we have clearly defined shadows on Earth.

Light and Color

We usually think of sunlight as white, but it is actually made up of a spectrum of colors. You can see this spectrum beautifully displayed as a rainbow arching across the sky after a light rain. The same bands of color can also be created by passing sunlight through a prism, a triangular piece of glass.

As you already know, refraction occurs when a wave strikes a boundary and begins to move in a different direction. In this case, the prism acts as a boundary, and when the sunlight hits it, it bends, or refracts. The white light separates into its component colors because each color of light refracts by a different amount.

Each color of light can be thought of as a wave of a certain wavelength. In the spectrum of colors, red has the longest wavelength, and violet has the shortest wavelength. As the drawing on page 231 shows, red light refracts the least, and violet light refracts the most.

As we've seen, white light is made up of many colors. But why is it that when we look at most objects, we see only a single color? The answer is that objects reflect some wavelengths of light and absorb others. For example, a leaf appears green because it reflects the wavelengths associated with green. This reflected light is what we see. The leaf absorbs all other wavelengths of light.

A black surface absorbs almost all the light that strikes it. A mirror or white surface reflects almost all light. During reflection, light changes its direction of travel much as a tennis ball changes direction after striking a solid wall.

THE REFRACTION OF LIGHT BY A PRISM

white light →

A prism separates white light into light of various colors.

Color

red
orange
yellow
green
blue
indigo
violet

wavelength

longer

shorter

THE FORMATION OF A RAINBOW

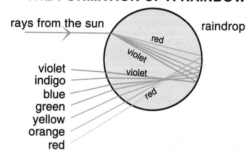

rays from the sun   raindrop

red
violet
violet
red

violet
indigo
blue
green
yellow
orange
red

EXERCISE 11

Directions: Answer the questions below.

1. Complete each sentence by filling in the blanks with the correct word(s) from the reading passage.

   a. Space that contains no matter is called a _____.

   b. Each color of light can be thought of as a wave that has a certain

   _____.

2. From the information given in the reading passage, determine if each of the following statements is true or false. Circle *T* if it is true or *F* if it is false.

   T F   a. An asphalt road appears almost black because it reflects all the sunlight that strikes it.

   T F   b. A red car appears red because it absorbs all wavelengths of light except wavelengths associated with red light.

   T F   c. On a hot summer day, a green shirt will keep you cooler than a white shirt.

   T F   d. A mirror reflects almost all the light that strikes it.

ANSWERS ARE ON PAGE 320.

GED Practice

EXERCISE 12

Questions 1-5 refer to the following definitions of five properties common to water, sound, and light waves.

straight-line movement—a wave travels in a straight line from its source

reflection—a wave will reflect (reverse its direction of travel) after striking a smooth surface

refraction—a wave will bend (change the angle of its forward motion) as it moves across a boundary, different wavelengths (colors) of light bending by different degrees

diffraction—a wave will spread out into a region behind or around a barrier

wavelength—a wave can be described as a series of crests and troughs, the distance between two crests (or troughs) being the wavelength

1. When you hear a child shout from the other side of the house, the sound of the shouting must travel through doorways and around corners in order to reach you. This is an example of the wave property known as

   (1) straight-line movement
   (2) reflection
   (3) refraction
   (4) diffraction
   (5) wavelength

2. After a rainstorm, you can sometimes see the rainbow spectrum of colors displayed in a drop of oil on the street. What property is demonstrated by the light as it strikes the oil?

   (1) straight-line movement
   (2) reflection
   (3) refraction
   (4) diffraction
   (5) wavelength

3. The echo of a person walking down an empty alley demonstrates the property of

   (1) straight-line movement
   (2) reflection
   (3) refraction
   (4) diffraction
   (5) wavelength

4. Emilio, a fisherman, spends most of his day sitting in a boat on the ocean. His boat bobs up and down about every seven seconds. Which property of waves is most related to Emilio's up and down movement?

   (1) straight-line movement
   (2) reflection
   (3) refraction
   (4) diffraction
   (5) wavelength

5. Amelia stood in the sunshine and looked at her shadow on the sidewalk. The property of light waves that is demonstrated by the presence of a shadow is

   (1) straight-line movement
   (2) reflection
   (3) refraction
   (4) diffraction
   (5) wavelength

ANSWERS ARE ON PAGE 320.

ELECTRICITY AND MAGNETISM

ELECTRICITY

KEY WORDS

electric current—the movement of electrons
circuit—a complete path in which an electric current flows
conductor—a material in which an electric current can be made to flow
static electricity—electricity that consists of motionless charges

---

In 1877, when the famous physicist Hermann von Helmholtz was taking members of the Imperial Court on a tour of his laboratory in Berlin, one of his guests looked at the electric wires and asked in amazement, "But, professor, how is it possible for electricity to flow through these thin little tubes?"

History doesn't tell us how Helmholtz answered this question, but today we have a pretty good idea about the nature of electricity. According to the atomic theory of matter, all matter is composed of atoms. Each atom has an equal number of negatively charged electrons and positively charged protons. Electricity involves the motion of these electrons and can be either of two types: static electricity or electric current.

Static Electricity: Electric Charges at Rest

Because most objects in nature are electrically neutral, having the same number of electrons as protons, we usually don't notice the electrical properties of things. However, what do you suppose would happen if you could upset this balance of positive and negative charges?

Here are a couple of examples in which you do just that. When you rub a comb through dry hair, the comb picks up extra electrons. These electrons actually leave your hair and electrically stick to the comb. The charged comb can then make your hair stand on end, and it can pick up small pieces of paper. You can also see this effect when you walk across a woolen carpet. Your body becomes charged with excess electrons picked up from the wool, and you can get quite a shock by touching a metal door handle.

In each of these examples of static electricity, electrons are transferred from one object to another. This transfer of electric charge takes place because the outermost electrons in many atoms are held loosely by the nuclei and can be removed easily.

Electric Current: Electric Charges In Motion

In static electricity, you observe effects of the presence of excess electric charges at rest. Now, what about charges in motion?

You can make electrons flow in many materials, particularly metals, much the way water flows in a hose. This flow of electrons is called an electric current. A material in which electric current can flow is called a conductor. A material in which it can't flow is called a ***nonconductor***, or an ***insulator***. You have probably seen electrical insulation, the rubber material that covers electric wires and cables. Electric current cannot flow through insulation. Insulation protects you from electric shock when you touch current-carrying wires.

Electric current that moves in one direction only is called ***direct current (DC)***. You can set a direct current in motion by attaching a battery to the ends of a copper wire. The battery produces an electric force that pushes electrons away from the negative terminal and toward the positive terminal. But for a current to flow, you must set up a complete circuit. You must connect the wires so that there is an electrical path that electrons can move along from one side of the battery to the other. A break anywhere in the circuit will stop the current's flow.

In a direct current circuit, electrons flow in a complete path from the negative terminal of the battery to the positive terminal.

The most common household power source is the wall socket. A wall socket provides an ***alternating current (AC)***—a current in which the electrons flow first in one direction and then in the opposite direction. The current in most homes is called 60-cycle AC: the current goes back and forth in the wire 60 times in one second.

An electric circuit can be either a series circuit or a parallel circuit. In a ***series circuit*** there is only one path for electric current to take. A break anywhere in this circuit stops the electric current flow to every light or other device in the circuit.

In a *parallel circuit* there is more than one path for electric current to take. A break in one part of the circuit does not always stop the electric current from flowing through other lights or devices in the circuit.

SERIES CIRCUIT

PARALLEL CIRCUIT

If bulb A burns out, bulb B goes out.   If bulb C burns out, bulb D stays lit.

The amount of current that flows from any power source depends on the voltage. Commonly used batteries you see around home are the 1½-volt flashlight battery and the 9-volt smoke alarm battery. A wall socket, which produces a 120-volt signal, provides a much greater amount of current. This is why you can safely handle batteries but should not, under any circumstances, stick your finger in a wall socket!

EXERCISE 13

Directions: Match each item on the left with the phrase that best describes it on the right. Write the letter of the phrase on the line before the correct number.

_____ **1.** alternating current

_____ **2.** voltage

_____ **3.** insulator

_____ **4.** electrons

_____ **5.** direct current

(a) current that flows in one direction only

(b) the moving particles that make up an electric current

(c) a number that tells the strength of a battery

(d) current that alternately flows in each direction

(e) a material in which electric current can't flow

6. Complete each sentence by filling in the blanks with the correct word(s) from the reading passage.

    a. The two types of electricity are _____ and _____.

    b. A _____ is a material in which an electric current can be made to flow.

ANSWERS ARE ON PAGE 320.

EXERCISE 14

Questions 1 and 2 are based on the information on pages 234–235.

1. Which phrase is the best summary of what happens in a series circuit of lights?

    If one goes out,

    (1) one other goes out
    (2) they all go out
    (3) the rest stay on
    (4) half of the rest stay on
    (5) a circuit breaker trips

2. One light in the dining room burns out. While it's out, the rest of the lights in the room remain as bright as ever. What is the most reasonable conclusion you can draw from this fact?

    (1) The lights are wired as a parallel circuit.
    (2) The burned-out light caused a fuse to blow.
    (3) The lights are wired as a series circuit.
    (4) Another light will soon burn out.
    (5) There is a power outage at your house.

Questions 3 and 4 refer to the following diagram.

3. Below are three statements that refer to circuit A at left.

    A. Direct current is flowing in circuit A.
    B. Electrons are flowing from the positive terminal of the battery to the negative terminal.
    C. Disconnecting the wire at the positive terminal of the battery will turn off the light but not the bell.

    Which of the statements above is false?

    (1) A only
    (2) B only
    (3) C only
    (4) A and B only
    (5) B and C only

4. When a switch in a circuit is opened, the flow of current stops. Referring to circuit B at left, which one of the three switches (a, b, and c) could you open in order to turn off light 1 only?

    (1) a only
    (2) b only
    (3) c only
    (4) either a or c
    (5) either b or c

ANSWERS ARE ON PAGE 320.

SUPERCONDUCTIVITY

Imagine trains that float on cushions of magnetic force and speed across
the country at hundreds of miles per hour. Imagine computers only a fraction
of the size they are now and powerful electric motors the size of your thumb.
Will such devices be in our future? "Yes!" say many excited physicists today. In
fact, they predict that these are just three of many consumer products that may
result from one of the most exciting advances to take place in physics in
decades: superconductivity.

Superconductivity is an amazing phenomenon that involves electric
current—the flow of electrons through a conductor. In common conductors of
electricity like copper wires, electrons bump into each other, so there is
resistance to the flow of the current. Electrical resistance causes heat and
results in a loss of energy. For example, about 20 percent of the electrical
energy carried by high-voltage power lines is lost as heat.

In a superconductor, on the other hand, electrons do not collide with one
another. There is no electrical resistance. No energy is lost when electrons flow,
and no heat is created. Superconductors are perfect conductors of electricity.

No one knows exactly why superconductivity occurs. A popular hypothesis
is that electrons in a superconductor have a way of pairing together and then
moving in step with other electron pairs. This coordinated motion enables the
electrons to avoid collisions. You can think of this motion as being similar to
the organized movement of two-lane traffic on a very busy street.

Although superconductivity was first discovered in the element mercury in
1911, no practical applications were developed in the years that followed. The
most important obstacle was that materials that become superconductors would
do so only at extremely low temperatures. Mercury, for example, was found to
become superconducting only when its temperature was lowered to −452°F! At
any higher temperature, mercury is just as resistant as a regular conductor.
What's more, cooling mercury to this temperature requires immersing it in a
bath of liquid helium, a very expensive and scarce coolant.

Between 1911 and the early 1980s, only a few other superconducting
materials were discovered. Each of these was either a metal or metal alloy, and
each had to be cooled to hundreds of degrees below zero before
superconductivity would occur. Then, in the mid-1980s, physicists found that
certain types of ceramics also become superconductors and that they do so at
temperatures much higher than previously was believed possible. In fact, new
types of superconducting ceramics are now being developed with the hope that
room-temperature superconductors may someday be in common use.

EXERCISE 15

Directions: Match each item on the left with the phrase that is the best description on the right. Write the letter of the phrase on the line before the correct number.

_____ **1.** helium

_____ **2.** mercury

_____ **3.** superconductivity

_____ **4.** conductor

_____ **5.** ceramic

(a) the absence of electrical resistance

(b) any material that will transmit electricity

(c) a material recently discovered to have superconducting properties

(d) the first known superconductor

(e) a coolant when in liquid form

 GED Practice

EXERCISE 16

Questions 1–3 are based on the information on page 237.

1. The important advantage that superconductors have over regular conductors is that they

   (1) can be used inside computers to carry electric current
   (2) cost less to make than regular conductors
   (3) use less electric current than regular conductors
   (4) don't produce heat when electricity flows through them
   (5) don't produce magnetic fields when electricity flows through them

2. When a certain low temperature is reached, superconductivity occurs in a superconductor. It is believed that this happens because

   (1) the magnetic field surrounding the superconductor becomes very strong as the electric current is increased
   (2) the superconductor's electrical resistance disappears and no heat is produced when current flows through it
   (3) the superconductor's electrons become very small and move through the material very rapidly
   (4) the superconductor suddenly exhibits several new types of electron motion
   (5) the superconductor's electrons join in pairs and move through the material without colliding

3. The use of superconducting electric power lines could save utility companies billions of dollars each year. What assumption is made by scientists who claim that this will result in lower electricity costs to consumers?

   (1) After utility companies install superconducting power lines, consumers will use less electricity.
   (2) Consumers will get rebates for the installation of superconducting power lines.
   (3) Superconducting power lines will enable the construction of faster trains and result in lower train fares.
   (4) The money saved by utility companies in the transmission of electricity on superconducting lines will be passed along as savings to consumers.
   (5) After superconducting power lines are installed, many people who presently heat by gas or oil will switch to electricity.

ANSWERS ARE ON PAGE 321.

MAGNETISM

KEY WORD

pole—region of a magnet where the magnetic force is very strong

---

Centuries ago, the Greeks discovered that small pieces of a certain iron ore could both attract and repel other pieces of the same ore. Today this ore is called magnetite, and pieces of magnetite are referred to as **natural magnets**. The phenomenon the Greeks observed is called **magnetism**.

HAVE YOU SEEN MAGNETS DO THESE THINGS?

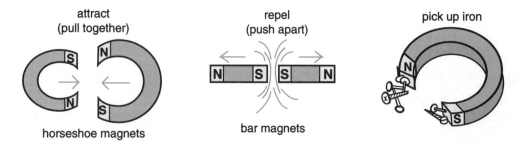

Magnets have two poles, or regions, where the magnetic force is very strong. When magnets are brought close together, they act in a way that reminds you of electric charges. Opposite poles attract each other: the north pole of one magnet is strongly attracted to the south pole of a second magnet. Like poles repel each other: north poles repel each other; so do south poles.

Two common magnets that you may have used at one time or another are the horseshoe magnet and the bar magnet. A horseshoe magnet, as its name implies, looks like a horseshoe. The poles are the two ends of the magnet. A bar magnet is in the shape of a straight bar. One end is the north pole, and the other end is the south pole. Horseshoe and bar magnets differ only in shape. Like all other magnets, each of these types always has only one north pole and one south pole.

When you use magnets, you will discover two more of their properties. First, you will find that a magnet can strongly attract metal such as iron, which itself is not a magnet, to either its north or south pole. And second, you will find that magnetic force, whether it attracts or repels, becomes less strong as you move farther away from a magnet.

Another type of magnet is called an electromagnet. An electromagnet is made by coiling a wire around a piece of iron and then running an electric current through the wire. The current-carrying wire creates a weak magnetic field that causes the magnetic atoms of iron to line up in the same direction. The total magnetic field that results is very strong. You may have seen pictures of small electromagnets being used to lift cars in a junk yard.

EXERCISE 17

Directions: The statements below refer to magnetism. Circle *T* for each statement that is true and *F* for each that is false.

T F   **1.** The north pole of any magnet is always attracted to the south pole of any other magnet.

T F   **2.** A bar magnet differs from a horseshoe magnet because a bar magnet will not attract iron.

T F   **3.** Magnetite is a name given to a type of natural magnet.

T F   **4.** The strength of a magnet increases as you move farther from the magnet.

ANSWERS ARE ON PAGE 321.

 GED Practice

EXERCISE 18

Questions 1 and 2 refer to the following passage.

When a wire carries an alternating electric current, both an alternating electric field and an alternating magnetic field are produced near the wire. These combined fields are called *electromagnetic fields*. In recent years, the presence of strong electromagnetic fields near electric power lines and weak fields near such household items as televisions, radios, and electric clocks has become a topic of concern. Many scientists think there may be growing evidence that overexposure to electromagnetic fields may be harmful to humans.

People living near high-voltage electric power lines have complained of excessive fatigue, unusual memory loss, headaches, and a feeling of overall discomfort. In response to these claims and out of concern for public health, scientists are investigating these health-and-safety issues.

No one yet knows what dangers, if any, are posed by electromagnetic fields. But until answers become available, the smart action is to reasonably limit your exposure to them.

1. Each of the following items, when turned on, has a surrounding electromagnetic field *except* a

 (1) hair dryer
 (2) car radio
 (3) television set
 (4) toaster
 (5) flashlight

2. When considering the degree of risk taken when in the presence of a strong electromagnetic field, which of the following is of *least* importance?

 (1) distance from the object creating the field
 (2) the strength of the field
 (3) time spent in the field
 (4) the type of object producing the field
 (5) personal sensitivity to the field

Questions 3–7 refer to the following definitions.

nonmagnetic—substances that are not attracted to a magnet at all

naturally magnetic—any material that occurs in nature as a natural magnet

ferromagnetic—any material that is strongly attracted by a magnet

paramagnetic—any material that is only slightly attracted by a magnet

diamagnetic—any material that is weakly repelled by a magnet

3. While playing with a magnet and a box of thumbtacks, Laurie noticed that the tacks strongly clung to both poles of the magnet. These thumbtacks would be best classified as

   (1) nonmagnetic
   (2) naturally magnetic
   (3) ferromagnetic
   (4) paragmagnetic
   (5) diamagnetic

4. The ancient Chinese used lodestone, a type of magnetic ore found in mountains and on sandy beaches, to make compasses for use in navigation. Lodestone can be classified as

   (1) nonmagnetic
   (2) naturally magnetic
   (3) ferromagnetic
   (4) paramagnetic
   (5) diamagnetic

5. When alchemists were trying to find a way to create gold, they knew that one property of gold was that it is weakly repelled by a magnet. Knowing this, you would classify gold as

   (1) nonmagnetic
   (2) naturally magnetic
   (3) ferromagnetic
   (4) paramagnetic
   (5) diamagnetic

6. Many gases, such as helium, are neither attracted to nor repelled by a magnet. These gases would be best classified as

   (1) nonmagnetic
   (2) naturally magnetic
   (3) ferromagnetic
   (4) paramagnetic
   (5) diamagnetic

7. Aluminum, which at first doesn't appear to be attracted by a magnet, is found to be slightly attracted to a very strong magnet. Aluminum is in a class of materials called

   (1) nonmagnetic
   (2) naturally magnetic
   (3) ferromagnetic
   (4) paramagnetic
   (5) diamagnetic

ANSWERS ARE ON PAGE 321.

NUCLEAR PHYSICS

RADIOACTIVITY

What do CAT scans and atomic bombs have in common? You may already know the answer: they both make use of radioactivity, a property of some types of atoms. The nuclei of radioactive atoms are unstable and break apart on their own. As an unstable nucleus breaks apart, it shoots out certain types of particles and rays. Nine of the elements are known to be radioactive.

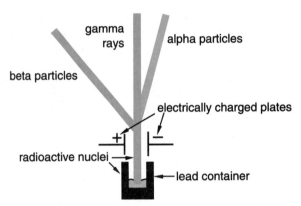

Alpha and beta particles and gamma rays are shot out as radioactive nuclei decay. Electronically charged plates can be used to separate these radiations.

There are three basic types of particles and rays given off by a radioactive nucleus:

- *Alpha particles.* An alpha particle is made up of two protons and two neutrons bound tightly together.

- *Beta particles.* A beta particle is an electron. It is identical to the electrons that orbit the nucleus of each atom.

- *Gamma rays.* A gamma ray is a high-energy electromagnetic wave. A gamma ray differs from visible light in that its energy is much higher and its wavelength is much shorter.

A given amount of a radioactive substance will decay (change into other substances because its nuclei are splitting) over a period of time. The rate at which the substance decays is given as a number called a ***half-life***. During one half-life, one-half of the radioactive nuclei present will have split into smaller nuclei. Different radioactive elements have different half-lifes. For example, the half-life of uranium-238 is 45,510,000,000 years, while the half-life of polonium is less than one-thousandth of a second.

Radioactive Decay of Uranium–238

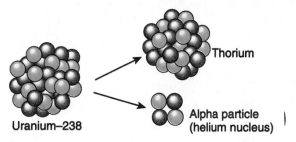

Uranium–238 → Thorium, Alpha particle (helium nucleus)

Below is an illustration of a radioactive decay curve for a fictitious element that has a half-life of one day. The element starts with 1,000 nuclei. Notice how many nuclei remain as each day (half-life) passes.

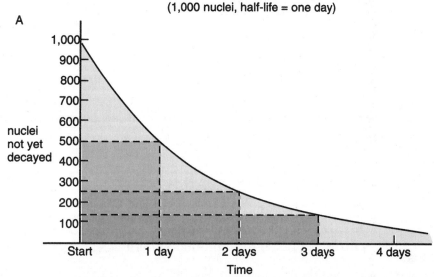

RADIOACTIVE DECAY CURVE
(1,000 nuclei, half-life = one day)

Notice that when one half-life (one day) has passed, only 500 nuclei have not yet decayed.

EXERCISE 19

Directions: Answer each question below.

1. Name the three types of particles and rays given off by radioactive nuclei as they

   decay. _____, _____, and _____

2. What is the name given to the length of time it takes one half of a group of

   radioactive nuclei to decay? _____

3. What two elements form when uranium-238 undergoes radioactive decay?

   _____ and _____

ANSWERS ARE ON PAGE 321.

Questions 1 and 2 are based on the information on pages 242–243.

1. Which of the following statements is false?

   (1) A radioactive element may emit one or more types of particles and rays.
   (2) Different radioactive elements have different half-lifes.
   (3) During radioactive decay, a nucleus breaks apart.
   (4) During one half-life, half of the radioactive nuclei will decay.
   (5) Radioactive decay occurs only when elements are X-rayed or blown up in atomic bombs.

2. According to the graph on page 243, the number of nuclei that remain when three half-lifes have passed is

   (1) 1000
   (2) 500
   (3) 250
   (4) 125
   (5) less than 100

ANSWERS ARE ON PAGE 321.

CHAIN REACTIONS AND NUCLEAR POWER

KEY WORDS

fission—the splitting of an atomic nucleus
fusion—the process of joining two atomic nuclei
chain reaction—the production of nuclear energy through fission of nuclei
nuclear reactor—a device in which controlled chain reactions occur

The discovery of radioactivity in 1896 was the first step toward a more complete understanding of atomic nuclei. Another discovery showed that many nuclei could be split into smaller nuclei if they were bombarded with particles such as protons or alpha particles.

The process of splitting a nucleus into two medium-sized nuclei is called fission. The fission of a nucleus causes the release of a large amount of nuclear energy. Scientists realized that a tremendous supply of energy could be released through the fission of very small amounts of elements such as uranium.

In 1942, Enrico Fermi, an Italian physicist working at the University of Chicago, produced the first controlled nuclear chain reaction. In a chain reaction, nuclei are split apart in a controlled way, and as a result a great quantity of nuclear energy is produced. (An example of an *uncontrolled* nuclear reaction is the explosion of an atomic bomb.)

By 1943, the first nuclear reactors were being built. A nuclear reactor is a device in which controlled chain reactions are carried out. Nuclear reactors are the heart of a nuclear power plant.

A nuclear power plant operates much the same way as a coal power plant. In each, heat energy is used to produce electrical energy. In the coal plant, heat is produced by the burning of coal in a boiler. In a nuclear plant, the heat comes from the fissioning of nuclei in a nuclear reactor. In each plant, the heat created is used to boil water to produce steam. The steam turns a turbine that is connected to an electric generator. The generator produces electrical power, which then flows down electric power lines on its way from each plant.

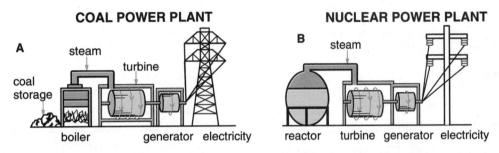

COAL POWER PLANT   **NUCLEAR POWER PLANT**

In both coal and nuclear power plants, water is heated to produce steam, which turns a turbine to create electricity.

Compared to other fuels, nuclear fuel produces an almost unbelievable amount of energy. At the present time, though, only one kind of atom found in nature can be used as nuclear fuel. This is U-235, a rare form of the element uranium. A piece of U-235 the size of a grain of rice can produce energy equal to that contained in three tons of coal or fourteen barrels of oil! One pound of U-235 can produce energy equal to that produced by 3,000,000 pounds of coal or 6,400 barrels of oil.

No one knows for sure how much U-235 is contained in Earth's crust. However, it is fairly scarce. In fact, it is estimated that with equal use, the known sources of uranium fuel would run out before fossil fuel sources (coal, oil, and natural gas) run out.

NUCLEAR FUSION

Someday it may be possible to obtain large amounts of power by a process called nuclear fusion. Nuclear fusion occurs when two nuclei are *fused*, or joined together. Nuclear fusion is the process that provides the energy given off by stars. On the sun, hydrogen atoms combine to form helium atoms, releasing tremendous energy in the process.

Unfortunately, fusion reactions can take place only in regions of extremely high temperature—near 100 million degrees Celsius! Because it is so difficult to produce this high temperature, nuclear fusion is not yet a practical energy source. Whether it ever will be is still a debated question. However, hydrogen—the fuel needed for nuclear fusion reactions—is available in abundance on Earth. It can be taken directly from ocean water.

EXERCISE 21

Directions: Briefly define what is meant by each of the following terms.

1. nuclear fission: _____

2. chain reaction: _____

3. nuclear reactor: _____

4. nuclear fusion: _____

GED Practice

EXERCISE 22

Questions 1–3 are based on the information on pages 244–245.

1. A nuclear power plant is similar to a coal power plant in the way it

   (1) uses an electric generator to turn a steam-driven turbine
   (2) produces nuclear waste
   (3) uses a steam-driven turbine to turn an electric generator
   (4) burns coal as a source of heat energy
   (5) uses nuclear fission as a source of heat energy

2. What is U-235?

   (1) a type of nuclear reaction
   (2) an electric generator in a nuclear power plant
   (3) a form of heat energy produced by nuclear fission
   (4) a type of fuel used in nuclear fusion
   (5) a type of fuel used in nuclear fission

3. All of the statements below were made by a scientist working at a nuclear power plant. Which statement is a prediction?

   (1) Nuclear fission produces radioactive by-products as waste materials.
   (2) By the year 2050, nuclear power plants will be the world's primary method of producing electrical power.
   (3) The reason that nuclear fusion power plants have not been developed is that no one knows how to build one.
   (4) When U-235 fissions, a tremendous quantity of energy is released.
   (5) Accidents like Three Mile Island and Chernobyl remind us just how dangerous nuclear power plants can be.

ANSWERS ARE ON PAGE 321.

WRITING ACTIVITY 2

   Nuclear power is also used in the manufacture of nuclear weapons. While some people support the continued buildup of nuclear arms, others are strongly opposed. Do you think that the U.S. should keep manufacturing nuclear weapons, or do you think we should stop?

   Pick one side of the issue and write one or two paragraphs defending your point of view. Be sure to support your reasons with specific examples.

ANSWERS WILL VARY.

OUR ENERGY FUTURE

KEY WORDS

solar energy—energy from the sun
geothermal energy—energy from Earth's crust
hydroelectric power—energy from running water

In this chapter, we've discussed the major forms of energy available to us: fossil fuels (oil, coal, and gas) and nuclear energy. Each of these energy sources has its problems. The supply of fossil fuels is limited and will not last forever. In addition, the burning of fossil fuels creates a dangerous form of pollution.

Nuclear energy, seen by some as a promising source of energy, is also limited, and there is no known way of disposing of radioactive waste. Scientists are doing research on alternative forms of energy, hoping that one of these, or a combination of them, may someday fill our energy needs.

SOLAR ENERGY

The term *solar energy* refers to any of a number of uses of sunlight. The great advantage of energy from the sun is that it is unlimited and does not pollute the environment. Homes and office buildings can be heated using solar energy. Passive solar heating is achieved through the greenhouse effect—simply using captured sunlight to heat a glass-walled room. Active solar heating can be accomplished by using solar collectors. A solar collector (a device that is most often placed on a building's roof) uses sunlight to heat a fluid that slowly passes through it. The heated fluid is then pumped from the collector and is circulated through the pipes of a building's heating system.

Another mechanism that runs on energy from the sun is the solar cell, a device that produces electricity when sunlight strikes it. Solar cells have a wide range of possible uses. At present, though, solar cell use is pretty much limited to spacecraft and to a small number of low-energy consumer items such as watches and hand-held calculators. Large solar cells are expensive to make and cannot yet be considered a reasonable alternative to other methods of generating power. However, if technological advances can bring the costs down, you may one day see solar cells power automobiles, homes, and a wide range of consumer products.

GEOTHERMAL ENERGY

Geothermal energy is energy that comes from Earth's hot interior. You already know about two forms of geothermal energy that aren't under our control: volcanoes and earthquakes. But some forms of geothermal energy can be controlled and used to our advantage.

In certain places, scientists can drill wells into Earth's crust and tap into naturally occurring bodies of hot water or steam. This energy can then be used to turn turbines that produce electricity. Iceland's electricity is produced in this way.

Though the amount of geothermal energy available in Earth's crust is almost unlimited and nonpolluting, technical difficulties prevent it from seriously being considered a major energy source in the near future. Some of the hot springs are so far under Earth's crust that it is very hard to get the heat up to the surface.

WIND AND WATER ENERGY

Wind energy has been used for several centuries to power windmills in Europe. Now windmills are being designed in many places in the world to provide a small amount of electricity to cities near strong wind areas. Although they are proving useful in some locations, windmills will probably not supply a very large share of the energy needed by future generations.

The most important form of water energy in the United States is the energy of flowing rivers. Flowing water can be used to turn turbines and produce electricity. At present, hydroelectric power provides about 5 percent of the energy used in the United States.

Ocean water also contains a great amount of energy, both as ocean waves and in the heat energy held in ocean water. But harnessing that energy has proved difficult. A machine large enough to capture a significant amount of energy from ocean waves would have to be more than a mile long. Many technical problems remain to be solved before the ocean could become a practical energy source.

DECISIONS ABOUT ENERGY USE

With all these energy sources available, the United States itself will not run out of energy in the near future. We have enough coal alone to last for several centuries. But, as you've seen, having energy sources isn't the whole story. Today's most immediate concern is not whether energy is available but is about the price we'll have to pay in order to continue to use those sources.

The dangers of air pollution, the greenhouse effect, and nuclear waste will not go away by themselves. These effects are only controlled by laws that regulate the industries that are responsible. What's more, the technological advances needed in order to develop safe, nonpolluting, affordable energy sources will cost a lot of money, much of which will probably be paid by taxpayers. For these reasons, the future of energy in the United States very much depends on what we citizens decide. In our society, pollution control and technological advances end up being as much political questions as scientific ones.

EXERCISE 23

Directions: Rushing water in a river is an example of uncontrolled energy. When river water is used to turn turbines and create electricity, we say that the energy is controlled. On each line below, write *controlled* or *uncontrolled* to indicate the use of energy being described.

_____ **1.** a raging house fire

_____ **2.** a race car being driven at 200 miles per hour

_____ **3.** a campfire

_____ **4.** an erupting volcano

_____ **5.** a telephone ringing

 GED Practice

EXERCISE 24

Questions 1 and 2 are based on the information on pages 247–249.

1. What are the two main reasons that geothermal and solar energy are not being used more than they currently are?

   (1) excessive cost and pollution-control problems
   (2) scarcity of the resource and excessive cost
   (3) technical problems and pollution-control problems
   (4) technical problems and excessive cost
   (5) scarcity of the resource and technical problems

2. Which of the following is *least* likely to be the main factor that determines which type of energy will provide most of the power used in the United States during the twenty-first century?

   (1) potential profits made by power companies
   (2) unforeseen natural disasters
   (3) technological advances in energy production
   (4) the supply of remaining fossil fuels
   (5) industrial competition from foreign countries

ANSWERS ARE ON PAGE 322.

GED Practice
PHYSICS

Questions 1–5 refer to the following diagram and passage.

microwaves   stirrer   waveguide
antenna
magnetron

A microwave oven uses *microwaves* (low-energy light waves) to cook food. When the oven is turned on, electricity flows into a device called a magnetron, which changes electrical energy into microwaves. The microwaves are given off by the antenna and are guided to the stirrer by a hollow tube known as a waveguide. The stirrer reflects the microwaves evenly throughout all parts of the oven's interior. Reflective surfaces on the microwave's walls and a reflective screen on the see-through door also help ensure an even distribution of microwave energy throughout the oven during cooking.

Microwaves are absorbed only by the water molecules in food items. Because water is dispersed evenly in many foods, these foods cook evenly and quickly. This is unlike a conventional oven, which heats food by hot air, cooking the outer layers of the food first, and heating all inner surfaces of the oven as well.

A microwave oven also differs from a conventional oven in that materials such as glass, paper, and most plastics can be safely used as cookware. Microwaves pass through these materials and are not absorbed.

1. According to the passage, the function of the waveguide is to guide microwaves

   (1) to the magnetron
   (2) to the stirrer
   (3) around the food item
   (4) to the antenna
   (5) from the power cord

2. While heating leftover pizza on a paper plate in her microwave oven, Jill noticed that the plate was getting warm. What is the best explanation of this discovery?

   (1) The plate felt dry but contained a lot of water.
   (2) The heated pizza was warming the plate.
   (3) The microwave oven was not working properly.
   (4) The air in the oven was being warmed by microwave energy.
   (5) The air in the porous plate was being heated by microwaves.

3. Carl's microwave no longer cooks food evenly. His last turkey was cooked well done on one side and only warmed on the other. The most likely reason is that

   (1) the power cord is broken
   (2) the oven door was open while the turkey was cooking
   (3) the magnetron is not working correctly
   (4) the antenna is not working correctly
   (5) the stirrer is not operating correctly

4. The reflective screen on a microwave's glass door is a safety feature most likely meant to

   (1) allow you to see into the oven
   (2) protect the door against breakage
   (3) keep microwaves from leaving the oven
   (4) keep heat from leaving the oven
   (5) keep heat from getting into the oven

5. You can conclude that a microwave oven is more energy efficient than a conventional oven because a microwave oven

   (1) heats only what it is cooking
   (2) doesn't use electricity to heat food
   (3) heats food uniformly
   (4) doesn't produce visible light energy
   (5) uses microwave energy to heat food

Questions 6–9 refer to the following information and diagrams.

In Experiment A and Experiment B, a fixed amount of gas is contained in a cylinder.

The volume available to the gas is determined by the position of a movable piston.

The purpose of the experiments is to determine how changes in volume and temperature affect the pressure of a confined gas.

EXPERIMENT A

As the piston is moved down in the cylinder, the temperature of the gas is kept constant.

EXPERIMENT B

The volume of the gas is kept constant as the temperature of the gas is increased.

6. What is the main conclusion that can be drawn from Experiment A?

    (1) Gas temperature increases as the volume in which the gas is confined is decreased.
    (2) Gas temperature decreases as the volume in which the gas is confined is increased.
    (3) Gas pressure increases as gas temperature is increased.
    (4) Gas pressure increases as the volume in which the gas is confined is decreased.
    (5) Gas pressure decreases as the volume in which the gas is confined is decreased.

7. Information obtained from Experiment A would be of most interest to someone who designs

    (1) parachutes
    (2) steam engines
    (3) snow skis
    (4) airplane wings
    (5) bicycle frames

8. What is the main conclusion that can be drawn from Experiment B?

    (1) Gas pressure increases as the volume in which the gas is confined is decreased.
    (2) Gas pressure decreases as the volume in which the gas is confined is decreased.
    (3) Gas pressure increases as the temperature of the gas is increased.
    (4) Gas pressure decreases as the temperature of the gas is increased.
    (5) Gas pressure increases as both the volume and temperature of the gas are increased.

9. Information obtained from Experiment B would be of most interest to someone who designs

    (1) pressure cookers
    (2) hot-air balloons
    (3) kites
    (4) canoes
    (5) coffee cups

ANSWERS ARE ON PAGE 322.

POST-TEST ANSWER GRID

1 ① ② ③ ④ ⑤   23 ① ② ③ ④ ⑤   45 ① ② ③ ④ ⑤

2 ① ② ③ ④ ⑤   24 ① ② ③ ④ ⑤   46 ① ② ③ ④ ⑤

3 ① ② ③ ④ ⑤   25 ① ② ③ ④ ⑤   47 ① ② ③ ④ ⑤

4 ① ② ③ ④ ⑤   26 ① ② ③ ④ ⑤   48 ① ② ③ ④ ⑤

5 ① ② ③ ④ ⑤   27 ① ② ③ ④ ⑤   49 ① ② ③ ④ ⑤

6 ① ② ③ ④ ⑤   28 ① ② ③ ④ ⑤   50 ① ② ③ ④ ⑤

7 ① ② ③ ④ ⑤   29 ① ② ③ ④ ⑤   51 ① ② ③ ④ ⑤

8 ① ② ③ ④ ⑤   30 ① ② ③ ④ ⑤   52 ① ② ③ ④ ⑤

9 ① ② ③ ④ ⑤   31 ① ② ③ ④ ⑤   53 ① ② ③ ④ ⑤

10 ① ② ③ ④ ⑤   32 ① ② ③ ④ ⑤   54 ① ② ③ ④ ⑤

11 ① ② ③ ④ ⑤   33 ① ② ③ ④ ⑤   55 ① ② ③ ④ ⑤

12 ① ② ③ ④ ⑤   34 ① ② ③ ④ ⑤   56 ① ② ③ ④ ⑤

13 ① ② ③ ④ ⑤   35 ① ② ③ ④ ⑤   57 ① ② ③ ④ ⑤

14 ① ② ③ ④ ⑤   36 ① ② ③ ④ ⑤   58 ① ② ③ ④ ⑤

15 ① ② ③ ④ ⑤   37 ① ② ③ ④ ⑤   59 ① ② ③ ④ ⑤

16 ① ② ③ ④ ⑤   38 ① ② ③ ④ ⑤   60 ① ② ③ ④ ⑤

17 ① ② ③ ④ ⑤   39 ① ② ③ ④ ⑤   61 ① ② ③ ④ ⑤

18 ① ② ③ ④ ⑤   40 ① ② ③ ④ ⑤   62 ① ② ③ ④ ⑤

19 ① ② ③ ④ ⑤   41 ① ② ③ ④ ⑤   63 ① ② ③ ④ ⑤

20 ① ② ③ ④ ⑤   42 ① ② ③ ④ ⑤   64 ① ② ③ ④ ⑤

21 ① ② ③ ④ ⑤   43 ① ② ③ ④ ⑤   65 ① ② ③ ④ ⑤

22 ① ② ③ ④ ⑤   44 ① ② ③ ④ ⑤   66 ① ② ③ ④ ⑤

Science Post-Test

Directions: This Science Post-Test will give you the opportunity to evaluate your readiness for the actual GED Science Test.

This test contains 66 questions. Some of the questions are based on short reading passages, and some of them require you to interpret a chart, graph, or diagram.

You should take approximately 95 minutes to complete this test. At the end of 95 minutes, stop and mark your place. Then finish the test. This will give you an idea of whether or not you can finish the real GED Test in the time allotted. Try to answer as many questions as you can, choosing the best of five answer choices and blackening in the grid. A blank will count as a wrong answer, so make a reasonable guess for questions you are not sure of.

When you are finished with the test, turn to the evaluation chart on page 279. Use the chart to evaluate whether you are ready to take the actual GED Test and, if not, what areas need more work.

Questions 1 and 2 refer to the illustration below.

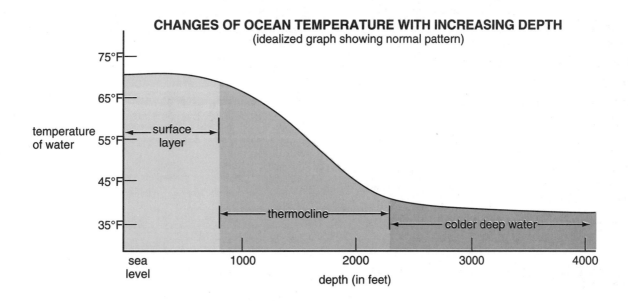

CHANGES OF OCEAN TEMPERATURE WITH INCREASING DEPTH
(idealized graph showing normal pattern)

1. A thermocline can best be described as a

   (1) temperature distribution in the ocean
   (2) layer of warm water close to the surface
   (3) layer of cold water beneath the warm surface
   (4) transition region between the warm surface and the much colder deep water
   (5) region of nearly constant temperature just beneath the warm surface

2. Which of the following would be the *most likely* to upset the ocean's normal temperature distribution?

   (1) an earthquake near the ocean shore
   (2) an erupting volcano on the ocean bottom
   (3) a violent rainstorm on the ocean surface
   (4) a hot sunny day when there is no wind
   (5) a hurricane passing over the ocean surface

3. Any object that moves through air feels the effect of air resistance, a force that pushes against the object and slows it down. All of the following objects are designed to take advantage of air resistance except

   (1) a parachute
   (2) a kite
   (3) an electric fan
   (4) a golf club
   (5) a frisbee

Questions 4 and 5 refer to the following passage.

Did you ever wonder why the sky appears so blue on a clear day? What happens to the other colors of the rainbow that are also present in sunlight? The answer has to do with the scattering of sunlight by the atmosphere.

When you look at the daytime sky, you see only the light that travels to your eyes from the direction of your gaze. This light is blue, because only blue light is to a great degree scattered in all directions by atoms of nitrogen and oxygen, the main gases found in the earth's atmosphere. Other colors of light are less apt to be scattered, and they continue their straight-line movement through the atmosphere and away from your eyes.

4. According to the passage, scattering causes blue light to

   (1) change color
   (2) change its direction of movement
   (3) return to space instead of striking Earth
   (4) lose its energy
   (5) become invisible

5. What information would scientists first need to know before they could determine the color of the daytime Martian sky as it is seen from the surface of Mars?

   (1) the amount of sunlight that strikes the Martian atmosphere
   (2) the types of gases that make up the Martian atmosphere
   (3) the color of the Martian surface
   (4) the average temperature on the Martian surface
   (5) the types of rocks and soil that make up the Martian surface

6. Two identical negatively charged spheres are suspended by string from support stands. Which of the drawings below correctly illustrates how the charged spheres will react when the stands holding them are moved close together?

(1)

(2)

(3)

(4)

(5)

Questions 7 and 8 refer to the following information.

Methane (CH_4), also called *natural gas*, is commonly used as fuel for heating and cooking. When methane burns, it combines with oxygen gas (O_2) and produces carbon dioxide gas (CO_2) and water (H_2O). The equation of this chemical reaction is written as:

$$CH_4 + 2O_2 \longrightarrow CO_2 + 2H_2O + energy$$

7. For each molecule of methane gas that burns, how many molecules of CO_2 gas form?

   (1) one
   (2) two
   (3) three
   (4) four
   (5) six

8. Which of the following statements about the reaction equation above is true?

   (1) There are more atoms of oxygen on the left side of the arrow than on the right side.
   (2) There are fewer atoms of oxygen on the left side of the arrow than on the right side.
   (3) There is an equal number of molecules of oxygen gas on each side of the arrow.
   (4) There is an equal number of atoms of oxygen on each side of the arrow.
   (5) No oxygen gas is represented in the reaction equation.

Questions 9 and 10 refer to the following information given below.

In a television commercial, an oil company salesman makes the following four statements about a synthetic car oil.

   A. Syn 1 is the most efficient oil you'll ever use in your car.

   B. Using Syn 1, you'll need to change your oil only once every 35,000 miles.

   C. The new Syn 1 oil costs only $4.49 per quart.

   D. Syn 1 is available wherever high-quality automotive products are sold.

9. Which of the statements above implies that scientific tests have determined the amount of wear received by an engine that uses Syn 1 oil?

   (1) A only
   (2) B only
   (3) C only
   (4) D only
   (5) B and D only

10. Which of the above statements are most likely based on opinion rather than facts?

   (1) A and B only
   (2) A and C only
   (3) A and D only
   (4) B and C only
   (5) C and D only

POST-TEST

Questions 11 and 12 refer to the following illustration.

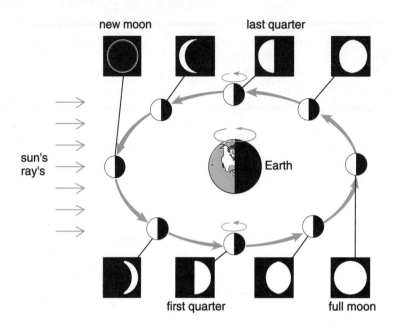

11. According to the illustration above, a full moon occurs when

(1) the moon is between the sun and Earth
(2) the moon is not visible from Earth
(3) the sun is between Earth and the moon
(4) the moon and Earth are the same distance from the sun
(5) Earth is between the sun and the moon

12. What can you conclude by observing the different shapes in which the moon appears to us on Earth?

(1) Moonlight is light produced by the moon.
(2) Moonlight is light from Earth that reflects off the moon's surface.
(3) Moonlight is sunlight that reflects off the moon's surface.
(4) The direction of the moon's rotation (spinning motion) is opposite to that of the Earth.
(5) During a full moon, the entire surface of the Earth is lit by sunlight.

Questions 13–15 refer to the following passage.

Geologists believe that Earth's surface is made up of many slowly moving rigid plates. Devastating earthquakes often occur along the boundary line where two plates meet. An example is the earthquake activity along the San Andreas fault, in California. Along this fault, or collision boundary, the slowly moving Pacific plate pushes against the continental plate and causes a buildup of pressure. Occasionally a sudden slippage occurs, and a tremendous amount of earth-shaking energy is released. Such an earthquake destroyed the city of San Francisco in 1906.

The San Andreas fault can be drawn on a map as a line that runs throughout the length of California. This fault passes near San Francisco in the north and Los Angeles in the south, two major population regions on the West Coast. Slippage anywhere along the San Andreas fault can result in major earthquakes in nearby areas and smaller earthquakes throughout the entire state of California.

No one can predict for sure just where or when the next major earthquake will strike. Every point along the fault must be considered at equal risk. For this reason, many buildings in cities near the fault zone are specially designed to be earthquake-proof.

13. A fault can best be described as

(1) a line drawn between two recorded earthquakes
(2) a boundary line between two crustal plates
(3) a boundary line that divides a state into two regions
(4) a boundary line that separates a region of high population from a region of low population
(5) a boundary line between two major population centers

14. Which of the following is *not* a conclusion that can be drawn from information given in the passage?

(1) In California, some buildings are constructed with earthquake danger in mind.
(2) The San Francisco earthquake of 1906 resulted from slippage along the San Andreas fault.
(3) People living along the San Andreas fault are more likely to be injured in an earthquake than people living in other parts of California.
(4) Major earthquake danger is less in San Francisco than in Los Angeles because San Francisco has already had a major quake in this century.
(5) Because the islands of Japan also lie along a fault, Japan also faces the danger of earthquakes.

15. A geologist is trying to predict when an earthquake might occur in or near Redding, California. Each of the following will be important to this study *except*

(1) the history of earthquakes in and around the city of Redding
(2) the pattern of yearly weather conditions in and around the city of Redding
(3) the distance Redding lies from the San Andreas fault
(4) the types of land formations around Redding
(5) the history of earthquake activity in other areas of California that are geologically similar to the Redding area

POST-TEST

Questions 16–19 refer to the following passage.

Selective breeding is a method used to improve the traits of animals or plants that are commercially valuable. In selective breeding, only those plants and animals that have desirable traits are mated.

Hybridization is the selective breeding of two organisms that have distinct genetic differences even though they are members of the same species and are able to mate. The purpose of hybridization is to produce a new individual (a hybrid) that inherits desirable traits from each parent organism. However, hybrids may inherit undesirable traits as well.

An example of a hybrid animal is the mule, a cross between a female horse and a male donkey. The mule gets its size and strength from the horse. Its endurance and surefootedness come from the donkey. Like many hybrids, though, the mule is sterile—unable to produce offspring.

Inbreeding, the opposite of hybridization, is the selective mating of plants or animals that have nearly identical genetic makeup. Inbreeding can produce generations of nearly identical offspring. In plants, inbreeding is done by self-pollination. Self-pollination insures that only the one parent-plant's genes are passed on. Inbreeding in animals is done by mating close relatives. The breeding of thoroughbred horses and purebred dogs are good examples of inbreeding.

16. If a pet store advertises that a dog is a purebred cocker spaniel, which of the following can you assume to be true about the dog?

A. The dog will have traits that are very similar to the traits of other purebred cocker spaniels.
B. The dog will have only the favorable traits of its parents.
C. Both parents of the dog are purebred cocker spaniels.
D. Only one parent of the dog is a purebred cocker spaniel.

(1) A and B only
(2) A and C only
(3) A and D only
(4) B and C only
(5) B and D only

17. The main purpose of hybridization is to produce organisms that

(1) are incapable of breeding
(2) are gentically identical to each other
(3) have a unique combination of desirable traits
(4) have no inheritable traits
(5) are genetically identical to their parents

18. From the information given in the passage, you can conclude that hybrid organisms are produced only when

(1) the offspring of the mating organisms are sterile
(2) organisms from two different species mate
(3) an offspring inherits only desirable traits
(4) genetically different members of the same species mate
(5) genetically identical members of the same species mate

19. Which of the following is *not* a hybrid?

(1) a pink rose, produced by crossing a red rose with a white rose
(2) a tangelo, produced by crossing a grapefruit with a tangerine
(3) a first-generation cockapoo, the result of breeding a purebred cocker spaniel with a purebred poodle
(4) a golden retriever, the result of breeding a purebred golden retriever with its second cousin
(5) popcorn, usually created by crossing two kinds of corn

Questions 20–22 refer to the following passage.

Potential energy is stored energy—energy available to be used. Four common forms of potential energy are gravitational, chemical, nuclear, and elastic.

When a rock simply sits on top of a mountain, it has gravitational potential energy. If the rock is knocked loose, it rolls down the mountain due to the pull of the force of gravity. As it rolls and gains speed, its gravitational potential energy is changed to kinetic energy—energy of motion.

Chemical potential energy is stored chemical energy such as that found in a flashlight battery. When a flashlight is turned on, the battery's stored energy is changed into light energy. Another example of stored chemical energy is glucose, the food sugar from which your body cells get their energy. During exercise, your muscles change the energy stored in this sugar into body heat and into the kinetic energy of body movement. A third example is the energy stored in coal. Coal's chemical potential energy is changed to heat when it is burned.

The energy stored in the nucleus of atoms is called nuclear potential energy. At a nuclear power plant, this energy is released and changed to heat. The heat is used to boil water and create the high-pressure steam needed to turn the electricity-producing turbines.

Elastic potential energy is energy that is stored in a stretched or compressed object such as a spring. A spring in a windup watch is an example. As the spring slowly unwinds, its stored energy is changed to the kinetic energy of the watch's moving hands.

20. Which of the following is the best restatement of information given in the passage?

(1) Potential energy and kinetic energy are both forms of stored energy.
(2) Potential energy and kinetic energy are both forms of energy of motion.
(3) Potential energy is energy of motion, while kinetic energy is stored energy.
(4) Potential energy is stored energy, while kinetic energy is energy of motion.
(5) Potential energy always changes into kinetic energy.

21. Of the following, which is the only object that is *not* designed to make practical use of stored chemical energy?

(1) boat oars
(2) a fireplace
(3) a bicycle
(4) a bathtub drain
(5) an automobile engine

22. Which of the following would be *least* relevant in determining whether a newly discovered source of potential energy might have great practical value?

(1) the amount of the new energy-containing material that is available for use
(2) whether the new source is a form of gravitational, chemical, nuclear, or elastic potential energy
(3) the cost of changing the potential energy of the new source into usable forms of energy such as heat
(4) whether there are technical problems that must be solved before the energy can be used
(5) whether use of the new source produces dangerous waste products

POST-TEST

Questions 23–27 refer to the following passage.

An ecosystem is a community of plants, animals, and nonliving things. Ecosystems may be found in forests, grasslands, deserts, mountains, and bodies of water. Each type of ecosystem depends on three cycles that make community life possible.

In the carbon dioxide–oxygen cycle, plants take carbon dioxide gas from the atmosphere and use it for photosynthesis, the production of food sugar. As plants use carbon dioxide gas, they give off oxygen gas. Animals, on the other hand, breathe in oxygen and give off carbon dioxide as a waste product. The cycle is completed when plants and animals die and carbon dioxide gas forms from their decomposing bodies.

In the water cycle, both plants and animals take in water for life activities. To complete the cycle, plant leaves give off water vapor in a process called transpiration. While transpiring, a plant uses evaporating water to help eliminate waste products formed from plant activity. Animals give water back to the atmosphere when they exhale and when they perspire (sweat).

In the nitrogen cycle, plants get nitrogen, which they need in order to grow plant tissue, from nitrates (nitrogen compounds in the soil). Nitrates are produced in the soil by a two-step process. First, nitrogen-fixing bacteria break down the proteins of decaying plant and animal remains and produce ammonia. Then, nitrifying bacteria change this ammonia to nitrates. The nitrates are used to produce healthy plants that then become food for animals. With the death and decomposition of plants and animals, the nitrogen cycle is completed.

23. The animal that is well known for being adapted to an ecosystem in which the water cycle may be very unpredictable is a

    (1) penguin
    (2) swordfish
    (3) camel
    (4) frog
    (5) duck

24. According to the passage, carbon dioxide gas is produced and returned to the atmosphere when

    (1) animals exhale
    (2) plants carry on photosynthesis
    (3) animals perspire
    (4) plants transpire
    (5) water decomposes

25. Which of the following would be most disruptive to the balance of atmospheric carbon dioxide gas and oxygen gas?

    (1) a huge forest fire
    (2) a major earthquake
    (3) a tidal wave on the ocean
    (4) a volcanic eruption
    (5) a major flood

26. In soil that is overwatered and does not drain well, a second type of bacteria, called denitrifying bacteria, thrives and breaks down ammonia before it is converted to nitrates. From this fact, you can conclude that overwatering a houseplant can

    (1) speed up plant growth
    (2) destroy denitrifying bacteria in the soil
    (3) result in a breeding ground for small insects
    (4) prevent the plant's roots from obtaining carbon dioxide
    (5) inhibit normal plant growth

27. Which of the following items of information would be *least* important to a biologist who wants to determine whether certain farmland could be used to grow bok choy, an Oriental vegetable?

    (1) the types of ammonia compounds in the soil
    (2) the types of bacteria that live in the soil
    (3) the types of crops previously grown on the land
    (4) the amount of dead plant and animal remains in the soil
    (5) the average amount of rain that falls on the land during the bok choy growing season

Questions 28 and 29 refer to the following information.

A lever is a simple tool that is used to help a person do some types of work. As shown in the drawings below, a lever is a rigid bar that is free to rotate about a fixed point called the fulcrum. The fulcrum is the only part of the lever that doesn't move. The object to be moved is called the load. The position on the lever where the person applies force (pushes or lifts) is called the effort. Depending on the relative positions of the fulcrum, load, and effort, each lever is placed in one of three classes. The first two classes of levers are shown below.

CLASSES OF LEVERS

28. A bottle opener is a familiar lever used to pry the cap off a bottle. Referring to the definitions in the passage, you would classify the bottle opener pictured below as a

   (1) first-class lever, with fulcrum at point A
   (2) second-class lever, with fulcrum at point A
   (3) second-class lever, with fulcrum at point C
   (4) first-class lever, with fulcrum at point B
   (5) second-class lever, with fulcrum at point B

29. A double lever is a tool made by combining two levers of the same class. For example, the pair of pliers shown below is a double lever. Notice that in a double lever the object on which work is performed is considered the load. In the pliers, for example, the gripped nut is the load.

The nutcracker below is also a double lever. Which of the following correctly identifies the effort, fulcrum, and load?

   (1) A = effort, B = fulcrum, C = load
   (2) A = effort, B = load, C = fulcrum
   (3) A = load, B = fulcrum, C = effort
   (4) A = fulcrum, B = load, C = effort
   (5) A = fulcrum, B = effort, C = load

Questions 30–35 refer to the following passage.

Important characteristics of the six most familiar groups into which most animals can be classified are given below.

Fish. Because they live only in water, most fish have two organs that no other animals have: gills and an air bladder. Fish use gills to take dissolved oxygen out of water. The air bladder, a thin-walled sac that acts as a float, controls the level at which they swim. To reproduce, fish lay soft eggs, depositing them on the bottom of the ocean or other body of water where they live.

Insects. Insects are six-legged creatures whose bodies are divided into three distinct regions. Many insects have wings and fly. Other insects have neither legs nor wings. Most insects go through a four-stage development process in which the young look nothing like the adult. To reproduce, insects also lay eggs.

Amphibians. Amphibians live for a time in water and for a time on land. Young amphibians live only in water. As they mature, though, they develop features that allow them to live on land. However, amphibians do not become total land animals. Like fish, amphibians must reproduce and lay eggs in water.

Reptiles. Reptiles are land animals. Unlike fish and amphibians, they lay an *amniote egg*—an egg that is surrounded by a protective membrane and tough shell. Reptiles are also characterized by a dry body covering of some type of horny scales or plates.

Birds. Birds are the only type of animals that are well adapted to life in the air, in the water, and on land. Bird flight is accomplished by the movement of a pair of feather-covered wings. Birds, like reptiles, lay amniote eggs.

Mammals. Of all the animals, mammals have the most highly developed organ systems and brains. Most mammals give birth to live young, offspring that look similar to their parents from the moment of birth. Young mammals are nourished with milk from the mammary glands of their mother.

30. Chameleons are best known for their ability to change color in order to match their environment. A chameleon's scaly skin may turn green, yellow, white, brown, or black. Since it lays an amniote egg, the chameleon is best classified as a

    (1) fish
    (2) insect
    (3) amphibian
    (4) reptile
    (5) mammal

31. Although a bat has eyes, it does most of its flying and hunting at night. The offspring of a bat are born live and receive nourishment from the glands of the mother bat. Knowing this, you would classify the bat as a

    (1) fish
    (2) amphibian
    (3) reptile
    (4) bird
    (5) mammal

32. A salamander is a timid, harmless animal that has a thin, elongated body and a long tail. Most species have four short legs. Salamanders live near streams and ponds in which the female lays her soft eggs. The larvae (young form of the salamander) grow in the water, and they eventually develop lungs that allow them to live on land. A salamander would be placed in the class of animals known as

    (1) fish
    (2) amphibians
    (3) reptiles
    (4) birds
    (5) mammals

33. The killdeer gets its name from the sound it makes—it seems to be saying, "Kill-deer." Killdeers build their nests in fields, where the female usually lays four spotted eggs. They are often seen flying around fields where they feast on crop-destroying insects. Killdeers belong to the class of animals known as

(1) fish
(2) amphibians
(3) reptiles
(4) birds
(5) mammals

34. A whale spends all of its life in the ocean. But unlike almost all other marine animals, whales do not lay eggs. Instead, they give birth to live young. After birth, whales are nourished from milk obtained from the glands of the mother whale. A whale is best classified as a

(1) fish
(2) insect
(3) amphibian
(4) reptile
(5) mammal

35. The seahorse gets its name from the shape of its head, which looks very much like a tiny horse. This five-inch-long animal lives only in. water. It uses its tail to cling to plants or floating vegetation. The female lays about 200 eggs, which she deposits in a pouch on the underside of the male seahorse's body. A seahorse can best be classified as a

(1) fish
(2) amphibian
(3) reptile
(4) bird
(5) mammal

36. A new roller coaster in an amusement park travels in a loop as shown in the illustration below.

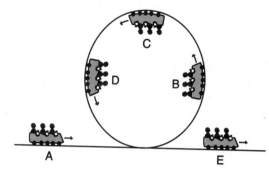

In which of the five indicated positions is the potential energy (stored energy) of the passenger car the greatest?

(1) A
(2) B
(3) C
(4) D
(5) E

Question 37 refers to the following graphs.

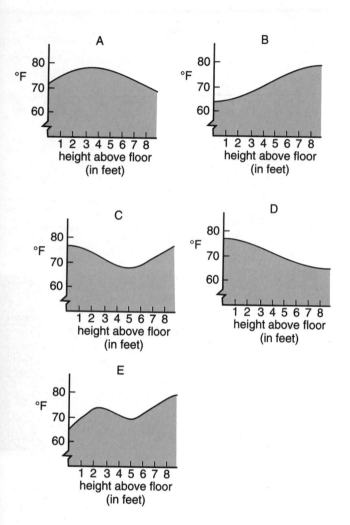

38. The pressure of a gas in a closed container can be increased by increasing the temperature of the gas or by adding more gas to the container. Which of the following *does not* utilize these properties of gas pressure?

(1) an automobile tire
(2) a sail on a sailboat
(3) a pressure cooker for use in home cooking
(4) a basketball
(5) a pressure-relief valve on a car radiator

39. An important principle of science is that matter is neither created nor destroyed during physical or chemical changes. Rather, the matter is changed from one form to another. Which of the following is *not* an example of matter changing from one form to another?

(1) boiling water changing into steam
(2) burning wood changing into ashes
(3) sugar dissolving in water
(4) the energy of a plucked guitar string changing into sound
(5) gasoline in a car engine changing into a mixture of hot exhaust gases

37. Remembering that warm air tends to rise above cold air, which of the following readings most likely represents the temperature readings taken in a room in which the doors and windows are closed?

(1) A
(2) B
(3) C
(4) D
(5) E

Questions 40–43 refer to the following passage.

The discovery that Earth acts as a giant magnet led to the development of the magnetic compass, a useful direction-finding device. The most popular type of compass consists of a magnetized needle that is in a case and is free to rotate around its center point. The needle is a type of bar magnet and has both a north pole and a south pole. You simply hold this compass in your hand and watch the needle naturally line up with the direction of Earth's magnetic field. From the direction the needle points, you can determine the direction you're traveling, or, if standing still, you can determine what direction one object is from a second object.

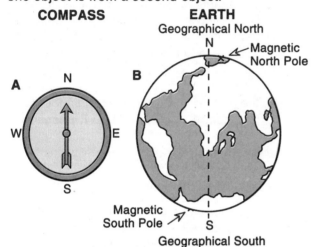

COMPASS   **EARTH**
Geographical North

Magnetic
South Pole

Geographical South

Scientists have discovered that at all points on Earth's surface, the north pole of a compass needle is attracted to and points toward Earth's north magnetic pole. The north magnetic pole—so named because it is located in the Northern Hemisphere—is a point about 1,200 miles from the north geographical pole (the northernmost point on Earth). Similarly, the south pole of a compass needle is attracted to and points toward Earth's south magnetic pole, a point located in Antarctica, about 1,200 miles from the south geographical pole (the southernmost point on Earth). Because scientists know that magnetic fields can be produced by electricity, they believe that Earth's magnetic field is caused by electric currents within Earth.

40. According to the passage, scientists believe that Earth's magnetic field is caused by

(1) deposits of magnetic rock
(2) the development of the compass
(3) the force of gravity
(4) electric currents within Earth
(5) the two magnetic poles

41. Which of the following people would have the *least* use for a compass?

(1) a mountain climber
(2) a mechanic
(3) an explorer
(4) a map maker
(5) a pilot

42. A hiker's compass is most apt to give an incorrect reading when the hiker

(1) is in a strong wind
(2) reaches the top of a high mountain
(3) walks along the shore of a large lake
(4) is in a rainstorm
(5) passes beneath electric power lines

43. Imagine that a person stands on Earth's north geographic pole and looks at his compass. The north pole of the compass needle will

(1) point toward a place that's north of where he stands
(2) point toward a place that's south of where he stands
(3) freely rotate and not point in any particular direction
(4) point straight at his feet
(5) point in any direction that he faces.

POST-TEST

Questions 44–48 refer to the following passage.

It is standard medical procedure to check a pregnant woman's blood Rh factor. The Rh factor is a protein found in the blood of about 85 percent of all people. Those who have the Rh factor are said to be Rh positive, while those who don't are said to be Rh negative.

If an Rh-negative person receives Rh-positive blood, he or she develops Rh-positive antibodies that will attack Rh-positive blood. This is usually not a problem the first time it happens because the Rh-positive blood mixes thoroughly with the Rh-negative blood before the antibodies form. However, if the person receives Rh-positive blood a second time, the result may be serious and possibly fatal. This is because antibodies are already present and attack the new blood immediately. The antibodies cause the unmixed Rh-positive blood to form clumps that can block small blood vessels.

A difficult situation may arise when a pregnant woman is Rh negative and her partner is Rh positive. Since their child inherits genes from both parents, the fetus can be either Rh positive or Rh negative. If the fetus is Rh positive, the mother's blood may develop Rh-positive antibodies, and some of these antibodies may pass into the fetus's blood. This condition occurs only when there are tiny tears in the membranes that normally keep the mother's blood completely separate from the blood of the fetus. Fortunately, this seepage of blood from mother to fetus does not occur in every pregnancy.

If Rh-positive antibodies do enter the blood of an Rh-positive fetus, the fetus becomes anemic and jaundiced and may die before (or shortly after) birth. To save the child's life at birth, his or her blood is almost entirely replaced by transfused blood. On rare occasions, blood transfusions have even been done to an endangered fetus before birth.

Even if an Rh-negative mother delivers a healthy Rh-positive baby the first time, a second baby born at a later time may be in danger. This is because the mother's blood may now contain Rh-positive antibodies produced during the first pregnancy. To avoid this problem, doctors can give a woman a shot at the time of her first delivery that will prevent her blood from developing Rh-positive antibodies during future pregnancies.

44. According to the passage, a problem pregnancy can develop when

   (1) the mother is Rh positive, the father is Rh negative, and the fetus is Rh positive
   (2) the mother is Rh negative, the father is Rh negative, and the fetus is Rh negative
   (3) the mother is Rh positive, the father is Rh positive, and the fetus is Rh positive
   (4) the mother is Rh negative, the father is Rh positive, and the fetus is Rh positive
   (5) the mother is Rh negative, the father is Rh positive, and the fetus is Rh negative

45. Before allowing a transfusion of Rh-positive blood to an Rh-negative patient, a doctor will want to check to see if the patient

   (1) has ever had a blood transfusion before
   (2) has ever had a problem pregnancy
   (3) is married to an Rh-negative person
   (4) has an Rh-negative mother and an Rh-positive father
   (5) has Rh-positive antibodies in his or her blood

46. The discovery of the importance of the Rh factor during pregnancy has most likely resulted only in

   (1) fewer pregnancies in which Rh-positive babies are born to Rh-negative mothers
   (2) a decrease in early deaths of babies born in countries where modern medical care is available
   (3) a method of stopping Rh-positive antibody production during any pregnancy
   (4) the careful screening of marriage partners by Rh-negative women
   (5) a better understanding of the effectiveness of birth control methods

47. A man who is Rh-negative is given a transfusion of Rh-positive blood. The transfusion would probably cause the man's blood to

(1) become Rh-positive
(2) become Rh-negative
(3) become neutral
(4) produce Rh-positive antibodies
(5) produce Rh-negative antibodies

48. Suppose a doctor's patient is pregnant and has Rh-negative blood. Which of the following additional items of information would the doctor need in order to plan to protect the health of the developing fetus?

(1) whether the patient has other children
(2) whether the father of her fetus is also the father of her other children
(3) whether either of the patient's parents has Rh-positive blood
(4) whether the father of her fetus is Rh positive
(5) whether the fetus is male or female

Questions 49 and 50 refer to the following information.

From person to person, differences exist in the surface proteins found in red blood cells. Because of these differences, each person can have any one of four types of blood. These four blood types are named A, B, AB, and O. The chart shows which kinds of blood transfusions are possible. A transfusion is the use of one person's donated blood in the body of a second.

BLOOD TYPES AND TRANSFUSION POSSIBILITIES		
Blood Type	Can Receive Blood from	Can Donate Blood to
A	O, A	A, AB
B	O, B	B, AB
AB	A, B, AB, O	AB
O	O	A, B, AB, O

49. According to the chart, a person with blood type B can give blood only to people of blood type

(1) B
(2) O or B
(3) AB or B
(4) O or A
(5) A or AB

50. A person who can give blood to any other type is called a universal donor. A person who receives blood from all types is called a universal recipient. With these definitions in mind, let A, B, AB, and O each stand for a person with that particular blood type. Which of the following conclusions can be drawn from the chart?

(1) A is a universal donor and AB is a universal recipient.
(2) B is a universal donor and O is a universal recipient.
(3) AB is both a universal donor and a universal recipient.
(4) O is a universal donor and AB is a universal recipient.
(5) AB is a universal donor and O is a universal recipient.

Questions 51–54 refer to the following passage.

One of the most controversial medical advances of the late twentieth century is the method of pregnancy known as surrogate motherhood. A surrogate mother is a woman who, on behalf of a couple (or a single person) desirous of a child, carries a fetus throughout pregnancy and birth. Then, immediately after delivery, the surrogate gives the child to the waiting couple.

A woman may become a surrogate mother by one of two methods. In the first method, she is artificially inseminated. A doctor uses a tube to place the man's sperm (sex cells) inside her uterus. She becomes pregnant when one of her own eggs becomes fertilized. In this type of pregnancy, the surrogate is actually the biological mother of the fetus she is carrying.

In the second method, a doctor implants a fertilized egg inside the surrogate mother's uterus. In this case the surrogate is not the biological mother of the fetus. The couple for whom she is carrying the fetus are the biological parents. The surrogate's only role is to provide the uterus in which the fetus grows until childbirth. For both methods, the surrogate is known as the birth mother because she actually carries and gives birth to the baby.

Most often, a surrogate mother is sought by a couple who, for some reason or another, are unable to have a child of their own. They choose this method of pregnancy because they desire that at least one or both of them be the biological parent of the child, even though a second woman carries the fetus. A surrogate mother may be hired, or she may be a friend or relative who volunteers her services.

Surrogate motherhood is controversial because it raises new types of issues concerned both with law and with human values. There are legal concerns about the rights of the couple, the rights of the surrogate mother, and the rights of the fetus or newborn baby. These rights are very hard to determine, especially in a situation in which either the couple or the surrogate wants to change any part of the contract or agreement concerning the child.

51. Which of the following is *not* a restatement of information presented in the passage?

   (1) A surrogate mother is unable to have children of her own.
   (2) A surrogate mother may be paid for her services.
   (3) A surrogate mother may be the biological mother of the fetus she carries on behalf of others.
   (4) A surrogate mother may be made pregnant by the implantation of a fertilized egg.
   (5) A surrogate mother may or may not be the biological mother of the fetus she carries on behalf of others.

52. When a couple hires a woman to be a surrogate mother, risks are taken by everyone involved. From the possible situations listed below, choose the one that poses the *least* risk to the surrogate.

   (1) The surrogate mother gives birth to a child with a birth defect, and the couple who hired her bring a lawsuit against her.
   (2) The couple change their minds after the pregnancy is under way and decide that they don't want a baby.
   (3) The couple refuse to pay the surrogate mother.
   (4) The surrogate mother becomes emotionally attached to the baby and does not want to give the baby up.
   (5) The child, born from a surrogate mother, may someday have difficulty adjusting to the facts surrounding his or her birth.

53. Which of the following could be a value of a couple who chooses to seek a surrogate-mother arrangement? Surrogate motherhood is

(1) against the laws of nature
(2) too risky to the health of the surrogate
(3) a reasonable option for people who can't have children
(4) against the law
(5) not fair to either mother

54. Which of the opinions voiced below is *least likely* to be expressed by people who oppose the use of surrogate mothers?

(1) Pregnancy is risky to the woman giving birth, and it is not fair to place this risk on a surrogate mother.
(2) A surrogate mother will not provide necessary prenatal care since she doesn't intend to keep the child.
(3) People who are unable to have children of their own should choose adoption rather than using a surrogate mother.
(4) A surrogate mother should be paid at least the minimum hourly wage for every hour of pregnancy.
(5) Surrogate motherhood is not a natural process and should be banned.

55. Ancient alchemists used a process called calcination to convert limestone ($CaCO_3$) into lime (CaO). The same process, which is simply the controlled heating of limestone, is still used today in the cement industry. By comparing the chemical formulas of limestone and lime, determine which of the following formulas represents the gas given off during calcination.

(1) O_2
(2) CO
(3) C_2O
(4) CO_2
(5) C_2

56. *Addiction* is the body's dependence on a drug, caused by continual use of the drug over a period of time. Which of the following is *not* an example of addiction?

(1) Lian still takes a painkiller, even though her broken arm stopped hurting two weeks ago.
(2) Sean has smoked for 23 years and now plans to quit.
(3) Richard eats an average of 4,000 calories each day he works in temperatures below freezing.
(4) Elise, hooked on heroin, is seeking treatment in a drug rehabilitation center.
(5) Feroz drinks three bottles of beer each night, but says he can stop any time he wants.

57. Large plants have a *vascular system*, a system of tubes through which plants transport water, minerals, and food to all parts of the plant: from the roots, through the stems, and throughout the leaves. Which of the following human systems is functionally most like a plant's vascular system?

(1) respiratory system
(2) reproductive system
(3) digestive system
(4) circulatory system
(5) nervous system

POST-TEST

Questions 58–61 refer to the following information.

OBSERVATIONS AT THE END OF EACH WEEK			
	First Week	*Second Week*	*Third Week*
Open Toast	No mold is observed.	Several spots of mold are observed on toast.	Mold covers much of the toast.
Enclosed Toast	No mold is observed.	No mold is observed.	Two spots of mold are observed on toast.

Bread mold is the common fungus that is often seen growing on bread and other foods. To study the factors that influence the growth of this tiny plant, Kristen, a nutritionist, planned an experiment.

In her experiment, Kristen wanted to find out if bread-mold spores (seeds) are airborne (present in and carried by air). To investigate this question, Kristen toasted a piece of bread until it was crisp, and then she quickly placed it in a jar. She immediately sealed the jar with a tightly fitting lid. She then placed another piece of crisply toasted bread in a second jar. She did not place a lid on this second jar. She placed the two jars side by side on a table and observed them for three weeks. The results of her experiment are recorded in the table above.

58. In her experiment, Kristen toasted the bread because toasting

(1) attracts bread-mold spores
(2) keeps bread from spoiling
(3) provides nutrients for bread-mold spores
(4) gives the bread a pleasant smell
(5) destroys bread-mold spores that may already be on the bread

59. The best summary of the information presented in the chart above is that

(1) bread mold forms on bread whether or not the bread is toasted
(2) bread mold forms on toast only when the toast is enclosed
(3) the rate of bread-mold growth on toast depends on exposure to fresh air, moisture, and temperature
(4) the rate of bread-mold growth on toast depends on the length of time the toast is exposed to fresh air
(5) bread mold forms on toast less quickly than it forms on bread that is not toasted

60. Which of the following is a hypothesis that is *not* supported by evidence presented on the chart?

(1) Even a temporary exposure to air can result in bread becoming contaminated with airborne bread-mold spores.
(2) Bread-mold spores grow better on bread that is not toasted because heat destroys certain nutrients.
(3) More bread-mold spores grew on the open toast than the enclosed toast because the open toast had more exposure to bread-mold spores in the air.
(4) Bread-mold spores can be made inactive and possibly destroyed by the high temperatures resulting from toasting.
(5) By increasing the number of bread-mold spores on a piece of toast, you increase the amount of mold that actually grows.

61. Assuming that bread-mold spores are present in air, which of the following experiments would provide the best evidence concerning the effect of *moisture* on bread-mold growth?

(1) Place one piece of fresh bread in a dry jar, and a second piece in a jar to which ten drops of water have been added. Seal both jars.
(2) Place one piece of fresh bread in each of two dry jars. Seal one jar and leave the second jar open.
(3) Place one piece of fresh bread in each of two dry jars. Add ten drops of water to each jar, and seal both jars.
(4) Place two pieces of fresh bread in a single dry jar and leave the jar open for two hours. Then seal the jar.
(5) Place one piece of fresh bread in each of two dry jars. Add ten drops of water to each jar and leave each jar open.

Questions 62 and 63 refer to the following information.

Rhythms are patterns of behavior that take place periodically. Communities of living organisms exhibit daily, seasonal, and annual rhythms. An example of a daily rhythm is shown by hawks and owls. Hawks are diurnal animals and hunt only during the day, while owls are nocturnal animals and hunt only at night.

Migration is a seasonal rhythm. Animals migrate to find a warmer climate and new sources of food or to find a more suitable place to nest and produce their young. For example, ducks migrate at the start of winter from Canada to regions of warmer climate nearer the equator. When the winter is over, the ducks return to Canada.

Hibernation, an annual rhythm, is a deep type of sleep that many animals go into during winter months. A true hibernating animal does not wake up during hibernation. Woodchucks and ground squirrels are true hibernators. Bears are not. Although bears sleep most of the winter, they do wake up often. Frogs, snakes, and lizards are also not true hibernators. However, they do spend their winters buried in mud, in a similar deep sleep.

62. Sleeping every afternoon is an example of

(1) a daily rhythm
(2) a seasonal rhythm
(3) an annual rhythm
(4) true hibernation
(5) a nocturnal behavior pattern

63. Which of the following is a conclusion that can be drawn from the passage?

(1) Woodchucks go hunting more often in winter.
(2) Bears sleep throughout the entire winter.
(3) Salmon migrate each year in order to breed.
(4) Ducks cannot live year-round in a cold climate.
(5) Owls migrate only at night.

Question 64 refers to the map below.

OCEAN CURRENTS OF THE WORLD

64. To which of the following studies would the map above be of *least* relevance?

(1) the study of ocean currents
(2) the science of weather prediction
(3) the study of volcanoes
(4) the study of aquatic animal migration
(5) the study of ocean navigation

Questions 65 and 66 refer to the following information.

As part of a study of the causes and effects of lead pollution in the United States, the Environmental Protection Agency compiled the data shown in the graphs below.

GRAPH A: LEAD USED IN GASOLINE

GRAPH B: AVERAGE BLOOD LEAD LEVEL IN AMERICAN ADULTS

65. Which of the following is a conclusion that is supported directly by information in either of the graphs above?

    (1) Lead is a dangerous pollutant present in exhaust gases of cars that burn leaded (regular) gasoline.
    (2) By 1980, Americans were using less than half the yearly amount of gasoline that they had used in 1976.
    (3) Government regulations were responsible for the decrease in the amount of lead used in gasoline after 1976.
    (4) By 1980, the amount of lead pollution in the environment had been reduced to less than half of its 1976 value.
    (5) By 1980, the amount of lead used in gasoline had decreased to less than half its 1976 value.

66. Which of the following facts is needed in order to establish a cause-and-effect relationship between the two graphs above?

    A. Americans bought more unleaded gasoline in 1976 than in 1980.
    B. When leaded gasoline burns, particles of lead enter the atmosphere.
    C. Lead can enter the human bloodstream when a person breathes in air.

    (1) A only
    (2) B only
    (3) A and C only
    (4) B and C only
    (5) A, B, and C

ANSWERS BEGIN ON PAGE 276.

POST-TEST

Post-Test Answer Key

1. **(4)** As shown on the graph, the surface layer is about 70°F, and the deep water is about 40°F. The thermocline is the transitional area between the two temperature regions.

2. **(2)** A volcano would be most disruptive because it would cause deep ocean water to boil, thus creating a region of hot water in what is normally a cold region of ocean. The other answer choices would do little to upset the normal pattern of ocean temperatures.

3. **(4)** Each of the other objects works by interacting with air resistance in some way, either by pushing against air or by having air push against it. Although a golf club swings through the air, air resistance does not make the club hit any harder.

4. **(2)** The passage states that blue light is scattered by air into the direction of your gaze. Thus, scattering changes the direction of movement of blue light.

5. **(2)** The passage states that scientists know how different colors of light are scattered by different types of gases in Earth's atmosphere. Knowing the types of gases that make up the Martian atmosphere would enable a scientist to determine which color (or colors) of sunlight striking Mars would be scattered. This color would be the color of the sky as seen from Mars.

6. **(3)** The spheres carry like charges and will push away from each other. This follows the principle that like charges repel and unlike charges attract.

7. **(1)** The substances that are formed appear on the right-hand side of the chemical equation. Neither CH_4 nor CO_2 has a number preceding it, so you know that when one molecule of methane burns, only one molecule of CO_2 is formed.

8. **(4)** There are an equal number of oxygen atoms on each side of the equation. You can count them; you also know that this must be true if the equation is correct.

9. **(2)** Statement B implies that the number 35,000 is based on scientific evidence resulting from tests on engines using Syn 1.

10. **(3)** Statement A can't be supported by evidence, because the Syn 1 company can't know how its oil will compare to oil you use in the future. Statement D is also an opinion: the quality of stores where Syn 1 is sold is a matter of personal opinion.

11. **(5)** A full moon in indicated by the box at the lower right-hand side of the diagram. As you can see from looking at the moon in orbit, a full moon occurs only when Earth is between the sun and the moon.

12. **(3)** Half of the moon's surface is lit by sunlight at any given point in its orbit. However, we see only part of this bright surface. As you can see from the diagram, most of the time part of the side of the moon that's facing us is sunlit and part of it is dark. The moonlight that we see must be reflected sunlight.

13. **(2)** In the first paragraph, a fault is described as a collision boundary between two moving crustal plates.

14. **(4)** According to the passage, it is impossible to predict exactly where the next major quake will strike. San Francisco and Los Angeles are at equal risk.

15. **(2)** Weather conditions are not relevant in determining earthquake danger.

16. **(2)** A purebred results from inbreeding, the mating of nearly genetically identical animals. Thus, statements A and C must be true; B and D are incorrect.

17. **(3)** The passage states that hybrids are produced to create individuals with the desirable traits of each parent. None of the other answer choices is a correct restatement of information in the passage.

18. **(4)** Hybrids are produced when members of the same species mate—members that have distinct genetic differences. Only choice (4) names these two criteria.

19. **(4)** Each of the other choices is a result of breeding two organisms that are genetically very different. Answer (4) is an example of inbreeding, not hybridization.

20. **(4)** The passage refers to each form of potential energy as stored energy and to kinetic energy as energy of motion.

21. **(4)** A bathtub drain is designed to allow water to flow down through it, a use of stored gravitational energy. Boat oars make use of stored chemical energy (food energy) in the person rowing; a fireplace uses stored chemical energy in wood; a bicycle uses energy stored in the cyclist; an engine uses the stored energy in gas.

22. **(2)** The type of energy is not important. The relevant factors are availability, cost, safety, and feasability.

23. **(3)** A camel can go for a long period of time without drinking water. It does this by storing a supply of water within its own body, an ability that enables the camel to survive in the uncertain conditions of a desert.

24. **(1)** Animals give off carbon dioxide as a waste product of their breathing process.

25. **(1)** A huge forest fire both consumes a great amount of oxygen gas and releases a great amount of carbon dioxide gas. None of the other answer choices would greatly affect the oxygen–carbon dioxide balance.

26. **(5)** When ammonia is broken down before it is converted into nitrates, the nitrogen cycle is interrupted. Nitrates are necessary for plant growth.

27. **(3)** The types of crops previously grown would have the least effect on a new crop.

28. **(2)** The fulcrum is at point A, the point that doesn't move. Point B is the load because the edge of the cap is lifted up. Point C, the handle, is the effort—the point where force is applied. The relative positions of these three points make this a second-class lever.

29. **(2)** The effort is the place where you apply force. As with the pliers, the gripped object is the load. The fixed point is the fulcrum.

30. **(4)** A chameleon lays an amniote egg and has scaly, horny skin—common characteristics of reptiles. The chameleon is a small lizard.

31. **(5)** Bat offspring are nourished from the glands of the mother bat, a type of feeding that is an identifying characteristic of mammals.

32. **(2)** A salamander is an amphibian and must return to the water to reproduce. As implied in the description, adult salamanders live on land.

33. **(4)** A killdeer flies and lays eggs, two of the main identifying characteristics of birds. Some insects also fly and lay eggs, but *insect* is not given as an answer choice.

34. **(5)** Although it lives only in water, the whale gives birth to live young and then nourishes the newborn from the glands of the mother. Whales are mammals.

35. **(1)** Because the seahorse lives only in water and lays eggs, you know it's a type of fish.

36. **(3)** The stored energy is greatest when the passenger car is at its highest point.

37. **(2)** You'd expect that a room in which the air is stagnant (not moving) would have a temperature distribution such as that shown in graph B: the lower temperature air would be near the floor and the higher temperature air near the ceiling, with a smooth transition region in between.

38. **(2)** Only the sail on the sailboat is not an example of an object that has something to do with either gas being added to a closed container or an enclosed gas being heated.

39. **(4)** The guitar string stops moving because energy changes from one form to another. Each of the other answer choices deals with *matter* changing from one form to another.

40. **(4)** The last paragraph of the passage states that scientists believe that Earth's magnetic field is caused by electric currents within Earth.

41. **(2)** Of the people listed, a mechanic would have the least concern about the accuracy of directions. Each of the others would need to have an accurate compass.

42. **(5)** Because the passage states that magnetic fields can be produced by electricity, it is reasonable (and correct) to conclude that strong magnetic fields may surround electric power lines. These fields interfere with the proper working of a compass.

43. **(2)** When you stand on the north geographic pole, every other point on Earth is south of you, including the north magnetic pole.

44. **(4)** Answer (4) is a correct restatement of information contained in the second paragraph of the passage. None of the other alternatives is correct.

45. **(5)** A transfusion of Rh-positive blood to an Rh-negative patient could be made in an emergency situation as long as the recipient did not have Rh-positive antibodies in his or her blood. None of the other answers is relevant to the danger that this type of transfusion may involve.

46. **(2)** Discovery of the Rh-factor problem has led to medical treatment of affected babies. It has not resulted in a cure available for a woman's first pregnancy, any change in how people choose mates, or a better understanding of birth control.

47. **(4)** When Rh-positive blood is introduced into the body of an Rh-negative person, Rh-positive antibodies form.

48. **(4)** The doctor will want to check the father's blood to see if he is Rh positive. If he is, the doctor will want to be prepared to take steps to protect the fetus throughout pregnancy and birth.

49. **(3)** Look for B in the "Blood Type" column. If you follow the row for type B, you see that type B can donate blood only to type B or type AB.

50. (4) Only O can give blood to all of the other types, while only AB can receive blood from all of the other types.

51. (1) Choice (1) is false, since some surrogate mothers bear children of their own. When a woman is artificially inseminated, the fetus grows from one of her eggs. All of the other answer choices are true and are restatements of information presented in the passage.

52. (5) Only choice (5) is not a direct risk to the surrogate. This is a potential problem that the parents who raise the child may face.

53. (3) People who seek a surrogate-mother arrangement are likely to believe that they are making a reasonable choice.

54. (4) People who oppose the use of surrogate mothers do so for all reasons except answer (4). Choice (4) indirectly places a monetary value on human life, a position that would be unpopular morally and ethically.

55. (4) By comparing the chemical formula $CaCO_3$ with the formula CaO, you can see that one C atom and 2 O atoms are given off. Therefore, CO_2 is the gas that is given off.

56. (3) Eating 4,000 calories while working in freezing conditions may be a reasonable amount of food for these conditions. Each of the other choices describes an addiction.

57. (4) In the human body, the circulatory system carries oxygen and nourishment to all of the body's cells.

58. (5) To see if bread-mold spores come from air, Kristen had to first eliminate any spores that might be present on the bread she used. She toasted the bread to kill or deactivate any spores on it.

59. (4) Only choice (4) is a summary of information obtained from the chart. Choice (2) is false. The other choices may also be true, but the chart itself does not provide any supporting evidence.

60. (2) Only choice (2) is a hypothesis for which no supporting evidence is available on the chart. The chart says nothing about untoasted bread.

61. (1) Only choice (1) gives evidence in which moisture is the only variable that differs when comparing one bread sample with the other.

62. (1) An activity that takes place every day is a daily rhythm.

63. (4) Ducks go south for the winter, so it is reasonable to conclude that they could not live year-round in a cold climate. The passage says nothing about the migration of salmon or owls, so choices (3) and (5) are wrong.

64. (3) Ocean currents are not likely to have much bearing on volcanic activity.

65. (5) Graph A shows this decline. Answer choices (1), (3), and (4) are true, but no information about exhaust gases, government regulations, or forms of lead pollution (other than lead used in gasoline) is given in either graph. Answer (2) is not true and cannot be inferred as true from either graph.

66. (4) Both statements B and C are needed to establish a cause-and-effect relationship between the two graphs. The graphs show a decline in the average amount of lead in Americans' blood at the same time that the usage of lead in gasoline declined. Knowing B, you can reasonably conclude that less lead in gas results in less lead in the atmosphere. Knowing C, you can reasonably conclude that less lead in the atmosphere results in less lead in human blood.

Post-Test Evaluation Chart

Use the answer key on pages 276–278 to check your answers to the Post-Test. Then find the item number of each question you missed and circle it on the chart below to determine the reading skill and content areas in which you need more practice. Pay particular attention to areas where you missed half or more of the questions. The reading skills are covered on pages 17–79. These skills are absolutely essential for success on the GED Science Test. The numbers in boldface are questions based on graphics. For those questions that you missed, review the skill pages indicated.

Skill Area/ Content Area	Comprehension	Application	Analysis	Evaluation
Plant & Animal Biology (pages 81–111)	17, 24, **59**	19, 23, 25, 30, 31, 32, 33, 34, 35, 57, 62	18, 26, 47, 48, **58**, **60**, 61, 63	16, 27
Human Biology (pages 113–143)	**49**, 51	56	44, 45, **50**, **66**	46, 52, 53, 54
Earth Science (pages 145–173)	**1**, **11**, 13		**2**, **12**, 14	15, **64**
Chemistry (pages 175–211)	7, 8, 9, 55, **65**		10	
Physics (pages 213–251)	4, 20, **29**, **40**	3, **6**, 21, **28**, **38**, **39**, **41**, **43**	**37**, **42**	5, 22, **36**

PRACTICE TEST ANSWER GRID

1 ① ② ③ ④ ⑤   23 ① ② ③ ④ ⑤   45 ① ② ③ ④ ⑤

2 ① ② ③ ④ ⑤   24 ① ② ③ ④ ⑤   46 ① ② ③ ④ ⑤

3 ① ② ③ ④ ⑤   25 ① ② ③ ④ ⑤   47 ① ② ③ ④ ⑤

4 ① ② ③ ④ ⑤   26 ① ② ③ ④ ⑤   48 ① ② ③ ④ ⑤

5 ① ② ③ ④ ⑤   27 ① ② ③ ④ ⑤   49 ① ② ③ ④ ⑤

6 ① ② ③ ④ ⑤   28 ① ② ③ ④ ⑤   50 ① ② ③ ④ ⑤

7 ① ② ③ ④ ⑤   29 ① ② ③ ④ ⑤   51 ① ② ③ ④ ⑤

8 ① ② ③ ④ ⑤   30 ① ② ③ ④ ⑤   52 ① ② ③ ④ ⑤

9 ① ② ③ ④ ⑤   31 ① ② ③ ④ ⑤   53 ① ② ③ ④ ⑤

10 ① ② ③ ④ ⑤   32 ① ② ③ ④ ⑤   54 ① ② ③ ④ ⑤

11 ① ② ③ ④ ⑤   33 ① ② ③ ④ ⑤   55 ① ② ③ ④ ⑤

12 ① ② ③ ④ ⑤   34 ① ② ③ ④ ⑤   56 ① ② ③ ④ ⑤

13 ① ② ③ ④ ⑤   35 ① ② ③ ④ ⑤   57 ① ② ③ ④ ⑤

14 ① ② ③ ④ ⑤   36 ① ② ③ ④ ⑤   58 ① ② ③ ④ ⑤

15 ① ② ③ ④ ⑤   37 ① ② ③ ④ ⑤   59 ① ② ③ ④ ⑤

16 ① ② ③ ④ ⑤   38 ① ② ③ ④ ⑤   60 ① ② ③ ④ ⑤

17 ① ② ③ ④ ⑤   39 ① ② ③ ④ ⑤   61 ① ② ③ ④ ⑤

18 ① ② ③ ④ ⑤   40 ① ② ③ ④ ⑤   62 ① ② ③ ④ ⑤

19 ① ② ③ ④ ⑤   41 ① ② ③ ④ ⑤   63 ① ② ③ ④ ⑤

20 ① ② ③ ④ ⑤   42 ① ② ③ ④ ⑤   64 ① ② ③ ④ ⑤

21 ① ② ③ ④ ⑤   43 ① ② ③ ④ ⑤   65 ① ② ③ ④ ⑤

22 ① ② ③ ④ ⑤   44 ① ② ③ ④ ⑤   66 ① ② ③ ④ ⑤

Science Practice Test

This Science Practice Test will give you a second opportunity to evaluate your readiness for the actual GED Science Test.

This test contains 66 questions. Some of the questions are based on short reading passages, and some of them require you to interpret a chart, graph, or diagram.

You should take approximately 95 minutes to complete this test. At the end of 95 minutes, stop and mark your place. Then finish the test. This will give you an idea of whether or not you can finish the real GED Test in the time allotted. Try to answer as many questions as you can, choosing the best of five answer choices and blackening in the grid. A blank will count as a wrong answer, so make a reasonable guess for questions you are not sure of.

When you are finished with the test, turn to the evaluation chart on page 301. Use the chart to evaluate whether you are ready to take the actual GED Test and, if not, what areas need more work.

Questions 1 and 2 refer to the following drawings.

Fraternal Twins

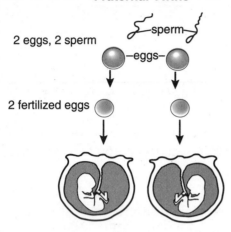

2 eggs, 2 sperm

sperm

eggs

2 fertilized eggs

2 genetically-different individuals who develop within separate fetal sacs.

Identical Twins

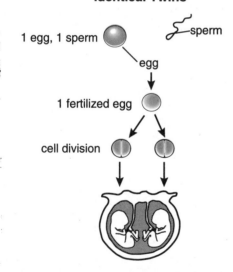

1 egg, 1 sperm

sperm

egg

1 fertilized egg

cell division

Cell division results in 2 genetically-identical individuals who develop in the same fetal sac.

1. From which fact can you deduce that Gary's twin brother Frank is Gary's fraternal twin?

   (1) Both Frank and Gary are teachers.
   (2) Frank's ears have a different shape from Gary's ears.
   (3) Frank weighs about thirty pounds more than Gary.
   (4) Frank and Gary each have fraternal twin daughters.
   (5) Frank and Gary are about the same height.

2. Which of the following characteristics is *least likely* to be shared by identical twins?

   (1) height
   (2) weight
   (3) eye color
   (4) shoe size
   (5) gender (male or female)

   ───────────────

3. In physics, *work* is defined as a process in which force is applied to an object with the result that the object moves. Which of the following activities would a physicist classify as work?

   (1) attempting to lift a rock that won't budge
   (2) mentally subtracting 194 from 331
   (3) swinging a bat but missing the ball
   (4) watching the Super Bowl on television
   (5) trying unsuccessfully to open a jar of jam

Questions 4 and 5 refer to the following passage.

Many animal behavior patterns are unlike those of humans. However, many of these behaviors hold clues for scientists who seek to improve human health. One behavior of great medical interest today is the squirrel's ability to hibernate.

Scientists know that when a squirrel hibernates, its bodily functions slow down. At the same time, the blood flow to the squirrel's brain almost ceases—a condition that would lead immediately to a stroke in humans. Without a continual supply of blood, human brain cells break down and die. These cells are not replaced, and permanent disability or death can result. The question is, why don't the brain cells of squirrels die during hibernation?

A clue may be found in the human brain, where a lack of blood causes brain cells to lose potassium and to gain calcium. Cells affected in this way surely die. By studying changes in the potassium and calcium levels in a hibernating squirrel's brain, scientists hope to discover what protects the squirrel. Understanding this, doctors someday may be able to help prevent strokes in some patients and to help stroke victims recover more fully.

4. According to the passage, which of the following can cause a stroke in a human?

   (1) a diet overly rich in calcium
   (2) an inability to hibernate
   (3) permanent disability or death
   (4) too little potassium in the blood
   (5) a restricted blood flow to the brain

5. Which is a hypothesis that is supported by information given in the passage?

   (1) Squirrels do not suffer strokes because they are able to replace dead brain cells.
   (2) The brain cells of a squirrel break down during hibernation but the squirrel is not harmed.
   (3) The brain cells of a squirrel do not contain potassium and calcium.
   (4) A squirrel's brain safely regulates its own cells' potassium and calcium levels during hibernation.
   (5) A dead brain cell can be brought back to life by injecting it with potassium.

Questions 6 and 7 refer to the following drawing.

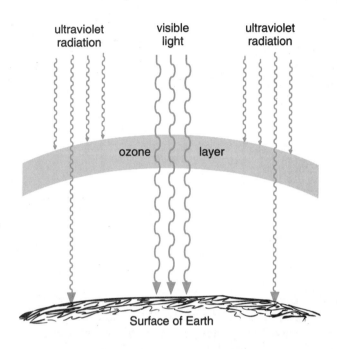

Surface of Earth

6. Which of the following is the best summary of information provided in the drawing above?

   (1) The ozone layer absorbs most ultraviolet radiation and visible light that strike it.
   (2) The ozone layer absorbs most ultraviolet radiation that strikes it but allows visible light to pass through.
   (3) The ozone layer protects Earth from all harmful effects of visible light.
   (4) The ozone layer protects Earth from all harmful effects of ultraviolet radiation.
   (5) Both ultraviolet radiation and visible light are present in sunlight.

7. If the ozone layer were partially destroyed by air pollutants, the most likely result would be

   (1) a decrease in the amount of visible light that reaches Earth's surface
   (2) an increase in the amount of visible light that reaches Earth's surface
   (3) a decrease in the amount of ultraviolet radiation that reaches Earth's surface
   (4) an increase in the amount of ultraviolet radiation that reaches Earth's surface
   (5) no change in the amount of ultraviolet radiation that reaches Earth's surface

PRACTICE TEST

Questions 8–10 refer to the following drawing and information.

DAYTIME CLOUDS   **NIGHTTIME CLOUDS**

sunlight

heat

Earth's surface   Earth's surface

Earth's surface is heated by sunlight. During the day, clouds stop much of this light from reaching the surface. Because of this, cloudy days are cooler than clear days. However, clouds in the night sky stop heat radiating off the warmed surface from escaping into space. Nighttime clouds form a protective blanket that keeps cloudy nights warmer than clear nights.

8. Clouds have a major effect on air temperature because of their ability to

   (1) reflect heat-producing light rays
   (2) absorb heat-producing light rays
   (3) transmit heat-producing light rays
   (4) reflect cold-producing light rays
   (5) absorb cold-producing light rays

9. During the winter, which of the following sky conditions produce the warmest nights?

   (1) partially cloudy day and partially cloudy night
   (2) cloud-covered day and cloud-covered night
   (3) clear day and cloud-covered night
   (4) cloud-covered day and clear night
   (5) partially cloudy day and cloud-covered night

10. Desert regions of Earth seldom are cloudy. Because of this, you can expect a desert temperature pattern to be characterized by

   (1) hot dry days and cold rainy nights
   (2) hot dry days and warm dry nights
   (3) hot rainy days and cold dry nights
   (4) hot dry days and cold dry nights
   (5) hot rainy days and cold rainy nights

Questions 11–13 refer to the following drawing and information.

THREE PHASES OF WATER (H₂0)

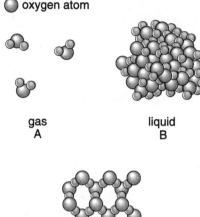

○ hydrogen atom

⬤ oxygen atom

gas
A

liquid
B

solid (ice)
C

As a gas (water vapor), H_2O molecules are widely separated, being much farther apart on the average than H_2O molecules in water or ice. Unlike most other liquids, though, water expands when it freezes. As water forms ice, H_2O molecules form a lattice-like structure in which they are farther apart than H_2O molecules in water.

11. Suppose you compare equal volumes of water vapor, liquid water, and ice. From heaviest to lightest, how do the weights of these three phases of water compare?

   (1) water heaviest, ice next, water vapor lightest
   (2) ice heaviest, water next, water vapor lightest
   (3) water vapor heaviest, ice next, water lightest
   (4) water heaviest, water vapor next, ice lightest
   (5) ice heaviest, water vapor next, water lightest

12. Which of the following is explained by the fact that H_2O molecules are farther apart in ice than in water?

   (1) Heat energy is needed to melt ice.
   (2) Ice sinks in water.
   (3) Ice is hard enough to break a tooth if you chew it.
   (4) Ice floats on water.
   (5) Water transmits light better than ice.

13. To quickly cool a bottle of soda pop, Jenny placed it in the freezer at noon. She forgot about the glass bottle until 6:00 P.M. When she opened the freezer, she found the bottle in pieces. Which of the following is the best explanation of what happened?

   (1) Lowering the temperature of glass below freezing causes glass to break.
   (2) The soda pop froze more quickly than the bottle.
   (3) The water vapor in the freezer expanded as it froze and crushed the bottle.
   (4) As the bottle froze, the glass expanded until it broke.
   (5) The soda pop expanded as it froze and broke the bottle.

PRACTICE TEST

14. *Electrolysis* is the use of an electric current to break down a substance into its component molecules. Electrolysis can be used to break down water (H_2O) into its two component gases—oxygen (O_2) and hydrogen (H_2).

    Remembering that the number of atoms of each element must be the same on both sides of a reaction equation, decide which equation below correctly describes the electrolysis of water.

    (1) $H_2O \longrightarrow H_2 + O_2$
    (2) $2H_2O \longrightarrow 2H_2 + O_2$
    (3) $3H_2O \longrightarrow 3H_2 + 2O_2$
    (4) $4H_2O \longrightarrow 4H_2 + O_2$
    (5) $5H_2O \longrightarrow 4H_2 + 4O_2$

15. *Adaptive radiation* refers to the pattern in which different species develop from a common ancestor in different ways. Which of the following pairs would *not* be a good example of adaptive radiation?

    (1) a giraffe and a frog
    (2) a deer and an elk
    (3) a shark and a salmon
    (4) a duck and a chicken
    (5) a horse and a zebra

16. *Convergent evolution* refers to the pattern in which unrelated organisms become alike in some features as they adapt to similar environments in similar ways. Which of the following pairs is *not* a good example of convergent evolution?

    (1) a whale (a mammal) and a bass (a fish)
    (2) a bat (a mammal) and a robin (a bird)
    (3) a penguin (a bird) and a seal (a mammal)
    (4) a cow (a mammal) and an alligator (a reptile)
    (5) a giraffe (a mammal) and an ostrich (a bird)

Question 17 refers to the following drawing.

A PARTIAL SOLAR ECLIPSE
(seen from Earth)

Dashed line indicates that part of the moon that cannot be seen from Earth.

17. Which of the following occur during a partial solar eclipse?

    A. The sun is partially blocked from view.
    B. The moon passes between Earth and the sun.
    C. The sun passes between the moon and Earth.
    D. The amount of sunlight reaching Earth decreases.

    (1) A and B only
    (2) A and C only
    (3) B and D only
    (4) C and D only
    (5) A, B, and D only

Question 18 refers to the following drawing.

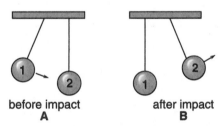

before impact   after impact
A   B

18. *Kinetic energy* is energy possessed by a body in motion. *Potential energy* is energy that is stored or is available for use. Which of the following statements explains the role that energy plays in the interaction shown above?

    (1) Kinetic energy is transferred from ball 1 to ball 2 at the time of impact.
    (2) Kinetic energy is transferred from ball 2 to ball 1 at the time of impact.
    (3) Potential energy is transferred from ball 1 to ball 2 at the time of impact.
    (4) Potential energy is transferred from ball 2 to ball 1 at the time of impact.
    (5) All kinetic energy is changed to potential energy at the time of impact.

Questions 19–22 refer to the following passage.

Gravity is a force of attraction that exists between any two objects in the universe. When you stand on a scale, the weight you measure is the force of attraction between your body and Earth. Your body pulls on Earth, while Earth pulls on your body. The scale measures the force that pulls you and Earth toward each other. When you throw a ball into the air, gravity (the force of attraction between the ball and Earth) pulls the ball back to the ground.

The strength of gravity depends upon the mass of each of the two objects: the larger each mass, the stronger the gravitational pull. The mass of an object is the amount of the material an object is made of. For example, the larger you are, the more mass you have and the more you weigh. You notice your weight (your attraction to Earth) because Earth's pull on you is very strong, due to Earth's huge size. When you throw a ball, there is also a gravitational force between you and the ball. However, you do not notice this force because your mass and the ball's mass are both very small.

The strength of gravity decreases as two objects move farther apart. When you climb a mountain, you increase your distance from the center of Earth. Because of this, you weigh less on the mountaintop than on the seashore. This difference is too little to notice, however. You have increased your distance from the center of Earth by only a very, very small percent—much too small to cause a noticeable change in weight.

19. Which of the following determine the strength of the gravitational attraction between two objects?

   A. the speed of each object
   B. the mass of each object
   C. the distance separating the objects
   D. the shape of each object

   (1) A and B only
   (2) A, B, and C only
   (3) B and C only
   (4) B, C, and D only
   (5) A, B, C, and D

20. While on the surface of the moon, astronauts noticed that they could jump much higher than back home on Earth. What can you conclude from this discovery?

   (1) The moon is at a very great distance from Earth.
   (2) Earth's gravity is not felt very strongly on the moon.
   (3) Earth has less mass than the moon.
   (4) The moon has less mass than Earth.
   (5) The moon has no atmosphere.

21. Electrons are negatively charged particles that circle an atom's positively charged nucleus. The gravitational force between the electrons tries to pull the electrons together. However, a repulsive *electrostatic force* between each pair of electrons keeps them widely separated from each other.

   Which of the following can you conclude about the electrostatic and gravitational forces acting on two electrons?

   (1) The repulsive electrostatic force is weaker than the attractive gravitational force.
   (2) The attractive electrostatic force is weaker than the repulsive gravitational force.
   (3) The repulsive electrostatic force is stronger than the attractive gravitational force.
   (4) The attractive electrostatic force is stronger than the repulsive gravitational force.
   (5) The electrostatic force and the gravitational force are the same strength.

22. Between which pair of objects is the gravitational force the strongest?

   (1) a bowling ball and a golf ball six feet apart
   (2) a baseball and a golf ball three feet apart
   (3) a bowling ball and a golf ball three feet apart
   (4) a baseball and a golf ball six feet apart
   (5) a bowling ball and a Ping-Pong ball three feet apart

Questions 23–25 refer to the following graph and information.

BLOOD PRESSURE OF CAROLYN McCARTHY

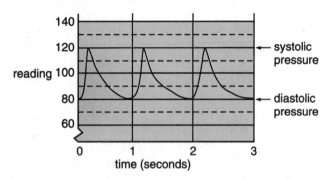

The human heart is like a pump whose job it is to force blood through arteries. One measure of how hard a heart is working is a *blood pressure reading*. A blood pressure reading such as 130/90 measures the pressure that blood exerts against the walls of a person's arteries during the heartbeat cycle. The first number (130), the *systolic pressure*, is the point of highest blood pressure, measured just as the heart beats. The second number (90), the *diastolic pressure*, is the point of lowest blood pressure, measured just before the heart beats. A rise in blood pressure can occur due to strenuous physical activity or can be caused by an illness or disease that causes the heart to work harder than normal.

The graph above records Carolyn McCarthy's blood pressure for three complete heartbeat cycles.

23. What is Carolyn McCarthy's blood pressure reading shown on the graph?

   (1) 80/120
   (2) 90/130
   (3) 120/40
   (4) 120/80
   (5) 130/90

24. What was Carolyn McCarthy's heartbeat rate (beats per minute) at the time this blood pressure reading was taken?

   (1) forty-five beats per minute
   (2) sixty beats per minute
   (3) seventy-five beats per minute
   (4) ninety beats per minute
   (5) one hundred five beats per minute

25. Hardening of the arteries (arteriosclerosis) is most prevalent among elderly patients. Arteries become less flexible and less able to carry blood, causing the heart to work harder during each beat. Which of the following most likely happens to a person's blood pressure when hardening of the arteries occurs?

   (1) Both systolic and diastolic pressures increase.
   (2) Both systolic and diastolic pressures decrease.
   (3) Systolic pressure increases while diastolic pressure decreases.
   (4) Diastolic pressure increases while systolic pressure decreases.
   (5) Systolic and diastolic pressures remain unchanged.

26. Buoyancy is the tendency of an object to float in a liquid or rise in a gas. Each of the following objects is designed to make use of the buoyancy principle except a

   (1) submarine
   (2) hot-air balloon
   (3) life preserver
   (4) parachute
   (5) canoe

Questions 27–31 refer to the following information.

The octopus was once considered a solitary animal with little ability to learn by observing other octopuses. However, learning-theory scientists have revised this opinion because of the results of a recent experiment.

In the experiment, one group of octopuses was trained to attack a red ball. Another group was trained to attack a white ball. Meanwhile, two groups of untrained octopuses watched: one group watched the red-ball tank; the other watched the white-ball tank. When both red and white balls were placed in the tanks with the untrained octopuses, each group attacked only the color of ball as did the group it had watched. Although octopuses have the largest brain of any invertebrate, this result surprised many scientists. This social learning skill had been considered to be beyond the ability of an octopus.

The statements in questions 27–31 can be classified into one of these five categories:

an experiment—a procedure used to investigate a problem

a finding—an experimental result obtained or a conclusion reached as part of the investigation

a hypothesis—a reasonable, but not proved, explanation of an observed fact

a prediction—an opinion about something that may occur in the future

a nonessential fact—a fact that does not directly help the researcher understand the problem being investigated

27. Octopuses that observed a red ball being attacked chose to attack a red ball themselves.

     This statement is best classified as a(n)

   (1) experiment
   (2) finding
   (3) hypothesis
   (4) prediction
   (5) nonessential fact

28. An octopus has a soft, oval body and eight arms and lives mostly at the bottom of the ocean.

     You should classify this statement as a(n)

   (1) experiment
   (2) finding
   (3) hypothesis
   (4) prediction
   (5) nonessential fact

29. With further research, scientists will find that octopuses have a wide range of learning abilities as yet undiscovered.

     This statement is best classified as a(n)

   (1) experiment
   (2) finding
   (3) hypothesis
   (4) prediction
   (5) nonessential fact

30. To see if octopuses can learn by observation, untrained octopuses were allowed to watch trained octopuses attack colored balls.

     This statement is best classified as a(n)

   (1) experiment
   (2) finding
   (3) hypothesis
   (4) prediction
   (5) nonessential fact

31. The observational learning ability of an octopus most likely arose from its need to learn from other octopuses at an early age, since an octopus's parents die when it is hatched.

     You should classify this statement as a(n)

   (1) experiment
   (2) finding
   (3) hypothesis
   (4) prediction
   (5) nonessential fact

Questions 32–36 refer to the following passage.

AIDS (Acquired Immune Deficiency Syndrome) is a disease of the body's immune system—the system that enables the body to destroy germs that cause infections and illness. The first symptoms of AIDS may be weight loss, swollen lymph nodes, body weakness, persistent cough, and chronic yeast infections of the mouth or genital areas. Other symptoms may include pneumonia or a type of cancer characterized by the presence of purplish spots. Eventually, an AIDS patient may develop life-threatening infections and cancers that usually don't affect people with normal immune systems.

AIDS is caused by a virus known as HIV, the Human Immunodeficiency Virus. Once infected with HIV, a person may feel fine and show no symptoms of AIDS for years. However, even though an "HIV-positive" person looks healthy, he or she *is* infectious and can transmit this virus to other people. The HIV virus spreads from the blood of an infected person to the blood of the uninfected. And, because blood cells are present in semen and other body fluids, the HIV virus can spread during sexual activity.

AIDS is most commonly spread in one of three ways:

• by having unsafe sex with an infected person

• by sharing a needle with an infected drug user

• from an infected mother to the fetus during pregnancy or to the baby during delivery or breast-feeding

At present there are treatments for many of the symptoms of AIDS, but there is no cure for AIDS. You can, though, protect yourself from AIDS. You do this by making intelligent choices about sex partners and drugs. A high percentage of AIDS patients are people who have had unsafe sex with more than one partner and people who have shared needles during drug use.

32. AIDS is a disease of the

(1) respiratory system
(2) nervous system
(3) immune system
(4) skeletal system
(5) reproductive system

33. According to the passage, AIDS can spread from an infected person to an uninfected person during each of the following *except*

(1) drug use
(2) sexual activity
(3) childbirth
(4) breast feeding
(5) swimming

34. Each word or phrase below correctly describes AIDS *except*

(1) curable
(2) preventable
(3) most often fatal
(4) transmittable by people
(5) slowly developing

35. From information given in the passage, you can infer that a healthy immune system can protect a person against

(1) sexually transmitted diseases
(2) all types of immune-system viruses
(3) all types of infectious diseases
(4) some types of infectious diseases
(5) blood contaminated with the HIV virus

36. To help prevent the possible spread of AIDS in a dental office, a dentist should take each of the following reasonable steps *except*

(1) wearing of disposable plastic gloves
(2) refusing to do dental work that causes gums to bleed
(3) disinfecting all dental instruments before use with each patient
(4) placing blood-soaked items in a plastic bag for safe disposal
(5) washing his or her hands with soap and water before seeing each new patient

37. Each of the following shows a relationship between electricity and magnetism *except* the fact that

   (1) the needle of a magnet deflects when the magnet is near a lighted lamp
   (2) an electric current flows through a coiled wire while a magnet is moved near the coil
   (3) the needle of a magnet points in the wrong way when the magnet is beneath electric power lines
   (4) a stereo speaker sounds fuzzy when a strong magnet is moved near it
   (5) a 12-volt battery causes twice as much current to flow through a light bulb as does a 6-volt battery

38. Glacial rock deposits found on the eastern coast of South America are almost identical to deposits found on the west coast of Africa. Which of the following hypotheses is best supported by this discovery?

   (1) South America and Africa were formed at about the same time.
   (2) Glacial rock deposits were carried from Africa to South America by early explorers.
   (3) Glacial rock deposits floated from Africa to South America.
   (4) During the last ice age, glaciers formed near the poles and moved toward the equator.
   (5) South America and Africa were once part of the same land mass.

39. Which of the following measurements would enable a scientist to compute the speed at which light travels through space?

   A. measuring the distance between Earth and the moon
   B. measuring the time between sunrise and sunset
   C. measuring the time it takes the moon to revolve around Earth
   D. measuring the time it takes for light to travel from Earth to the moon and back

   (1) A and C only
   (2) A and D only
   (3) B and C only
   (4) D only
   (5) C and D only

PRACTICE TEST

Questions 40 and 41 refer to the following drawing.

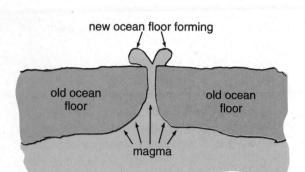

Question 42 is based on the following drawing.

40. According to the drawing above, new ocean floor results from

  (1) magma forcing its way down through a crack in the old ocean floor
  (2) magma forcing its way up through a crack in the old ocean floor
  (3) magma forming from minerals deposited in ocean water
  (4) the change of old ocean floor into magma
  (5) erosion of underwater mountains due to the flow of magma

41. The process in which new ocean floor is formed is most like what process that takes place on Earth's surface?

  (1) earthquake
  (2) soil erosion
  (3) volcanic eruption
  (4) tornado
  (5) avalanche

42. The Sierra Nevada mountains in the western United States are fault-block mountains. Knowing this, you can conclude that the fault lines beneath these mountains

  (1) spread apart as they run deeper beneath Earth's surface
  (2) close together as they run deeper beneath Earth's surface
  (3) stay the same distance apart as they run deeper beneath Earth's surface
  (4) alternately spread apart and close together as they run deeper beneath Earth's surface
  (5) cross each other beneath Earth's surface

Questions 43–45 refer to the following passage.

An *aurora* is a magnificent display of colored light that appears occasionally in the night sky. Auroras are seen most often in regions around the North Pole and South Pole. Called *Northern* or *Southern Lights*, auroras are caused by electrically charged particles from space colliding with air molecules in Earth's upper atmosphere.

The stream of fast moving, charged particles that cause an aurora comes from the sun. Called a *solar wind*, this stream is created when hot gas storms occur on the sun's surface. These storms, known as *solar flares*, emit highly energetic particles into space. As the resulting solar wind approaches Earth, its particles are guided toward the poles by Earth's magnetic field. A glowing curtain of colored light results.

43. According to the passage, what is an aurora?

   (1) a flow of electrically charged particles from the sun
   (2) the guidance property of Earth's magnetic field
   (3) a luminous display in the sky seen at night
   (4) gas molecules in the upper atmosphere
   (5) a solar storm that emits electrically charged particles

44. What is the most reasonable conclusion you can draw about a year in which there was an above-average number of auroras?

   (1) The number of solar storms was above average.
   (2) The number of severe winter storms on Earth was above average.
   (3) The average distance between Earth and the sun was less than normal.
   (4) An above-average number of people living in southern states reported seeing auroras.
   (5) More auroras occurred that year at the North Pole than at the South Pole.

45. Which of the following conclusions is *not supported* by information given in the passage?

   (1) Earth's magnetic field is strongest near the North Pole and South Pole.
   (2) Air molecules that are struck by electrically charged particles can emit light.
   (3) Violent gas storms occur on the sun's surface.
   (4) Electrically charged particles race from the sun at the speed of light.
   (5) Residents of Alaska are more apt to see an aurora than residents of Florida are.

———

46. A basketball is dropped from point A as shown in the drawing below. The ball hits the floor, rises to point C, and then drops again. The ball is momentarily motionless when its center is across from points A, B, and C.

At what point is kinetic (motion) energy and gravitational potential (stored) energy equal for the basketball?

   (1) point A
   (2) point B
   (3) point C
   (4) halfway between point A and point B
   (5) halfway between point A and point C

Questions 47 and 48 are based on the following information.

In an advertisement, a pharmaceutical company makes the following claims about their new pain reliever.

A. Doctors who know their stuff prefer Pain Blocker to any other pain relief medicine on the market today.

B. Pain Blocker contains no aspirin.

C. Pain Blocker tastes great.

D. Pain Blocker has FDA approval for use with children.

47. Which of the above claims requires chemical analysis to check for accuracy?

(1) A only
(2) B only
(3) C only
(4) D only
(5) B and C only

48. Which of the above claims are most likely based on opinion rather than fact?

(1) A and C only
(2) A and D only
(3) B and C only
(4) B and D only
(5) C and D only

49. Suppose the fossils of several types of extinct fish are found in the cliffs of an inland mountain. Which of the following are the two most reasonable hypotheses that might explain this discovery?

A. Prehistoric humans ate the fish and later moved to these cliffs, where they died.
B. The fish was a type of flying fish that flew to this mountain and died.
C. Birds carried the remains of the fish to these cliffs.
D. These cliffs were once under water.

(1) A and C
(2) A and D
(3) B and C
(4) B and D
(5) C and D

50. *Transpiration* is a process in which a plant loses water through tiny pores called *stomata*, located on the undersides of its leaves. Transpiration cools the plant and helps ensure a continual flow of mineral-rich water up the stem. Which of the following serves humans in a similar way?

(1) taste buds
(2) hair follicles
(3) sweat glands
(4) fingernails
(5) skin cells

51. Each of the following is designed to use the reflection property of light *except*

(1) a mirror
(2) a camera lens
(3) high-gloss paint
(4) car wax
(5) a ceiling light

Questions 52–54 refer to the following information.

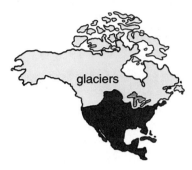

glaciers

For unknown reasons, Earth passes through periods called *ice ages*, when much of its surface is covered with huge sheets of ice called *glaciers*. During an ice age, which may last several hundred thousand years, the average temperature on Earth drops about 6°C lower than the average temperature today. Land formations are forever changed and whole species of animals and plants die out.

The period between ice ages are warm periods called *interglacials*. The average temperature of an interglacial is about 3°C higher than the average temperature today.

52. Which of the following is the most likely sign that an ice age is coming to an end?

    (1) a decrease in Earth's average temperature
    (2) the formation of huge glaciers
    (3) the movement of glaciers
    (4) the drifting apart of the continents
    (5) the melting of glaciers

53. Which of the following is a hypothesis that attempts to explain why an ice age begins?

    (1) The next ice age may begin within the next million years.
    (2) Variations in the distance between Earth and the sun may lower Earth's temperature.
    (3) An ice age may have been responsible for the extinction of dinosaurs.
    (4) An ice age is a time during which much of Earth's surface is covered with ice.
    (5) During the last ice age, the average temperature of Earth was about 6°C lower than it is today.

54. The total amount of water (both liquid water and ice) on Earth has changed very little, if at all, since Earth first formed. Which of the following conclusions logically follows from this fact?

    During an ice age,

    (1) there is mainly snow and very little rain
    (2) there is mainly rain and very little snow
    (3) the oceans totally freeze
    (4) ocean levels are higher than they are today
    (5) ocean levels are lower than they are today

55. When sunlight is absorbed by an object, the absorbed energy causes the object to warm up. Knowing that dark-colored objects absorb more sunlight than light-colored objects, which of the following conclusions is most reasonable?

    On a hot sunny day, you'll keep coolest by

    (1) wearing dark-colored clothes and staying out of direct sunlight
    (2) wearing light-colored clothes and staying in direct sunlight
    (3) wearing dark-colored clothes and staying in direct sunlight
    (4) wearing light-colored clothes and staying out of direct sunlight
    (5) wearing a light-colored jacket over dark-colored clothes and staying out of direct sunlight

Questions 56–60 refer to the following passage.

A plant is commonly referred to according to its characteristic features and life cycle. Five types of plants are described below.

Annuals. Annuals produce flowers, fruits, and seeds each year. At the end of the growing season, the plant dies and only the seeds survive until the next year. New plants grow from the seeds that germinate the next year.

Vegetable biennials. Vegetable biennials are vegetables that have a two-year life cycle. The seeds germinate the first year. Roots, a short stem, and leaves also form. In the second year, the stem grows. Flowers, fruits, and seeds are produced. Vegetable biennials are usually harvested during their first year of growth.

Flower biennials. Flower biennials have the same characteristics as the vegetable biennials listed above. The distinguishing difference between the two types of biennials is that flower biennials are known for their flowers and are not harvested as food.

Herbaceous perennials. Herbaceous perennials are plants that live for more than two growing seasons. The roots of these perennials grow slowly during the winter and produce new shoots each spring. Herbaceous perennials are foliage-like (soft and leafy) and do not contain wood.

Woody perennials. Woody perennials also live for more than two growing seasons. But, unlike herbaceous perennials, woody perennials stop growing during the winter. They resume their growth in the spring. Woody perennials are characterized by stiff wooden trunks and branches.

56. A peony is a small plant that has large showy flowers. Peonies are a favorite yard flower and resurface year after year once they're planted, although the above-ground part of the plant dies at the end of each growing season. Peonies belong to the group called

   (1) annuals
   (2) vegetable biennials
   (3) flower biennials
   (4) herbaceous perennials
   (5) woody perennials

57. The foxglove has drooping purple and white flowers and leaves that are used to produce the heart medication called digitalis. Foxglove has a two-year life cycle but is not harvested for human consumption. Foxglove is best placed in the group known as

   (1) annuals
   (2) vegetable biennials
   (3) flower biennials
   (4) herbaceous perennials
   (5) woody perennials

58. An apple tree lives for many years, producing blossoms and apples each year. Because of its long life and strong wooden trunk and branches, the apple tree is in the group known as

   (1) annuals
   (2) vegetable biennials
   (3) flower biennials
   (4) herbaceous perennials
   (5) woody perennials

59. The pea plant is a very popular vegetable that is harvested in great quantity for human consumption. The seeds of the plant, commonly called peas, must be planted each year to start new plants. The rest of the plant dies at the end of each growing season. The pea plant belongs in the group known as

(1) annuals
(2) vegetable biennials
(3) flower biennials
(4) herbaceous perennials
(5) woody perennials

60. Carrots, unlike pea plants, have a two-year life cycle. However, carrots are usually harvested for consumption during their first year of growth. Carrots belong to the group called

(1) annuals
(2) vegetable biennials
(3) flower biennials
(4) herbaceous perennials
(5) woody perennials

61. Humus is a dark-colored material that is made up of the decaying remains of dead plants and animals. Each of the following would be a good use of humus *except* as part of a

(1) planting mixture
(2) garden fertilizer
(3) subsoil for a yard
(4) walking path
(5) food supply for home-grown worms

62. *Diffusion* is a process by which the atoms or molecules of one substance penetrate into a second substance. Each of the following is an example of diffusion *except*

(1) freezing meat
(2) evaporating water
(3) soaking up spilled pop with a paper towel
(4) putting cream in coffee
(5) using air freshener

63. A heat pump is a process or a machine that transfers heat from a first object, which is cooled, to a second object, which is heated. Which of the following operates on the principle of a heat pump?

(1) a fan
(2) a stove
(3) a refrigerator
(4) a fireplace
(5) an automobile engine

Questions 64–66 refer to the following circle graphs.

DAILY CALORIE CONSUMPTION

Current American Diet

Recommended American Diet

64. Which suggestion is the best summary of the recommended dietary changes shown on the graphs above?

(1) Eat less carbohydrates and more fat.
(2) Eat less protein and more carbohydrates.
(3) Eat less fat and more protein.
(4) Eat less fat and more carbohydrates.
(5) Eat less carbohydrates and more protein.

65. What assumption is most likely made by a person who decides to change his or her diet as recommended by the graphs above?

(1) These dietary changes are recommended only for overweight people.
(2) These dietary changes are recommended only for underweight people.
(3) The graphs resulted from a scientific study that related eating habits to good health.
(4) Food costs will not increase if the recommended dietary changes are made.
(5) The recommended dietary changes will result in the eating of fewer calories at each meal.

66. What information would you need to know in order to determine whether eating a 350-calorie cheeseburger or a 350-calorie fish sandwich best follows the recommended dietary changes?

A. the fat content of each sandwich
B. the carbohydrate content of each sandwich
C. the weight of each sandwich

(1) A only
(2) A and B only
(3) A and C only
(4) B and C only
(5) A, B, and C

ANSWERS BEGIN ON PAGE 299.

Practice Test Answer Key

1. **(2)** Ear shape is inherited, and a difference in ear shape indicates a difference in genetic makeup. This fact tells you that Frank and Gary are fraternal twins.

2. **(2)** Of the choices listed, only weight is something that the twins have some control over (by choosing their own diets). Height, eye color, foot size, and gender are not under personal control.

3. **(3)** Even though you miss the ball, you do work when you swing the bat. None of the other listed activities describe moving an object.

4. **(5)** You can infer from the second paragraph that if blood flow to a human brain is restricted, a stroke (death of brain cells) can occur.

5. **(4)** Paragraph 3 tells you that it is the loss of potassium and increase of calcium that causes brain cells to die. Choice (4) is a hypothesis that explains how a squirrel's brain cells might be protected during hibernation by preventing this loss.

6. **(2)** The drawing indicates that most of the ultraviolet radiation does not pass through the ozone layer, but visible light does. Choice (2) puts in words what the picture shows.

7. **(4)** Choice (4) is a logical conclusion. A thinner ozone layer would allow more ultraviolet radiation to pass through. This is happening today and explains the worldwide concern about protecting the ozone layer.

8. **(1)** As the drawing indicates, clouds reflect much of the heat-producing light rays that strike them.

9. **(3)** A clear day allows the land surface to warm, while a cloudy night helps keep the warm land from radiating heat back into space.

10. **(4)** Without clouds, sunlight warms the land during the day, and the warm land radiates the heat back into space at night, causing cold nights. The lack of clouds creates dryness.

11. **(1)** Water is heaviest because it is the densest. The illustration shows the molecules closely packed together. Water vapor is the lightest because its molecules are farthest apart, as shown in the illustration.

12. **(4)** Ice floats because a given volume of ice weighs less than the same volume of water. Ice is not as dense as water.

13. **(5)** This has happened to just about everyone. Most drinks are mainly water, and water expands as it freezes and easily breaks a glass container.

14. **(2)** Only equation (2) gives an equal number of hydrogen atoms (four) on each side of the reaction equation as well as an equal number of oxygen atoms (two).

15. **(1)** A giraffe is a mammal, while a frog is an amphibian. Of all the pairs of animals listed, these two are the least likely to have developed from a common ancestor. Each other pair has similar characteristics.

16. **(4)** Each pair of animals listed has something in common except a cow and an alligator. For example, in choice (1) both animals have fins and tails used for swimming. In choice (5), both animals have developed long necks for help in finding food.

17. **(5)** Statement C is wrong; the sun never passes between Earth and the moon. Each of the other statements is correct.

18. **(1)** At the moment of impact, ball 1 has all kinetic energy and ball 2 has potential energy. After impact, ball 2 has all the kinetic energy and ball 1 has none. Kinetic energy is transferred from ball 1 to ball 2 at the moment of impact.

19. **(3)** According to the passage, the strength of gravity depends only upon two things: the mass of each object and the distance separating the objects.

20. **(4)** The astronauts weigh less on the moon because the moon has less mass than Earth. The mass of the astronauts, though, is the same on the moon as it is on Earth.

21. **(3)** Because the electrons are held apart, you can conclude that the repulsive electrostatic force is stronger than the attractive gravitational force.

22. **(3)** To make such a comparison, choose the two heaviest objects the least distance from each other.

23. **(4)** As shown on the graph, the first number (the systolic pressure) is 120, while the second number (the diastolic pressure) is 80.

24. (2) Since three complete beats occur in a three-second time interval, you can conclude that Carolyn's heart rate is one beat per second, or sixty beats per minute.

25. (1) Since each reading (systolic and diastolic) is related to how hard the heart is working, you can conclude that both values will increase any time the heart is forced to work harder, as happens with hardening of the arteries.

26. (4) With the exception of a parachute, each object listed is designed either to float in a liquid or to rise in a gas.

27. (2) This is something the scientists observed.

28. (5) This is an interesting fact but has nothing to do with this particular experiment.

29. (4) This statement is a prediction that only time will prove to be correct or incorrect. It is not a hypothesis because it does not attempt to explain a finding.

30. (1) This statement tells what the scientists actually did as an experiment.

31. (3) This statement is a hypothesis because it attempts to explain where the newly discovered learning ability of the octopus actually came from or how it arose.

32. (3) AIDS causes a breakdown in the immune system's ability to respond to disease.

33. (5) There is no indication that the HIV virus can be transmitted during swimming.

34. (1) At present AIDS is not curable. However, ongoing medical research is investigating a number of possible approaches to developing a cure for AIDS.

35. (4) A healthy immune system does protect against some but not all infectious diseases. An example of an infectious disease that the immune system can't prevent entirely is the common cold.

36. (2) Because almost all dental work involves some bleeding around the gums, choice (2) is not a reasonable step.

37. (5) Each of the choices except (5) illustrates a particular interaction between electric and magnetic phenomena.

38. (5) Choices (1) and (4) do not explain the similarity between the separate continents. Choices (2) and (3) are implausible. Only choice (5) is a reasonable hypothesis that explains the similarity of two separate land masses.

39. (2) A scientist would need to know the distance between Earth and the moon and the time it takes for light to travel from Earth to the moon. By dividing the total distance light travels by the time of travel, a scientist can determine the velocity of light: velocity = distance ÷ time

40. (2) Choice (2) says in words what the drawing shows: magma moves upward through a crack in the old ocean floor.

41. (3) In a volcano, magma moves up through a crack in Earth's surface. New land is formed as magma (now lava) pours out of a volcano.

42. (1) As the drawing shows, fault lines along the edges of a fault-block mountain spread apart as they run deeper beneath Earth's surface.

43. (3) This choice is a restatement of the first sentence of the selection.

44. (1) According to the passage, an aurora is directly related to the presence of solar storms.

45. (4) Each choice except (4) can be inferred from information given in the passage. The passage does say the solar wind is fast moving but says nothing about the speed of light.

46. (4) At points A, B, and C, the ball is motionless and has no kinetic energy. Only when the ball is halfway between point A and B is half of its energy kinetic and half potential.

47. (2) Only a chemical analysis of Pain Blocker can confirm that it contains no aspirin.

48. (1) Statements A and C are opinions that can't be proved true or false. Statements B and D are alleged facts that can be checked.

49. (5) It is more likely that birds, rather than humans, carried fish to the cliffs where they then ate them. Statement B is highly unlikely. Statement D is highly probable.

50. (3) Sweat glands enable a human to lose water from his or her body surface in order to cool down during hot weather and during exercise.

51. (2) A camera lens is designed to make use of the refraction property of light, the bending of light as it travels from one medium to another. Each of the other choices uses the reflection property.

52. (5) Only the melting of glaciers signals a warming trend, an end to an ice age. None of the other choices shows a warming of Earth.

53. (2) Only choice (2) is a hypothesis that explains the conditions that might have caused an ice age. The other choices are predictions or facts that do not explain why ice ages occur.

54. (5) The ocean is the main reservoir of water on Earth, and during an ice age ocean levels decrease as glaciers form.

55. (4) Light-colored clothes are always the coolest when you're outdoors. To stay the coolest, you are also advised to stay out of direct sunlight.

56. (4) Peonies grow year after year, a characteristic of perennials. They are herbaceous because they are soft and leafy flowers and do not contain wood.

57. (3) With a two-year life cycle, foxglove is a biennial. As a flower that is not eaten, it is classified as a flower biennial.

58. (5) An apple tree has a wood trunk and wooden branches. Because it grows year after year, it is a woody perennial.

59. (1) Since the pea must be replanted each year, it is classified as an annual.

60. (2) Because carrots have a two-year life cycle and they are eaten, they are classified as vegetable biennials.

61. (4) Humus tends to be wet, gooey, and slippery, not the kind of surface typical of a walking path.

62. (1) When meat freezes, it loses heat, and its molecules slow down. However, no diffusion takes place. In each of the other choices diffusion occurs.

63. (3) A refrigerator operates on the principle of a heat pump. It takes heat from food placed in it and transfers this heat to the room in which the refrigerator is sitting.

64. (4) Choice (4) says in words what the graph recommends. Notice that protein consumption is the same on both graphs.

65. (3) The person assumes, though the graphs do not specify, that these graphs are based on scientific studies of healthful diets.

66. (2) The weight of the sandwich depends very much on water content and so is not a determining factor. Each of the other choices alone would not be enough to make a determination.

Practice Test Evaluation Chart

Use the answer key on pages 299–301 to check your answers to the Practice Test. Then find the item number of each question you missed and circle it on the chart below to determine the reading skill and content areas in which you need more practice. Pay particular attention to areas where you missed half or more of the questions. The reading skills are covered on pages 17–79. These skills are absolutely essential for success on the GED Science Test. The numbers in boldface are questions based on graphics. For those questions that you missed, review the skill pages indicated.

Skill Area/ Content Area	Comprehension	Application	Analysis	Evaluation
Plant & Animal Biology (pages 81–111)		15, 16, 27, 50, 56, 57, 58, 59, 60, 61	5, 49	28, 29, 30, 31
Human Biology (pages 113–143)	4, **23**, **24**, 32, 33, 34, 35		**1**, 25	**2**, 36
Earth Science (pages 145–173)	**6**, **8**, **40**, 43	**9**, **41**	7, **10**, **17**, 38, **42**, 44, **52**, **53**, 54	45
Chemistry (pages 175–211)	14, **64**		**11**, **12**, **13**, 48, **65**	47, **66**
Physics (pages 213–251)	**18**, 20, 39	3, 22, 26, 51, 55	19, 21, 46, 62, 63	37

PRACTICE TEST

Answer Key

CHAPTER 1: COMPREHENDING SCIENCE MATERIALS

EXERCISE 1
page 19

1. **(2)** Answers (1) and (3) are both mentioned, but they are details.
2. **(3)** All three paragraphs discuss how scientists are trying to find life on distant planets.

EXERCISE 2
page 20

(4) The passage does not discuss any of the issues mentioned in choices (1), (2), (3), or (5). Choice (4) is a restatement of facts from the first two sentences of the passage.

EXERCISE 3
page 22

1. **(1)** Paper is represented by the largest piece of the circle.
2. **(3)** Glass (10 percent) + metals (8 percent) make up 18 percent (10 percent + 8 percent) of the solid waste produced in the United States.
3. **(2)** To find 12 percent of 100 pounds, multiply as follows: $\frac{12}{100} \times 100 = 12$ pounds.
4. **(3)** Only answer choices (2) and (3) relate to information found on the graph, and choice (3) is the only fact that supports the author's argument.

EXERCISE 4
page 24

Only statements 1, 3, 5, and 8 should be checked.

EXERCISE 5
page 25

1. **(4)** Answer (4) is the only detail actually given in the passage. Answer (1) is not true, and (2) is an opinion.
2. **(3)** Only rain is mentioned as the way that pesticides enter groundwater.

EXERCISE 6
page 26

1. A transparent object lets most of the light pass through it. Only a small part of the light is reflected or absorbed. Examples include glass and water.

2. An opaque object allows no light to pass through it. Light is either absorbed, reflected, or both. Examples include wood and metal.

EXERCISE 7
page 27

1. **(4)** According to the drawing, precipitation includes "snow, rain, hail, etc." Each of these falls to Earth.
2. **(5)** On the drawing, the word *evaporation* is used with forms of moisture that are returning to the atmosphere (shown by arrows pointing upward).
3. **(3)** The best answer choice is (3) because all of the other processes described are details.

EXERCISE 8
page 28

1. The author thinks quite highly of robots.
2. The author implies that a robot costs less than an employee.
3. You can infer that the work done by a robot is as good as or better than work done by a regular employee.
4. You can infer that the author is an owner. Assembly-line workers are not enthusiastic about losing their jobs to robots.

EXERCISE 9
page 29

1. **(3)** The author is not proud of how humans have treated Earth. All of the other choices represent the author's attitude correctly.
2. **(5)** The author is expressing concerns about all life on Earth, the concerns most often voiced by environmental protection groups.
3. **(2)** The passage points to species that have become extinct by human actions. Based on this, you can infer that the main point is that human actions can help save life on Earth or help destroy it.

EXERCISE 10
page 31

1. **(1)** The point on the line above 20 minutes corresponds to a temperature almost midway between 40° and 60°. The best answer would be 48°.
2. **(4)** The point on the data line directly to the right of 32°F lies between the 40- and 50-minute point.
3. **(3)** At 50 minutes, the water is partially, but not completely, frozen.

CHAPTER 2: APPLYING SCIENCE CONCEPTS

EXERCISE 1
page 34

2, 4, 5 Numbers 1 and 3 are not inherited traits.

EXERCISE 2
page 34

1, 2, 4 Numbers 3 and 5 relate to heat but not to expansion or contraction.

EXERCISE 3
page 35

1. (5) The passage defines a vestigial organ as an organ that seems to have no purpose.
2. (3) Because the tailbone has no known use, it is considered a vestigial organ. Each other organ mentioned has a use of some kind, although the use may be limited.
3. (2) Iron at 212°F is the densest (heaviest) material listed and is at the highest temperature, both conditions that contribute to a high speed of sound.
4. (5) Sound needs air or some other medium through which to travel. Vacuumlike conditions exist between Earth and space.

EXERCISE 4
page 37

1. (5) The relationship is commensal because the beetles nutritionally benefit but do not harm the ants.
2. (3) The relationship is parasitic because the fungus harms the chestnut tree as it takes nutrients from it.
3. (2) The relationship is saprophytic because the bacteria take nutrients from the remains of dead organisms.
4. (1) The relationship is predator-prey because the lioness kills and eats another organism.
5. (4) The relationship is mutualistic because both fungus and algae benefit from living together as a lichen.

EXERCISE 5
page 38

1. (3) You would need to know the purpose of animal migrations in order to answer the question correctly.
2. (3) The Rocky Mountains are far from the ocean, so the tide would not affect them.

EXERCISE 6
page 39

1. (2) The nuclear waste issue is considered to be one of the most important issues facing the nuclear industry today. It is frequently discussed on TV and in newspapers.
2. (4) Reducing the amount of money spent on acid rain research only prolongs the problem; it does not help reduce it.
3. (2) Of the choices listed, explosion of rocket fuel has proved to be the main danger to astronauts; it was the cause of the destruction of the space shuttle *Challenger* in 1986.
4. (3) Dressing warmly may help you recover more quickly, but each of the other choices directly helps you keep from spreading the cold virus.
5. (5) Where the liquid was purchased has nothing whatever to do with deciding on an antidote—a doctor's chief concern.

EXERCISE 7
pages 40-41

1. (3) Molars are used for the hard chewing required to adequately soften a piece of cut steak.
2. (1) Incisors are used for biting things off food held outside the mouth.
3. (2) Most people automatically try to bite a piece of string with their canine teeth.
4. (4) Molars are at the back of the mouth; therefore, they would be the hardest to clean.
5. (2) Of the choices listed, a wet highway is the place where a thin film of water is most likely to form. The reflection of sunlight off a wet highway is particularly dangerous to drivers.
6. (4) Furniture polish is applied as a thin film on a furniture surface, causing a shiny look.
7. (3) Both glass and a thin film of water have a smooth surface, which is why you can see your reflection in them.
8. (3) Both ceilings and walls of most rooms are coated with rough plaster, the purpose of which is to spread ceiling and lamplight evenly into all parts of each room.

CHAPTER 3: ANALYZING SCIENCE MATERIALS

EXERCISE 1
page 44

1. O
2. F
3. H
4. F
5. O
6. H
7. F

EXERCISE 2
page 44

Answers may vary.
1. Fact: One possible answer is that a home computer can perform thousands of calculations each second.

2. Hypothesis: One possible answer is that based on what is already known about computers, scientists believe that the human mind stores and sorts information in the same way a computer does.
3. Opinion: One possible answer is that a thinking computer would be a great benefit to our society.

EXERCISE 3
page 45

1. **(3)** Only answer (3) is a fact. Answers (1) and (2) are predictions, and (4) and (5) are not correct.
2. **(5)** Only answer (5) is a hypothesis. Answers (1) and (3) are facts, and answers (2) and (4) are opinions.
3. **(2)** There is evidence available to support each of the other choices. Only (2) is a personal belief that is not supported by fact.

EXERCISE 4
page 47

1. **(2)** Only answer choice (2) is supported by the graph. Of the specific causes named, the cancer bar is second in height only to the heart disease bar.
2. **(1)** Only (1) is an opinion that can't be proved. Each of the other answer choices is a fact.
3. **(4)** Only answer choice (4) is a reasonable explanation of an observed fact.

EXERCISE 5
pages 48-49

Answers may vary.
1. The writer assumes that life exists on one or more other planets.
2. The astronaut assumes that unmanned spacecraft can't do an adequate job and that some information will be obtained through space travel.
3. Rhoda assumes that cold water will freeze more quickly than warm or hot water.
4. People assume that these drugs work and that there will be no serious side effects.
5. Doctors assume that there is always a chance that a medication may harm a developing fetus.
6. Astrologers assume that the positions of stars and planets can tell us something about human beings.

EXERCISE 6
page 49

Statements 1 and 4 would need to be true if Jerry is correct. Statements 2 and 3 are simply facts, and 5 is irrelevant.

EXERCISE 7
page 50

1. **(3)** To support nuclear power, a person would have to believe that a safe disposal method for radioactive waste will someday be invented.

2. **(1)** Choice (1) is the most reasonable because many of the problems of storing radioactive waste, such as leaking storage drums, have become known only in recent years. The dangers of radioactive materials of any kind have been known about for a much longer time.
3. **(5)** B, C, and D all support the opinion that nuclear power plants should be closed, while reason A does not.

EXERCISE 8
page 52

1. c
2. e
3. b
4. a
5. d

EXERCISE 9
page 53

1. An increase in temperature could result in the evaporation of Earth's oceans.
2. A decrease in temperature could result in the freezing of Earth's oceans.

EXERCISE 10
page 53

1. **(5)** Of the answer choices, only the death of tropical forests is a direct effect of an ice age. Answer (2) is not an effect—it is part of the definition of what an ice age is.
2. **(2)** Only answer (2) is a cause that could have brought about the end of the Mesozoic era. Each of the other answers is related to the Mesozoic era, but none of these answers is a cause.
3. **(4)** According to the passage, dinosaurs died because of the death of the tropical forests, the lush vegetation that was their food supply.

EXERCISE 11
page 54

1. Tooth was not properly brushed.
2. Bacteria in plaque eats through tooth enamel.
3. Cavity exposes nerve in tooth.
4. Bacterial infection reaches tooth root.

EXERCISE 12
page 55

1. **(3)** The purpose of a solar panel is to capture sunlight energy and use it as needed to heat a building.
2. **(2)** The pump is the only part of the system that controls fluid circulation.
3. **(1)** As shown in the drawing, the heat exchanger warms the air that passes next to it.
4. **(3)** The solar panel is not heated by sunlight at night. So, you can infer that the heat storage device is used as the source of heat at night.

EXERCISE 13
page 57

Only choice 1 should be checked.

EXERCISE 14
page 57

1. **(3)** Of the choices given, only answer (3) is a general rule that is both practical and reasonable.
2. **(5)** Only answer (5) is a conclusion that follows directly from the observation and your knowledge that a burning candle consumes oxygen.

EXERCISE 15
page 59

1. moderate breeze
By looking in the "What Happens" column, you can see that both types of gales would be too strong for children to play in.
2. gale
During a gale, tree branches break.
3. strong gale

EXERCISE 16
page 60

1. **(2)** Comparing diameters, you see that the diameter of Venus is closest to that of Earth.
2. **(3)** The comparative size of Earth is found in the column that gives the diameter (distance across) of each planet.
3. **(5)** Hydrogen and helium are the elements out of which the four largest planets are made.
4. **(1)** The planets with the longest days rotate (spin) most slowly.
5. **(4)** A small arrow indicates that the exercise ended after 3 minutes.
6. **(3)** As shown on the graph, the greatest distance between the two line graphs occurs just before the exercise is over.
7. **(5)** By the three-minute point, student A's heart rate has leveled out at 170 beats per minute. You can reasonably infer that this rate would continue during two more minutes of exercise.
8. **(1)** An hour after quitting the exercise, student A's heart rate would most likely return to its normal before-exercise level of 70 beats per minute.
9. **(4)** If two students exercise at different rates, differences in heart rates are to be expected. In this case you would be unable to compare physical condition, which is not as dependent upon students being the same sex, height, age, or upon time of day.

CHAPTER 4: EVALUATING SCIENCE MATERIALS

EXERCISE 1
page 64

All the choices except 2 and 5 relate to smoking but not to the health risks involved.

EXERCISE 2
page 65

1. **(3)** Only answer (3) mentions a legal definition of being too drunk to drive.
2. **(4)** Any car could have a burned-out headlight, regardless of whether or not the driver was drunk.
3. **(2)** You determine that light, the faster of the two, will reach you more quickly.

EXERCISE 3
page 66

1. from north to south
2. from west to east
3. **(3)** Volcanic eruptions have nothing to do with prevailing winds.

EXERCISE 4
page 67

1. **(4)** Beaks for capturing fish and sieving would be found on birds that obtain food from water sources.
2. **(1)** Both insect-eating and tearing beaks are used by birds for attacking small land animals.
3. **(4)** The beak designed for seed eating (D) belongs to birds adapted to a diet of land plants.
4. **(5)** Sieving is used to take tiny, often-invisible food particles from the water. Each of the other beaks is designed for grabbing visible foods.
5. **(5)** The brain size of a bird has nothing to do with its beak structure.

EXERCISE 5
page 68

(3) Two animals that eat the same foods often must live in different parts of a forest.

EXERCISE 6
page 69

1. **(2)** Only choice (2) gives a link between a high-fat diet and a known health risk.
2. **(4)** Only choice (4) links the man's weight to his health by a medical opinion, given by the doctor's recommendation.
3. **(4)** Gasoline will float on water only if the two liquids are not miscible and if water has a greater density than gasoline.

4. (5) For alcohol to float on oil, alcohol and oil can't be miscible, and the density of alcohol must be less than that of oil.

EXERCISE 7
page 71

Only numbers 1, 4, 6, 8, and 9 should be checked.

EXERCISE 8
page 72

1. (4) Only choice (4) is true for both drawings A and B.
2. (5) The teeter-totter will balance only when the weight of each child is the same. To determine if this is the case, you need to know the weight of each child.

EXERCISE 9
page 73

1. Betty must choose between her religious values and the value she places on having children.
2. Jay had to choose between his political values and the value he places on his job.
3. Rosario must choose between the value she places on a clean environment and the value she places on saving money.

EXERCISE 10
page 76

1. a. identify a problem
  b. collect information
  c. form a hypothesis
  d. perform experiments
  e. draw conclusions
2. to have a second group of plants with which to make a comparison as the treated plants grew
3. If only one plant grew in each planter, it would not be possible to establish a reliable pattern of differences.

EXERCISE 11
pages 76-77

1. (3) The brick and the paper clip fall at the same rate, as do the rock and the paper clip.
2. (4) Although the leaf and the paper clip are about the same weight, the leaf has a much larger surface. The difference in amount of surface might account for the difference in rate of falling.
3. (5) Wanda must drop two very light objects: one that has a small surface (the spoon) and one that has a large surface (the paper).
4. (4) Since the moon has no air, it also must have no air resistance. However, unlike the space shuttle, the moon does have gravity.

EXERCISE 12
page 78

1. (5) Choice (5) is the best because it describes the use of both a control group and an experimental group. Choices (1) and (2) do not use different size cages for each group of mice. Therefore, in these two designs no comparative information could be obtained.
2. (3) Answer choice (3) is the best. If he gets the same results with new groups of mice, he can be pretty sure that his hypothesis is correct. Using the same number of mice ensures that crowding will occur again in the smaller cage.
3. (1) The most relevant evidence would come from studies of people who live in crowded conditions similar to those of the crowded mice.
4. (3) Of the locations mentioned, an indoor shopping mall is most likely to have crowds of people who might panic in the event of a fire.

CHAPTER 5: PLANT AND ANIMAL BIOLOGY

EXERCISE 1
page 82

1. d   **4.** e
2. c   **5.** b
3. a

EXERCISE 2
pages 82-83

Comprehension
1. (3) The two paragraphs point out a variety of life forms living their daily lives.

Analysis
2. (1) While it's true that frogs eat insects, it is only an opinion that frogs are more important to humans than are worms.
3. (5) The meat in the control jar must be kept away from flies for the experiment to give conclusive results.
4. (4) Choice (3) is incorrect because the meat will rot whether inside or outside the jar. The cloth keeps flies from landing on the meat and laying eggs, so (4) is correct.

Evaluation
5. (2) Redi needed to start the experiment with meat that did not already contain fly eggs, or his experiment would have failed.

EXERCISE 3
page 85

1. growth   **4.** death
2. decline   **5.** maturity
3. beginning

EXERCISE 4
page 85

Comprehension
1. **(5)** This is stated directly in the passage.

Analysis
2. **(2)** Animals that are slow to respond to stimuli that warn of danger are not likely to live long.

Evaluation
3. **(4)** Only answer (4) deals with the instinct for survival, an important difference between an animal and a puddle.

EXERCISE 5
page 88

1. **a.** The roots anchor the plant and obtain water and minerals from the soil.
   b. The stem holds up the leaves and transports water to them.
   c. The leaves carry on photosynthesis (food production).
   d. The flower contains the reproductive structures.
2. **a.** stamen: produces pollen
   b. stigma: collects pollen
   c. style: moves pollen from stigma to ovary
   d. ovary: contains female sex cell; fertilization here leads to seed
   e. pollen: protects and moves male sex cell to female part of flower
3. Your answer should include any two: bees, butterflies, hummingbirds.
4. **a.** T
   b. F
   c. F

EXERCISE 6
page 89

Application
1. **(2)** The Venus's-flytrap responds to an insect's touch, an example of touch response.
2. **(5)** The best answer is circadian rhythm. These flowers open and close in twenty-four-hour cycles.
3. **(3)** The roots grow in the direction of gravity, an example of positive geotropism.
4. **(1)** The sunflower moves to follow the sun, an example of phototropism.
5. **(4)** Even though buried upside down, the plant's stem has turned upward, away from the direction of gravity.

EXERCISE 7
page 91

1. **1.** b   **4.** a
   2. e   **5.** d
   3. c

2. Animals' defenses help protect them from natural predators.

EXERCISE 8
pages 92-93

Comprehension
1. **(1)** Only choice (1) accurately sums up the main idea of the passage. Choices (2), (3), and (5) are only details, and (4) is not true.

Analysis
2. **(4)** If a hive is attacked, the worker bees sting the aggressor and then die. In this case, the bear is the aggressor.

Evaluation
3. **(3)** Choice (3) is true and is unlike any human social group, even a military unit. All the other choices are true of both humans and insects.

Comprehension
4. **(4)** Choices (2) and (5) are also true, but choice (4) best summarizes the point of the passage: the surprising intelligence level of chimpanzees.

Comprehension
5. **(3)** Scientists assume and believe that chimpanzees have learned tool-making skills on their own.

Evaluation
6. **(5)** Only by making detailed observations of chimpanzees in the wild were scientists able to discover this amazing animal's tool-making abilities.

EXERCISE 9
page 95

1. d   **4.** c
2. a   **5.** b
3. e

EXERCISE 10
page 96

Comprehension
1. **(5)** Cell walls are not found in animal cells.
2. **(2)** According to the passage, chromosomes, which contain hereditary information, are formed from chromatin during cell division.

Application
3. **(3)** It is chloroplasts that are used by green plants for photosynthesis.

EXERCISE 11
page 98

1. **F**   **4.** T
2. **T**   **5.** T
3. **F**

EXERCISE 12
page 98

Comprehension

1. (4) All organisms start life as a single cell.

Evaluation

2. (5) Only the type of cell will tell the cell's function. Choice (4) is not correct because an organ contains many types of tissues.

EXERCISE 13
page 101

1. Heredity
2. chromatin, nucleus
3. gene
4. two
5. chromosomes

EXERCISE 14
pages 101-102

Comprehension

1. (4) Only choice (4) is a correct summary of information given in the passage. Choice (1) is true, but it is a detail.

Application

2. (2) Of the various pairs, only choice (2) is a pair of animals that aren't similar in body shape and behavior.

Evaluation

3. (1) Identical twins have the same genetic makeup. If they were put in different environments, it would be easier to determine which traits are inherited and which are not.

Analysis

4. (4) All plants with at least one *T* gene are tall. Therefore, the *T* gene is dominant.
5. (4) Taking the four possible combinations of the two gene sets *Tt* and *Tt*, you get *TT*, *Tt*, *Tt*, and *tt*. Notice that we've written the capital *T* before the small *t*. You could also write *Tt* as *tT*.

EXERCISE 15
page 104

1. c   **4.** a
2. e   **5.** d
3. b

EXERCISE 16
page 105

Analysis

1. (2) With a limited food source, many frogs would die. And, with the death of its predator—the frog—the grasshopper population would increase.
2. (4) Population increases only when more organisms are born each year than die.

Evaluation

3. (5) Each of answers (1) through (4) will directly affect the bass in Waldo Lake.

EXERCISE 17
page 107

1. c   **4.** a
2. e   **5.** b
3. d

EXERCISE 18
pages 108-109

Comprehension

1. (2) Choice (2) is a summary of Darwin's theory. Choices (1) and (3) are not true. Choice (4) is a detail.

Analysis

2. (4) If the land animals are scarce, being able to capture water animals would be the most useful survival trait.

Evaluation

3. (1) A beak is most useful for capturing food, so choice (1) is correct.

Evaluation

4. (5) Only choice (5) deals with how organisms may change over long periods of time, the main idea of Darwin's theory of evolution.

Evaluation

5. (4) Darwin would say that both humans and chimpanzees have evolved, most likely from a common ancestor—given the similarity of our features.

Application

6. (1) Only choice (1) is a t. hat an animal might have some control over. by jumping a lot, a frog might strengthen its legs.

Evaluation

7. (4) If there was not much vegetation close to the ground, a giraffe would need to hunt high in trees for vegetation.

GED PRACTICE: PLANT AND ANIMAL BIOLOGY
pages 110-111

Analysis

1. (3) The first step in Oparin's theory involves the breakdown of methane and other gases in the atmosphere.

Analysis

2. (2) Besides being present as a pure gas, hydrogen is a component of each of the other three main gases.

Comprehension

3. (4) Nothing in the passage indicates that Oparin had either plant or animal cells in mind—only organisms in general.

Evaluation

4. (1) Oparin's theory hypothesizes how life may have started from *nonliving* substances.

Comprehension

5. (4) Distinctly different stages of development is the true feature of metamorphosis.

Analysis

6. (3) To live on land and breathe air, a frog must have lungs.

Analysis

7. (5) Choice (1) is true but has nothing to do with metamorphosis, and choice (3) is true of both species. Choices (2) and (4) are not true. Butterflies have an inactive or quiet stage before adulthood, frogs do not, choice (5).

CHAPTER 6: HUMAN BIOLOGY

EXERCISE 1
page 115

1. **a.** body structure and function
   b. *Homo sapiens*
2. **a.** similarities in the structure of organs
   b. similarities in chemical makeup

EXERCISE 2
pages 115-116

Comprehension

1. (5) Humans can create clothes, shelter, and other things that help them survive in harsh environments. Answer choice (3) is also a correct statement, but it is not a summary of the first two paragraphs.

Application

2. (2) Primates can walk erect on two legs. The gorilla is the only animal listed that fits this description.

Comprehension

3. (1) Genetic codes are like sets of instructions that tell cells what type of body structures to form.

Application

4. (5) A bird's forelimb is used for flying, while the forelimb of a human is used for arm and hand activity.

Analysis

5. (4) Since Darwin believed that all organisms evolve, it is most reasonable that he would conclude answer choice (4).

Evaluation

6. (3) Only answer choice (3) deals with evidence that possibly links the early history of humans with the early history of apes.

Analysis

7. (4) Human evolution occurs as changes take place in the human genetic code. Positive changes may be accomplished by genetic engineering.

Writing Activity 1
page 117

Answers will vary, but your list could include the following points:

Pro	Con
• We can't do without the medical knowledge gained through animal experimentation.	• Animal experimentation is cruel and should be stopped.
• I feel sorry for the animals, but I also think a human life is more important than an animal's life.	• Experimenting with animals is unfair, since animals can't speak up for their rights or, in a lab, fight back.

EXERCISE 3
page 120

1. two
2. left, right
3. neurons
4. right
5. bundles of nerve fibers
6. mind-brain problem

EXERCISE 4
page 120

Comprehension

1. (3) According to the reading selection, these nerve fibers are believed to allow the two halves of the brain to communicate with each other.

Application

2. (5) Answer choice (5) is correct because it is the left half of the brain that controls the right side of the body.

Evaluation

3. (2) Maddie can use statement A; some people are extremely intelligent, yet their brains are no larger than other people's brains. She also can use statement C; humans are smarter than elephants.

EXERCISE 5
page 122

1. T
2. T
3. F
4. T

EXERCISE 6
pages 123-124

Comprehension
1. **(1)** Increased average income is not mentioned in the passage, nor is it necessarily related to life expectancy.

Evaluation
2. **(4)** The amount of money spent on food is not important to know. It's the type of food that's purchased that is important.

Comprehension
3. **(3)** 75 − 47 = 28, or about 30

Comprehension
4. **(1)** The passage states that half the deaths in the U.S. each year are caused by heart and blood vessel disease.

Analysis
5. **(2)** Answer (4) is not true because poverty is also a source of stress. Answer (1) is not relevant, and (5) is false. Answer (3), while true, is not the most direct contributing factor to a higher incidence of heart disease.

Analysis
6. **(3)** This conclusion is most reasonable when you consider that only the underfed mice lived beyond average life expectancy.

Evaluation
7. **(2)** The time of day that the mice ate is not important. The researcher is interested, though, in the quantity of food eaten and the causes of death.

Evaluation
8. **(1)** Of the choices listed, only choice (1) would help improve your health.

Writing Activity 3
page 124

Your lists could include some of the following points:

Concerns	Benefits
• financial worries	• retirement
• illness or pain	• grandchildren
• family living far away	• wisdom

EXERCISE 7
page 126

Part A
1. b
2. e
3. d
4. a
5. c

Part B
6. heart disease, diabetes
7. **a.** 10 to 15 percent
   b. 55 to 60 percent
   c. 30 percent

EXERCISE 8
pages 127-128

Comprehension
1. **(5)** Excess calories are stored as body fat.

Application
2. **(3)** Of the professions listed, the accountant is apt to get less exercise than the people in answer choices (2), (4), and (5). The accountant also will not need the calories required by the pregnant woman, who needs extra calories for the growth of the fetus.

Comprehension
3. **(4)** Protein is found mainly in meat, a food not eaten by vegetarians.

Analysis
4. **(2)** During a high fever, a patient sweats a lot. Drinking water replaces this lost fluid and helps to lower body temperature.

Analysis
5. **(4)** Exercise uses up energy (food calories). Thus, the more you exercise, the more food calories that are used up and not stored as body fat.

Evaluation
6. **(3)** Answer choice (3) is not relevant because it does not include height, an important comparison factor.

Comprehension
7. **(2)** This information is given in the chart.
8. **(4)** This information is given in the chart.

EXERCISE 9
page 131

1. T
2. F
3. F
4. T
5. F

EXERCISE 10
page 132

Comprehension
1. **(1)** The purpose of the nervous system is to carry messages from one part of the body to another. In this way it acts as a communication network.

Application
2. **(3)** Of the choices given, only choice (3) is intentional. The others occur involuntarily.

Application
3. **(5)** Breathing occurs naturally and without conscious control.

Analysis
4. **(4)** An injury to the spinal cord in the lower back would affect all nerve impulses that try to travel to and from all lower points on the body, namely the legs.

5. (2) The nerve impulse must be sent from the girl's hand to her brain before she feels any pain. Then a nerve impulse is sent back to her hand, so her muscles contract and she pulls her hand away.

Evaluation
6. (3) Of the answer choices given, only choice (3) is related to the production of body heat as discussed in the reading selection.

EXERCISE 11
page 136

1. d
2. a
3. b
4. e
5. c

Writing Activity 4
page 136

Answers will vary, but your response could include the following points:

Yes	No
• In order to make an informed choice about sex, teenagers need to know the facts. They need to learn the facts from reliable sources such as parents or doctors—not from other teenagers.	• Discussing sex only puts ideas into children's heads—ideas that could get them into trouble.

EXERCISE 12
page 137

Comprehension
1. (1) According to the passage, the epiglottis performs this protective function.
2. (5) The circulatory system transports and delivers nutrients and oxygen to the body cells and waste carbon dioxide gas to the lungs.

Comprehension
3. (4) In the lungs, oxygen is absorbed by the blood and carbon dioxide is released as a waste product.

Comprehension
4. (5) An added fact—if you want to feel your heartbeat, you press your fingers lightly against an artery.

Analysis
5. (2) Choice (2) is always true. Answer choices (1), (3), (4), and (5) may be true, but they would not cause an extra burden to be placed on an overweight person's heart.

Evaluation
6. (4) Answer choices (1), (2), (3), and (5) are all true, but choice (4) is neither true nor false. Choice (4) is an opinion based only on human values.

EXERCISE 13
page 139

1. F
2. T
3. T
4. F
5. T

EXERCISE 14
pages 140-141

Comprehension
1. (1) Identical twins form from one fertilized egg, not two.
2. (4) The female egg cell has twenty-three unpaired chromosomes compared to forty-six chromosomes (twenty-three pairs) found in all other cells.

Analysis
3. (5) The mother-to-be should avoid all types of chemicals, including those such as paint that can be accidentally inhaled.
4. (4) If a woman finds out she's pregnant, it would be best for her to discontinue social drinking.

Comprehension
5. (3) Sickle-cell anemia causes red blood cells to become elongated and narrow.

Comprehension
6. (3) Since sickle-cell anemia is passed on genetically, it is not contagious.

Comprehension
7. (5) Based on the passage, only choice (5), that a person can carry a single sickle-cell gene and not suffer any of the symptoms, is true.

Analysis
8. (3) Since any of the four gene combinations shown beneath the children is equally likely to occur, there are two chances in four (or 50 percent probability) that a child will be an *NS* person.

Analysis
9. (2) As shown in Diagram B, there is one chance in four (or 25 percent probability) that this couple will have a child with sickle-cell anemia (*SS*).

GED PRACTICE: HUMAN BIOLOGY
pages 142–143

Comprehension
1. **(4)** According to the passage, both oxygen and nourishment are passed to fetal blood through the cells of the placenta.

Analysis
2. **(1)** According to the passage, fetal waste products (carbon dioxide being one) enter the mother's blood for later elimination.

Evaluation
3. **(5)** Choices (2), (3), and (4) are also true, but only choice (5) tells why smoking, drinking, or taking drugs can harm a fetus directly.

Analysis
4. **(4)** Only choice (4) results from atherosclerosis. Choices (2) and (3) are two of its causes, and choice (1) is its definition.

Comprehension
5. **(4)** None of the other choices are mentioned in the passage.

Comprehension
6. **(4)** These food items do not contain cholesterol, but they do contain high levels of saturated fat, which the body may convert to cholesterol.

Application
7. **(2)** Most bacon is high in both cholesterol and saturated fat.

Evaluation
8. **(3)** Of the facts listed, only choice (3) directly links diet with atherosclerosis.

CHAPTER 7: EARTH SCIENCE

EXERCISE 1
page 146

1. oceanographer
2. astronomer
3. paleontologist
4. geologist
5. meteorologist

EXERCISE 2
page 146

Analysis
1. **(1)** Only statement A is a hypothesis. Statement B is a fact, C is an opinion, and D is a prediction.
2. **(2)** Only statement B is a fact. Statement C is an opinion, A is a hypothesis, and D is a prediction.

Evaluation
3. **(5)** An environmental geologist would be most interested in toxic waste dumps because these dumps directly affect the safety of the environment.

EXERCISE 3
page 149

1. 1. d
   2. c
   3. e
   4. a
   5. b

2. **a.** Mercury
   b. third
   c. Pluto
   d. 6 trillion miles
   e. 100 billion
   f. 186,000

EXERCISE 4
page 150

Comprehension
1. **(4)** According to the article, Copernicus had the correct idea that the sun is at the center of a system of orbiting planets.

Evaluation
2. **(3)** Planets do not give off their own light, but the sunlight striking the planets enables us to see them. Distance from the sun and surface temperature are not relevant to our ability to see the planets.
3. **(5)** Both statements A and D give you reason to think that the sun orbits Earth. Statements B and C are true but not relevant.

EXERCISE 5
page 152

1. **a.** T   **c.** F
   b. F   **d.** T
2. **a.** twenty-four hours
   b. one year (365 days)
   c. rotation (or spin)
   d. tilt

EXERCISE 6
page 153

Application
1. **(1)** February is the hottest of the months listed. Remember, since the seasons are opposite, February in Brazil is like August in the United States.

Application
2. **(4)** In countries in North America, winter (and snow) occurs in December, January, and February.

Comprehension
3. **(2)** As shown on the diagram, Paris is eight time zones earlier than Seattle. Eight hours before 6:00 A.M. Saturday is 10:00 P.M. Friday.

Analysis
4. **(4)** The flight takes five hours, and an extra three hours is "lost" because of time zone changes. Thus, the flight reaches New York City at 4:00 P.M. (8:00 A.M. + 8 hours).

EXERCISE 7
pages 156-157

Comprehension
1. (1) The crust is the surface layer of Earth.

Comprehension
2. (2) Plate tectonics refers to the movement of rigid plates on Earth's surface.

Analysis
3. (4) Of the answer choices given, only (4) is a hypothesis that attempts to explain the shapes of the continents.

Evaluation
4. (2) Of the answer choices given, only (2) involves something (rain) not relevant to volcanic activity.

Evaluation
5. (3) Ancient European pottery would be, at most, several thousand years old, far too recent to have any relevance to questions concerning Pangaea.

Comprehension
6. (3) Granite and basalt are the two types of igneous rock indicated.

Comprehension
7. (3) As shown in the drawing, both heat and chemical change (as well as pressure) are needed to change sedimentary rock into metamorphic rock.

Writing Activity 2
page 157

Answers will vary, but some possible reasons for evacuation and possible problems are listed below.

Reasons	Problems
• Lives would be saved.	• Tax money would be wasted on people who were needlessly evacuated.
• Some people might be able to save valuable possessions.	• Factories, stores, and businesses would lose money because of the temporary shutdown.

EXERCISE 8
page 159

1. the layer of gases (air) that surrounds Earth
2. Ozone absorbs harmful ultraviolet rays.
3. carbon dioxide gas
4. 46 percent

EXERCISE 9
page 160

Application
1. (1) The troposphere extends to an altitude of about eight miles and, therefore, contains the cirrus clouds.
2. (5) The shuttle must first pass through the top layer of atmosphere called the thermosphere.
3. (4) The ionosphere is the layer that affects long-distance radio reception.
4. (3) The mesosphere is the layer above the stratosphere, which is the ozone layer.
5. (2) The damage is caused in the stratosphere, which is the layer containing ozone.

EXERCISE 10
page 162

1. 1. d   4. a
   2. e   5. b
   3. c
2. a. clear, pleasant weather
   b. wet or stormy weather

Comprehension
3. (2) In some, but not all, communities, air pollution level *is* given, especially when air quality is low.

EXERCISE 11
page 163

Comprehension
1. (3) According to the definitions on map symbols, an isotherm connects places with the same temperature.

Analysis
2. (5) The map shows winter conditions in the United States. December is the best answer.

EXERCISE 12
page 166

1. rock fragments and organic materials
2. By burrowing, they allow air and moisture to seep into the ground.
3. Weathering (the breaking of rock) occurs before erosion (the movement of broken rock).

EXERCISE 13
pages 166-167

Application
1. (4) Ocean waves are a type of water erosion.
2. (5) Gravity causes rocks to fall as a landslide.
3. (2) When rock is changed by an acid, chemical weathering is occurring.
4. (1) Freezing water breaks granite by the process of physical weathering.
5. (3) In a desert, wind blows piles of sand from one place to another.

Analysis

6. **(5)** There is no wind under water. Each of the other kinds of weathering and erosion does affect an underwater mountain chain.

Analysis

7. **(5)** Arranged in order, the steps show how a river with a slight bend causes the bend to increase and then get cut off to form the oxbow lake.

EXERCISE 14
page 170

1. 4 to 5 billion years
2. Any three of these: solid rock, caves, tar beds, ice
3. Cenozoic

EXERCISE 15
pages 170-171

Comprehension

1. **(3)** The second paragraph of the passage says that minerals slowly replace the original cell material in the fossil.

Analysis

2. **(4)** The passage says that petrified remains look very much like the original fossil. Therefore you can conclude that information about the fossil's shape is preserved and information about its weight, color, age, and chemical composition is lost.

Evaluation

3. **(2)** A tree's age at death can be determined by counting tree rings. The outline of these rings are preserved during petrification.

Analysis

4. **(3)** Coal is formed from the remains of a tropical forest and limestone from the remains of ocean life.

Application

5. **(5)** Of the answer choices given, only the sea worm is a form of ocean life, the types of fossils found in limestone.

6. **(3)** Of the animals listed, the extinct camel is the one most likely found in a desert, the most probable explanation of the sandstone.

Analysis

7. **(2)** The variety of types of layers indicates that answer choice (2) is the best answer.

GED PRACTICE: EARTH SCIENCE
pages 172-173

Comprehension

1. **(2)** The third paragraph of the selection states that scientists have discovered that many eruptions are preceded by small earthquakes.

Analysis

2. **(5)** If the magma temperature increases, the geyser water will reach boiling temperature more quickly and the time between eruptions should decrease.

Comprehension

3. **(5)** A geyser's eruption cycle is fairly predictable while a volcano's is not predictable at all at this time.

Comprehension

4. **(4)** Only choice (4) is supported by the drawing. Each of the other choices is not a true statement.

Application

5. **(2)** P-waves travel much more quickly than either L-waves or S-waves. Also, P-waves travel in all directions from the point of the quake.

Application

6. **(2)** Only between a Richter magnitude of 0 and 3 is a quake measurable but not felt.

Evaluation

7. **(4)** The magnitude of the P-wave could help determine the strength of the quake but not its location.

CHAPTER 8: CHEMISTRY

EXERCISE 1
page 176

1. d	**4.** a
2. e	**5.** c
3. b	

EXERCISE 2
page 176

Comprehension

1. **(3)** According to the essay, salicylic acid, the basic ingredient of aspirin, was used in its natural form (as found in willow bark) by the Native Americans.

Analysis

2. **(5)** Only statements B and C can be supported by facts. Statement A is a personal opinion that can't be proved true or false.

3. **(1)** There is no way to prove which science is the most difficult to learn.

EXERCISE 3
page 178

1. **a.** elements
   b. protons, neutrons, electrons
   c. neutron

2. a. F		**c.** T	
b. F		**d.** T	

EXERCISE 4
page 179

Comprehension

1. **(2)** Oxygen makes up 65 percent of average body weight, and hydrogen makes up 10 percent, for a combined total of 75 percent (65 percent + 10 percent = 75 percent).

Evaluation

2. **(5)** Carbon is listed as the second most abundant element in the first table, but is not listed at all among the nine specific elements shown in the second table.

EXERCISE 5
page 183

1. **a.** atomic number
   b. protons, neutrons
2. **a.** 11
   b. 12
   c. 11

EXERCISE 6
page 183

Comprehension

1. **(3)** The periodic table shows that atoms are listed by atomic number, the number of protons in the atom's nucleus.

Application

2. **(3)** According to the reading, elements that are listed in the same column have the same number of electrons in their outermost shells. In the periodic table, magnesium is listed in the same column as calcium.

Analysis

3. **(2)** Elements that are listed in the same row have the same number of shells. Reading the table from left to right, you can see that oxygen and lithium are both in the second row.

Application

4. **(1)** The atomic number of Fe is 26, which means 26 protons. The mass number is 56, which tells us there are 30 neutrons (56 − 26).

EXERCISE 7
page 185

1. **a.** two
   b. five
   c. six
2. C_4H_{10}

EXERCISE 8
page 185

Application

1. **(5)** The 2 in front stands for two molecules, while the subscript that follows an atom's symbol shows the number of atoms. Therefore, $2Fe_2O_3$ is the correct way to show two molecules of Fe_2O_3.

2. **(2)** The notation C_6 means that there are six atoms of carbon in the molecule. H_{12} indicates twelve atoms of hydrogen; 0_6 indicates six atoms of oxygen.

EXERCISE 9
page 187

1. **1.** c   **3.** a
   2. d   **4.** b

2. ionic bond: a bond formed when an electron transfers from one atom to another
   covalent bond: a bond formed when one or more electrons are shared between two atoms

EXERCISE 10
page 188

Comprehension

1. **(2)** Both unconsciousness and death are mentioned as effects associated with breathing concentrated carbon monoxide.

Analysis

2. **(4)** All answers will contribute to worker safety, but safe ventilation is of immediate importance to all employees because of the danger of carbon monoxide gas from car exhaust fumes.

3. **(2)** Answer (2) ensures that you minimize your breathing of carbon monoxide gas within an enclosed area.

Evaluation

4. **(3)** You can reasonably assume that light-headedness or dizziness may be the first effect felt by someone breathing too much carbon monoxide—a hypothesis that, along with the reading, supports conclusion (3).

Writing Activity 2
page 188

Your response might include the following points:
- Chemical weapons can have a greater negative impact on the environment than guns or nuclear weapons.
- Chemicals are unfair because they are invisible. There's no clear enemy to fight against.

EXERCISE 11
page 190

1. boiling point
2. freezing point
3. 32, 0; 212, 100

EXERCISE 12
page 191

Comprehension

1. **(3)** Find the point on the three-gallon system line that is directly to the right of −15°F on the vertical axis. This point lies directly above five quarts on the horizontal axis.

2. **(2)** Protection to 0° takes about five quarts, while protection to −20° takes about seven quarts. The answer is found by subtraction: seven quarts − five quarts = two quarts.

3. **(5)** No specific information is given for temperatures above 10°F or below −35°F.

Analysis

4. **(1)** The two graphed lines tell you that the larger system requires more antifreeze for every level of protection.

EXERCISE 13
page 192

1. physical change: a change in which a substance's appearance changes but those properties that enable you to identify it remain the same; for a physical change it's sometimes possible to restore a substance to its original form, but this is not possible for a chemical change.
   chemical change: a change in which a substance actually changes into other substances

2. **a.** chemical
   b. physical
   c. chemical
   d. physical

EXERCISE 14
page 193

Application

1. **(5)** When sugar is burned it undergoes a chemical change. The smell of burned sugar is caused by the sugar combining with another substance.

Analysis

2. **(2)** The room temperature determines whether thirty minutes is long enough for all the ice cream to warm to its melting temperature. If the room is cold, the ice cream may melt more slowly.

Application

3. **(3)** Iron left in a cool, wet place will rust, forming iron oxide. None of the other actions will cause a chemical change in the iron.

Evaluation

4. **(5)** The chemical structure of active chlorophyll is no longer in the leaves, an indication of chemical change.

5. **(5)** Statement C is true because melting an ice cube can be reversed by simply refreezing the water, whereas sanding a board cannot be reversed. Statement D is true because melting ice is a change of phase, and sanding results in a change of shape of an object.

Analysis

6. **(3)** Statement A is not true because a lighted match can't be restored to its original state. Statement D is not true because causing epoxy to harden is a purposeful, not destructive, action.

EXERCISE 15
page 195

1. **a.** chemical equation
   b. reactants, products
2. **a.** one
   b. twelve
   c. twelve

EXERCISE 16
page 195

Application

1. **(3)** The 3 at the beginning of the formula $3CO_2$ indicates that three molecules of CO_2 are formed.

Application

2. **(5)** To the right of the arrow in the chemical equation, there are three molecules of CO_2 and each molecule contains two atoms of oxygen— shown by the small 2 to the right of the O: $3 \times 2 = 6$.

EXERCISE 17
pages 196-197

Comprehension

1. **(3)** Paragraph 1 of the reading passage states that energy is released as (an exothermic) reaction takes place.

Comprehension

2. **(5)** The final paragraph states that many exothermic reactions require that heat energy be supplied before the reactions can start.

Evaluation

3. **(2)** Heat is required to dry the glue. Any reaction that requires heat is an endothermic reaction.

Application

4. **(3)** The result of the reaction in the equation is given on the right side of the arrow. Both carbon dioxide gas (CO_2) and heat energy are produced by the fermentation of alcohol.

Application

5. **(3)** Examples A, B, and D each use up heat to proceed, while Example C gives up heat as water cools.

Application

6. (2) As shown on the right side of the equation, six molecules of water (H_2O) appear as a product.

Application

7. (4) To the left of the arrow in the chemical equation, there are 12 molecules of water. Each molecule of water contains 2 atoms of hydrogen: $12 \times 2 = 24$. To the right, there are 6 molecules of water containing 12 atoms of hydrogen and 1 molecule of glucose containing 12 atoms of hydrogen: $12 + 12 = 24$.

Evaluation

8. (4) The heat energy provided by sunlight is required for photosynthesis to proceed. Any reaction that requires heat energy is endothermic.

Analysis

9. (2) According to the equation, water is used to produce the glucose that plants use for energy.

Evaluation

10. (5) Because plants use carbon dioxide to produce the glucose needed for growth, placing more of it in the air is thought by some growers to speed plant growth.

EXERCISE 18

page 198

1. d
2. c
3. b
4. a

EXERCISE 19

page 199

Application

1. (4) As mentioned in the reading, a carbonated soft drink consists of a gas dissolved in a liquid.
2. (1) Paint and paint thinner are both liquids.
3. (2) Punch mix is a solid, and water is a liquid.

Analysis

4. (2) The warmer cola tastes flat because a large amount of the dissolved carbon dioxide gas has escaped. Explanation (2) is consistent with this discovery.

Analysis

5. (1) Choice (1) is consistent with the observation, while choices (2) and (3) are not. Choices (4) and (5) are not relevant because the sugar was not stirred.

EXERCISE 20

page 201

1. **a.** carbon dioxide, water
   b. carbon
2. organic chemistry

EXERCISE 21

page 201

Comprehension

1. (4) Only salmon fat (oil) contains equal amounts of both saturated and unsaturated fats as indicated by the two bars being of equal height.

Comprehension

2. (3) By comparing the graphs of each product, you see that only choice (3) is correct.

Application

3. (4) The graph shows that safflower oil has less saturated fat than olive oil, and that salmon fat has less saturated fat than beef fat.

page 202

1. hydrocarbon: a compound that is composed of only hydrogen and carbon
2. polymer: a hydrocarbon containing a large number of carbon atoms

EXERCISE 23

page 203

Comprehension

1. (3) Methane would not be considered a polymer because it has only 1 carbon atom. Statements (1), (2), (4), and (5) are true for all three fuels mentioned.

Application

2. (5) You can deduce that this rule is true by counting the number of hydrogen and carbon atoms in propane and kerosene. Propane: 3C, 8H; Kerosene: 12C, 26H.
3. (4) Gasoline, at 45 percent, is the main petroleum product and is represented on the graph by the largest part of the circle.

Analysis

4. (3) Transportation fuels include gasoline (45 percent), diesel fuel (7 percent), and jet fuel (7 percent).
45 percent + 7 percent + 7 percent = 59 percent.

EXERCISE 24

page 205

1. strength, versatility, durability
2. any three: seabirds, seals, sea lions, turtles

EXERCISE 25
page 205

Analysis
1. (3) Method A leads to ocean pollution, and method C leads to air pollution even if the burning is done far from land.

Comprehension
2. (4) Its resistance to weathering and decay makes plastic difficult to dispose of, and this is the reason for the environmental concern.

EXERCISE 26
page 208

1. greenhouses
2. Carbon dioxide acts as a heat-trapping agent.

EXERCISE 27
page 208

Application
1. (2) Like a nursery greenhouse, a car lets sunlight in but does not allow the trapped heat to escape easily.

Analysis
2. (5) Only answer (5) is a cause of the greenhouse effect. Answers (1) and (4) are both results.

Evaluation
3. (3) The protection of polar bears is not related to the greenhouse effect. Each of the other answers is.
4. (1) Because all hydrocarbon fuels contribute to the greenhouse effect, the best answer is (1). Choices (2) and (3) are partial solutions but not as complete as (1). Choice (4) wouldn't work, and (5) probably wouldn't help.

EXERCISE 28
page 209

Evaluation
1. (4) Only a chemical analysis could determine whether Tri-State Oil contains no lead or lead products

Evaluation
2. (2) Only statements A and C concern what Tri-State Oil will do for your car.

Evaluation
3. (3) Only statement C, that Tri-State Oil will reduce the emission of carbon monoxide and other greenhouse gases, can be checked by doing a chemical analysis of the exhaust emitted from a car engine that runs on Tri-State Oil.

Evaluation
4. (5) By relating the advantages of using Tri-State Oil to reducing the greenhouse effect, the advertisement is appealing to a consumer's concern for the environment.

GED PRACTICE: CHEMISTRY
pages 210-211

Application
1. (3) The water level decreases as water evaporates from the lake's surface and is carried away by wind.

Application
2. (5) The grass and flower leaves provide a cool surface on which water vapor can condense into droplets.

Application
3. (1) Freezing occurs any time a liquid changes into a solid because of a drop in its temperature.

Application
4. (2) Melting occurs any time a solid changes into a liquid because of an increase in its temperature.

Application
5. (4) Boiling occurs any time a liquid's temperature rises to the point where vapor bubbles form in the liquid and the liquid begins rapidly changing to a gas.

Analysis
6. (3) In each example given in this problem set, the temperature determines the state of a substance.

Application or Analysis
7. (4) A little baking soda (a weak base) would cause orange juice (a weak acid) to taste a little less acidic.

Comprehension
8. (5) Acid rain is more acidic than regular rainwater (pH 6.2). Therefore the most reasonable choice is (5)—a pH value of less than 6.

Analysis
9. (1) A weak base would tend to neutralize the acidic soil without endangering people who come into contact with the grass.

Application
10. (3) Of the choices given, this combination is the only one that is slightly basic. The other choices would increase the acid level of the upset stomach.

CHAPTER 9: PHYSICS

EXERCISE 1
page 214

Part A
1. d	3. b
2. a	4. c

Part B

Comprehension

5. (3) The second paragraph of the chapter states that the world's population is increasing and worldwide standards of living are rising. As a result, more people can afford energy-consuming products, choice (3). While choice (2) is true and (4) is not, neither is mentioned. Choices (1) and (5) do not explain the cause of the worldwide increase in energy use.

Comprehension

6. (2) Only choice (2) is a reasonable conclusion based on the information given in the reading text.

Comprehension

7. (5) Biophysics is a word that results from combining the prefix *bio*, which means "life," and *physics*.

EXERCISE 2
page 215

Comprehension

1. (3) Only solar power, perhaps our main energy source in the future, is not mentioned on the graph.

Comprehension

2. (4) Adding the fossil fuel percents gives 22.9 + 28.7 + 28.1 = 79.7 percent, or about 80 percent.

Analysis

3. (2) According to the pie chart, natural gas (28.7 percent) is produced at a level of about three times that of nuclear power (9.2 percent): 9.2 percent × 3 = 27.6 percent.

EXERCISE 3
page 218

1. a. force: any push or pull that can affect either an object in motion or an object at rest

b. inertia: an object's natural resistance to any change in its motion

2. a. 3

b. 2

c. 1

d. 2

EXERCISE 4
pages 218–219

Application

1. (1) According to the discussion of Newton's first law, the fact that a force is needed in order to stop a moving object (such as a car without brakes) is the result of that object's inertia.

Analysis

2. (1) When a bullet is fired, hot gas caused by the explosion pushes the bullet forward and the rifle backward, into the shoulder of the person holding it. The pushing back of the rifle is called "recoiling."

Comprehension

3. (3) As indicated on the drawing, it is the escaping water that exerts a force on the sprinkler head, causing it to spin.

4. (3) The sprinkler rotates because of a reaction force felt by the sprinkler nozzles from the pressure of the escaping water. Reaction force is explained by Newton's third law.

Analysis

5. (5) Oil would allow the sprinkler head to rotate more easily and thus react to the water by rotating more quickly. Increasing the water flow would also increase the reaction force felt by the sprinkler nozzles.

6. (3) As you can calculate from the graph, an object's speed increases by 32 feet per second during each second of fall.

EXERCISE 5
page 222

1. constant

2. kinetic energy, potential energy

3. Friction

EXERCISE 6
page 222

Application

1. (2) The energy is partly kinetic and partly potential only at point B, where the ball is between its highest point (all potential energy) and lowest point (all kinetic energy).

Analysis

2. (3) The ball will have the greatest amount of force at its point of maximum kinetic energy, point C—its lowest point.

Evaluation

3. (5) The energy that was in the ball is not lost during impact. It is transferred to the building, breaking the building apart and creating sound and heat.

EXERCISE 7
page 224

1. T   **3. T**

2. F   **4. F**

EXERCISE 8
pages 224-225

Analysis

1. (2) Heat always flows from the hotter object (the iron) to the colder object (the water) until both objects reach the same temperature.

2. (5) Since heat causes matter to expand, the metal beams expand during times of high temperature. The gaps provide room for this expansion.

Comprehension

3. (2) Locating "normal body temperature" on the diagram, you can see that the correct reading is 37°C, or 98.6°F.

4. (4) Since 37°C is normal body temperature, 38°C is a slight fever. Choices (2) and (3) represent normal temperatures. Choice (1) is too low, and (5) is much too high.

Evaluation

5. (2) Because of the seriousness of a high fever, it is best to try to reduce the fever with a damp cloth and to seek immediate medical advice.

EXERCISE 9
page 228

1. F
2. T
3. T
4. T

EXERCISE 10
page 229

Comprehension

1. (3) According to the chart, a dog makes sounds (barks) at the frequency range of 450–1,080 cycles per second.

Comprehension

2. (4) According to the chart, the greatest hearing range is that of a dolphin—from 150 to 150,000 cycles per second.

Analysis

3. (2) As shown in the table, a dog can hear frequencies as low as 15 cps, while a human's lower limit is 20 cps.

4. (3) Grasshoppers can "speak" at frequencies as high as 100,000 cps but can hear only at frequencies as high as 15,000. No other animal listed has this unusual ability.

Evaluation

5. (3) The table shows that most animals can hear at both lower and higher frequencies than those at which they can "speak."

EXERCISE 11
page 231

1. **a.** vacuum
   b. wavelength
2. **a.** F   **c.** F
   b. T   **d.** T

EXERCISE 12
page 232

Application

1. (4) The sound waves must diffract—move around barriers like doorways and corners—in order to reach your ears.

2. (3) The light waves cross a boundary when passing through the oil. When light waves refract, the light is separated out into a spectrum of colors.

3. (2) The echoes are simply sound waves reflecting off the alley and the surrounding buildings.

4. (5) Emilio bobs up and down each time the crest of a new wave reaches him.

5. (1) The shape of Amelia's outline and the accompanying shadow is only possible because light moves in a straight line. If light curved around Amelia, she would see no shadow.

EXERCISE 13
page 235

1. d
2. c
3. e
4. b
5. a
6. **a.** static electricty, electric current
   b. conductor

EXERCISE 14
page 236

Comprehension

1. (2) In a series circuit, electricity has only one path to follow. If this path is broken, electricity stops flowing in the whole circuit.

Analysis

2. (1) When one light goes out, the circuit in which it is located is broken. Since the other lights don't go out, you can conclude that the electricity runs in a parallel circuit.

Application

3. (5) Statement B is false because electrons always flow away from the negative side of a battery. Statement C is false because a break in a circuit will stop the current flow to all points in that circuit: both light and bell turn off.

Analysis

4. **(2)** Only by opening switch b can you break the circuit that contains light 1 while at the same time not breaking the separate circuit that contains light 2.

EXERCISE 15
page 238

1. e   4. b
2. d   5. c
3. a

EXERCISE 16
page 238

Comprehension

1. **(4)** According to the passage, the main property of superconductors is that they do not produce heat when an electric current passes through them.

Analysis

2. **(5)** Only (5) is a possible cause of superconductivity. Answers (1) and (2) are simply observed properties of superconductivity, not causes. Nothing in the passage would lead you to infer that either (3) or (4) is correct.

Analysis

3. **(4)** Although it is certainly true that utility companies will save money, consumers will share in the savings only if the utility companies pass these savings along. Consumers probably will continue to use the same amount of energy, and they will not necessarily switch to electric heating from gas or oil.

EXERCISE 17
page 240

1. **T**   3. **T**
2. **F**   4. **F**

EXERCISE 18
pages 240–241

Application

1. **(5)** Of the choices listed, only a flashlight is not an electrical device.

Analysis

2. **(4)** Each choice except (4) is related either to one's total exposure to an electromagnetic field or to one's sensitivity to it, all risk factors.

Application

3. **(3)** The thumbtacks are strongly attracted by the magnet.
4. **(2)** Lodestone occurs naturally on Earth, so it is naturally magnetic.

Comprehension

5. **(5)** Weak repulsion is classified as diamagnetic.

Application

6. **(1)** Since helium shows no reaction to a magnet, it is classified as nonmagnetic.
7. **(4)** Slight attraction is classified as paramagnetic.

EXERCISE 19
page 243

1. alpha particles, beta particles, gamma rays
2. half-life
3. thorium and helium

EXERCISE 20
page 244

Comprehension

1. **(5)** Radioactive elements decay constantly.
2. **(4)** Find the point on the curve that lies directly above the "3 days" point on the horizontal axis. From this point, follow the dotted line across to the answer on the vertical axis: about 125 nuclei remain after three days.

EXERCISE 21
page 246

1. nuclear fission: splitting a nucleus by bombarding it with other particles
2. chain reaction: the production of nuclear energy by the controlled fission of nuclei
3. nuclear reactor: a device in which controlled chain reactions are carried out
4. nuclear fusion: joining together two atomic nuclei

EXERCISE 22
page 246

Comprehension

1. **(3)** In both nuclear and coal plants, steam is used to turn the turbine, which turns the electric generator.
2. **(5)** According to the article, U-235 is a type of fuel used in nuclear fission.

Analysis

3. **(2)** Only (2) is a statement about the future. Choices (1), (3), and (4) are facts, and (5) is an opinion.

EXERCISE 23
page 249

1. uncontrolled
2. controlled
3. controlled
4. uncontrolled
5. controlled

page 249

Analysis
1. **(4)** Technical problems and excessive cost are the most frequently given reasons that many energy sources are not yet widely used.

Evaluation
2. **(2)** Natural disasters may have a slight impact on energy production, but all the other choices are more relevant.

GED PRACTICE: PHYSICS
pages 250-251

Comprehension
1. **(2)** The first paragraph of the selection says that microwaves are guided to the stirrer by a hollow tube known as the waveguide.

Analysis
2. **(2)** Most likely the dry plate became warm because of its contact with the heated pizza. A microwave oven will not directly warm a paper plate.

Analysis
3. **(5)** The function of the stirrer is to spread microwaves evenly throughout the cavity. If food cooks unevenly, most likely the stirrer is not reflecting the microwaves properly.

Analysis
4. **(3)** Microwave radiation is a form of electromagnetic radiation that is best confined to the interior of the oven!

Analysis
5. **(1)** A conventional oven heats more than the food; on the other hand a microwave oven heats only the food being cooked. Therefore, you can conclude that the microwave oven is the more efficient of the two.

Analysis
6. **(4)** Experiment A illustrates the change in gas pressure as volume is decreased. Only choice (4), that gas pressure increases as the volume in which the gas is confined is decreased, correctly states the results shown in Experiment A.

Evaluation
7. **(2)** A steam engine uses the pressure of confined vapor to move a piston up and down. None of the other choices involve a confined gas.

Analysis
8. **(3)** Experiment B deals with the change in gas pressure as temperature is increased. Only choice (3), that gas pressure increases as the temperature of the gas is increased, correctly states the results shown in Experiment B.

Evaluation
9. **(1)** A pressure cooker keeps the volume of a gas (water vapor) constant as the pressure is increased by raising the temperature. This is very similar to results obtained in Experiment B.

Index

2002 Science Model Test 1

Directions: This model test will help you identify the skills you will need to be successful on the new 2002 GED Science Test. The test consists of 50 multiple-choice questions. Some of the questions are based on short reading passages, and some require you to interpret a diagram, a graph, or a map. Questions are based on information from the areas of earth science (including space science), physical science (including physics and chemistry), life science (including environmental and health science), and the National Science Education Standards guidelines.

You should take no longer than 80 minutes to complete this test. When you are finished, check your work with the answers and explanations at the end of the test. Use the evaluation chart on page 342 to determine the areas in which you will need more study before taking the 2002 GED Science Test.

MODEL TEST ANSWER GRID

1 ① ② ③ ④ ⑤   14 ① ② ③ ④ ⑤   27 ① ② ③ ④ ⑤   39 ① ② ③ ④ ⑤

2 ① ② ③ ④ ⑤   15 ① ② ③ ④ ⑤   28 ① ② ③ ④ ⑤   40 ① ② ③ ④ ⑤

3 ① ② ③ ④ ⑤   16 ① ② ③ ④ ⑤   29 ① ② ③ ④ ⑤   41 ① ② ③ ④ ⑤

4 ① ② ③ ④ ⑤   17 ① ② ③ ④ ⑤   30 ① ② ③ ④ ⑤   42 ① ② ③ ④ ⑤

5 ① ② ③ ④ ⑤   18 ① ② ③ ④ ⑤   31 ① ② ③ ④ ⑤   43 ① ② ③ ④ ⑤

6 ① ② ③ ④ ⑤   19 ① ② ③ ④ ⑤   32 ① ② ③ ④ ⑤   44 ① ② ③ ④ ⑤

7 ① ② ③ ④ ⑤   20 ① ② ③ ④ ⑤   33 ① ② ③ ④ ⑤   45 ① ② ③ ④ ⑤

8 ① ② ③ ④ ⑤   21 ① ② ③ ④ ⑤   34 ① ② ③ ④ ⑤   46 ① ② ③ ④ ⑤

9 ① ② ③ ④ ⑤   22 ① ② ③ ④ ⑤   35 ① ② ③ ④ ⑤   47 ① ② ③ ④ ⑤

10 ① ② ③ ④ ⑤   23 ① ② ③ ④ ⑤   36 ① ② ③ ④ ⑤   48 ① ② ③ ④ ⑤

11 ① ② ③ ④ ⑤   24 ① ② ③ ④ ⑤   37 ① ② ③ ④ ⑤   49 ① ② ③ ④ ⑤

12 ① ② ③ ④ ⑤   25 ① ② ③ ④ ⑤   38 ① ② ③ ④ ⑤   50 ① ② ③ ④ ⑤

13 ① ② ③ ④ ⑤   26 ① ② ③ ④ ⑤

Questions 1–5 refer to the following graph.

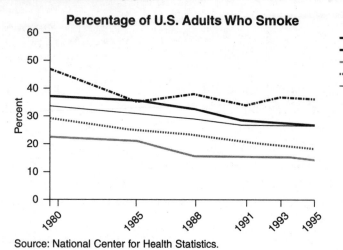

Percentage of U.S. Adults Who Smoke

Source: National Center for Health Statistics.

1. Which group has the highest percentage of adults who smoke?

   (1) African Americans
   (2) American Indians
   (3) Asian Americans
   (4) Hispanics
   (5) Caucasians

2. In 1988, approximately what percentage of Asian American adults reported smoking cigarettes?

   (1) 40 percent
   (2) 35 percent
   (3) 25 percent
   (4) 22 percent
   (5) 18 percent

3. What is the best description of the trend in smoking among American Indians?

   (1) The percentage of adult American Indian smokers has fallen steadily since 1980.
   (2) The percentage of American Indian smokers fell rapidly until 1988 and then leveled off.
   (3) Fewer adult American Indians smoke than do members of any other ethnic group.
   (4) The percentage of American Indian smokers has fallen and risen several times during the time period on the graph, and remains higher than other ethnic groups.
   (5) American Indians quit smoking in large numbers after 1993.

4. For what purpose might a scientist use the information in this graph to design programs to help people quit smoking?

   (1) to determine which groups most need health information about smoking
   (2) to design experiments that find ways to discourage people from smoking
   (3) to decide which groups most deserve to receive health care
   (4) to select a youth sample to target with anti-smoking information
   (5) to choose a geographic region in which to offer classes to stop smoking

5. For which group did the percentage of adult smokers decrease most steadily from 1980 to 1995?

   (1) Asian Americans
   (2) Hispanics
   (3) Caucasians
   (4) African Americans
   (5) American Indians

6. The chemical formula for carbon monoxide is CO. What does each molecule of carbon monoxide contain?

   (1) one atom of carbon dioxide and one atom of water
   (2) twice as much carbon as oxygen
   (3) one atom of carbon and one atom of oxygen
   (4) a positive charge
   (5) more oxygen than carbon dioxide

7. An electric circuit is a path followed by an electric current. The circuit consists of three parts: an energy source, an output device, and a connection that allows the current to flow from the source to the output device. An open circuit has gaps that prevent the current from completing its path. A closed circuit has no gaps.

   According to this definition of an electric circuit, what occurs when you use a light switch to turn off a lamp?

   (1) the switch removes the potential energy source
   (2) the switch creates a light wave
   (3) the switch opens a gap in the circuit
   (4) the switch closes a gap in the circuit
   (5) the switch removes the output device

8. A pulley is a simple machine in which a wheel reverses the direction of movement of a rope. A block and tackle is a system of fixed and moveable pulleys used together. Which statement best describes the input and output forces of the block and tackle shown?

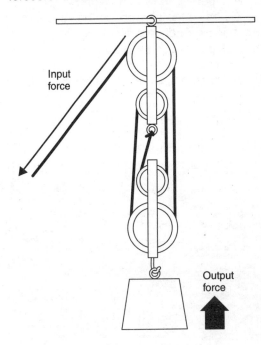

   (1) The input force is greater than the output force.
   (2) The output force is greater than the input force.
   (3) The distance the rope is pulled is greater than the distance the weight is lifted.
   (4) The distance the rope is pulled is less than the distance the weight is lifted.
   (5) The output force exceeds the input force and the weight is lifted a lesser distance than the rope is pulled.

9. To a scientist, work is defined as the amount of force needed to move something over a given distance. If Mickey sits at his desk and types on his computer for an hour, how much work has he done on the keyboard?

   (1) It depends on what he typed.
   (2) He has done no work on the keyboard.
   (3) It depends on how fast he typed.
   (4) It depends on how hard the keys were pressed.
   (5) He has done work on the computer monitor.

Questions 10–12 refer to the following map.

Recent Earthquakes in Alaska

Magnitude (size)

Source: U.S. Geological Survey

10. What does the map show?

   (1) the depth of recent earthquakes in Alaska
   (2) the location and severity of recent earthquakes in Alaska
   (3) the location of recent earthquakes in Europe
   (4) the number of earthquakes in the United States
   (5) the amount of damage caused by earthquakes in Alaska

11. What is the magnitude of the strongest earthquake shown on the map?

   (1) 1
   (2) 3
   (3) 4
   (4) 6
   (5) 9

12. Based on this map, which statement about the relationship between earthquakes and plate boundaries is correct?

   (1) Earthquakes tend to occur near plate boundaries.
   (2) Earthquakes can occur anywhere, but they are strongest near plate boundaries.
   (3) Earthquakes do the least damage when they occur near plate boundaries.
   (4) There is no relationship between earthquakes and plate boundaries.
   (5) Plate boundaries lie under the ocean, but earthquakes occur only on land.

Questions 13–16 refer to the following graph.

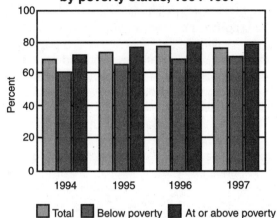

**Immunization Among Children
19 to 35 months of age,
by poverty status, 1994-1997**

■ Total   ■ Below poverty   ■ At or above poverty

Source: Centers for Disease Control and Prevention

13. About what percentage of all U.S. children were vaccinated in 1994?

(1) 60 percent
(2) 70 percent
(3) 75 percent
(4) 80 percent
(5) This information cannot be determined from the graph.

14. About what percentage of U.S. children below the poverty level were vaccinated in 1996?

(1) 60 percent
(2) 65 percent
(3) 70 percent
(4) 75 percent
(5) 80 percent

15. What general trend or trends does the graph show?

(1) More children who are below the poverty level receive vaccinations than children who are at or above the poverty level.
(2) Vaccination rates are higher than they need to be to prevent serious childhood illnesses.
(3) Vaccination rates decreased from 1994 to 1996.
(4) The state and federal governments should provide vaccinations.
(5) Although vaccination rates have increased, the percentage of poor children receiving vaccinations is less than for children at or above the poverty level.

16. Why might a scientist be interested in the information in this graph?

(1) to find out which clinics were successful in vaccinating children
(2) to predict the likelihood of serious outbreaks of disease
(3) to measure the number of children living in poverty
(4) to find out why wealthier children were more likely to be vaccinated
(5) to predict the worldwide rate of influenza in children

Questions 17–21 are based on the following paragraphs.

In many parts of New England, the forest floor is blanketed by many different wildflowers in spring. In other places, few species of wildflowers can be found. Scientists at Williams College in Massachusetts wondered what caused the difference.

Using old maps, Dr. Henry Art and his students found that the woodlots with the greatest diversity of wildflowers were those that had never been cleared for agriculture. Those with fewer varieties of flowers had been plowed repeatedly in the past, before they were returned to wild land. The trees in the two types of forests were nearly identical. Only the wildflowers differed. Why?

Dr. Art found that the difference was associated with seeds and ants. Some plant seeds are dispersed by wind, birds, and small mammals. All these plants, whether they are trees, shrubs, or wildflowers, can spread their seeds quickly over long distances—as fast and as far as a bird can fly or the wind can blow. Dr. Art found that neither animals nor the wind spread the seeds of many of the wildflowers that grew only in woodlots that had never been cleared; ants spread them. Dr. Art also found that the ants in these woodlots do not stray very far from their home base.

When a field is plowed, flowering plants are uprooted, and the ants that formerly dispersed their seeds are disturbed. When the field lies fallow, it will grow into a forest once more, and plants whose seeds are dispersed by wind and birds will quickly reappear. However, ants that do not stray far from their homes only re-colonize at a rate of 3 to 10 inches per year. So it may take 1000 years for the ants to spread even the length of a football field. Thus, the wildflowers that are spread only by the ants may also take 1000 years to spread across woodlots that were once plowed.

17. Which sentence best states the main idea of this investigation?

   (1) In many parts of North America, the forest floor is blanketed by many different wildflowers in spring.
   (2) The trees in the two types of forests were nearly identical.
   (3) Some woodlots in New England have a lower diversity of wildflowers because they were once plowed and have not yet been re-colonized.
   (4) When the field lies fallow, it will grow into a forest once more.
   (5) Ants re-colonize at a rate of only 3 to 10 inches per year.

18. What led Dr. Art to begin his study?

   (1) studying old maps
   (2) studying ant behavior in New England forests
   (3) comparing two different types of forests
   (4) asking a question about two different types of forests
   (5) measuring the distance birds travel

19. According to the passage, what has happened to areas once used for farming in New England?

   (1) They have grown into forests again.
   (2) They are used for scientific experiments.
   (3) They are now used for grazing.
   (4) They are still used for farming.
   (5) They have become colleges.

20. For what purpose did Dr. Art use old maps?

 (1) to pinpoint areas with the most wildflowers
 (2) to find locations with the most trees
 (3) to locate areas with the fewest ants
 (4) to find property that had never been owned by settlers
 (5) to search for land that had never been plowed

21. Which of the following might be concluded from reading about this investigation?

 (1) People can encourage ants to return by scattering seeds.
 (2) Human activities can affect the natural environment long after the activities have ended.
 (3) New England forests will be cleared for agriculture once again.
 (4) The author believes that farming is harmful to the earth.
 (5) Ants are more important than birds and animals in spreading seeds over a wide area.

Questions 22 and 23 are based on the following paragraph.

There are two kinds of energy: potential and kinetic. Potential energy also is known as stored energy because it is stored inside an object. When an object moves, all its stored potential energy becomes kinetic energy. Kinetic energy, also known as released energy, is energy that is currently being used to move something.

22. Which of the following is an example of kinetic energy?

 (1) a remote control car without batteries
 (2) a race car speeding down a racetrack
 (3) a race car being serviced in the pit lane
 (4) a person sitting on a stationary swing
 (5) a rock resting on a mountain road

23. Which of the following is an example of potential energy?

 (1) a tire bouncing down the street
 (2) a man running a race
 (3) a football flying through the air
 (4) a Frisbee in its owner's hand
 (5) a woman swimming free-style

2002 MODEL TEST 1

Questions 24–26 are based on the following diagram of the layers of Earth.

Cross-Section of Earth

Crust varies in composition and in thickness. It is thinner under oceans than under continents.

Boundary between inner and outer mantle

Inner core is made of solid iron.

Outer core is made of molten iron, with nickel, oxygen, and silicon.

Mantle is made of compounds of iron, magnesium, and silicon. Upper part is partially melted.

24. According to the diagram, which layer of Earth is completely molten?

(1) crust
(2) outer mantle
(3) inner mantle
(4) outer core
(5) inner core

25. According to the diagram, which statement about the mantle is *incorrect?*

(1) It is partly melted.
(2) It contains compounds of iron, magnesium, and silicon.
(3) It contains large amounts of nickel.
(4) There is a boundary between the inner and outer mantle.
(5) It lies beneath the crust.

26. According to the diagram, which layer varies in thickness?

(1) the crust
(2) the outer mantle
(3) the inner mantle
(4) the outer core
(5) the inner core

27. A lever is a simple machine that turns on a fixed support, called a fulcrum, and transmits effort and motion. Which of the following is an example of a lever?

(1) a pulley
(2) a hammer
(3) a screw
(4) a seesaw
(5) a swing

28. Benjamin Franklin's famous experiment involved tying a key to a kite string, then flying the kite in a thunderstorm. When lightning struck the kite, there was a spark on the key. What did this experiment demonstrate about lightning?

(1) It is electricity.
(2) It always strikes the highest point.
(3) It cannot electrocute someone.
(4) It never misses a target.
(5) It is attracted to paper and string.

Questions 29–32 refer to the passage below.

Comets, the wanderers of the night sky, are brilliant and exciting visitors from the far reaches of our solar system. Scientists believe that most comets are composed of rocks and water ice. Some have highly elliptical orbits that bring them close to the sun and swing them far out into space, beyond the orbit of Pluto.

The current view is that many comets arise from a huge cloud of similar objects—perhaps as many as 100 billion of them—orbiting the sun at a distance of about 1 light year. This cloud is called the Oort cloud, after Jan H. Oort, the Dutch astronomer who proposed the theory. The Oort cloud is near the boundary between the gravitational field of our sun and the gravitational fields of nearby stars.

Oort's theory states that every several thousand years the sun comes into proximity to these nearby stars. These "close encounters" perturb the orbits of the comets in the Oort cloud. As a result, other stars may capture some comets, some may be lost to interstellar space, and some may "fall" toward the sun. The comets we observe are in the last group— those whose disturbed orbits cause them to approach the inner solar system and come within our view.

29. According to the passage, which comets can be seen from Earth?

(1) those that fall into the inner solar system
(2) those that are in the gravitational fields of the stars
(3) all of the comets in the Oort cloud
(4) those that are in interstellar space
(5) only comets that are not composed of rock and water ice

30. Which statement about the Oort cloud is supported by the passage?

(1) Scientists have observed the Oort cloud with telescopes.
(2) Astronauts have traveled in the space within the Oort cloud.
(3) Scientists theorize from the movement of comets that the Oort cloud exists.
(4) The Oort cloud has existed for 100 billion years.
(5) Few scientists believe that the Oort cloud actually exists.

31. According to the theory, what causes the movement of comets?

(1) encounters between the sun and other stars
(2) changes in the strength of the sun's gravitational pull
(3) the gravitational pull of the outer planets' orbits
(4) a build-up of clouds in the gravitational field of our sun
(5) disturbing the boundaries of the Oort cloud

32. According to the theory, what affects the movement of all the objects in the solar system?

(1) friction
(2) gravity
(3) freezing
(4) kinetics
(5) orbits

Questions 33–36 to refer to the following map and information.

This map shows the range of the gray wolf in Canada and part of the northwestern United States. It also indicates some locations, outside of the wolf's present home range, where hunters have killed wolves in recent decades. Wolves had been a federally endangered species for many years, but they have recently made a comeback in the United States and gradually are extending their range, both naturally and with the efforts of wildlife scientists.

Gray Wolf Occurrences

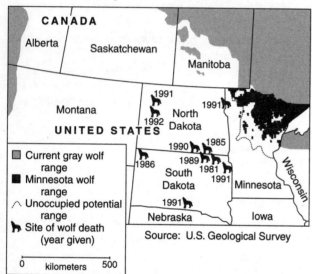

Source: U.S. Geological Survey

33. According to the map, the wolf's range extends into which states?

   (1) North Dakota and South Dakota
   (2) Montana and North Dakota
   (3) Minnesota and Wisconsin
   (4) Montana, Minnesota, and Wisconsin
   (5) Minnesota, North Dakota, and South Dakota

34. What definition of a wolf's range do the map and passage support?

   (1) the area in which it breeds and searches for food
   (2) the area in which the pack leaders live
   (3) the territory in which it is in danger of being killed
   (4) the area it travels through
   (5) the area in which it defends its young

35. How might a wildlife biologist use this map?

   (1) to decide when to observe wolves raising their young
   (2) to select areas that might also support fox populations
   (3) to choose areas to study to learn more about wolves
   (4) to learn more about the plant life needed to support wolves
   (5) to measure how far from its birthplace a young wolf travels

36. When did the earliest wolf death noted on the map take place?

   (1) 1981
   (2) 1985
   (3) 1986
   (4) 1991
   (5) 1992

Questions 37–39 refer to the following paragraphs.

The birth of the modern science of geology can be dated from the acceptance of the theory of uniformitarianism. James Hutton first offered this theory in the late eighteenth century. It states that the forces that shape Earth today have worked in a *uniform* way throughout Earth's history. Thus, observations of current geological processes can be used to interpret the record of past geological events.

In the early nineteenth century, uniformitarianism won out over a competing hypothesis, catastrophism, which states that Earth was shaped by a sequence of enormous, planetwide catastrophes. The theory implies that Earth's current form is complete and unchanging.

Hutton's realization was that the slow processes he saw all around him, such as rivers cutting through valleys and rocks sliding down valley walls, had gone on throughout Earth's history. He also recognized that, to shape Earth as we know it, these processes must have continued for extremely long periods of time. This powerful theory laid the groundwork for the modern study of our planet as dynamic and continually evolving.

37. In the first paragraph of this passage, what does the term *uniform* mean?

    (1) the same as
    (2) evolving
    (3) older than
    (4) competing with
    (5) winning

38. Why is uniformitarianism a powerful theory for use by scientists?

    (1) It provides a means to study other planets by studying events on Earth.
    (2) It ignores evidence of past catastrophes, such as volcanic eruptions.
    (3) It allows study of Earth's history by observing current geologic events.
    (4) It allows scientists to find the half-life of rocks and estimate Earth's age.
    (5) It says that Earth's geologic formations are permanent.

39. On what observation did Hutton base his idea of uniformitarianism?

    (1) Small, everyday events act over time to reshape Earth.
    (2) Catastrophes have little effect on Earth.
    (3) Everyday events cause changes in short periods of time.
    (4) The forces that shape Earth act on other planets as well.
    (5) Few changes take place on Earth's surface.

Questions 40 and 41 refer to the following illustration, which shows the frequency and wavelength of different kinds of energy on the electromagnetic spectrum.

Electromagnectic Spectrum

Wavelength, m

40. What is the frequency for visible light?

(1) 10^{10} Hz
(2) 10^{12} Hz
(3) 10^{14} Hz
(4) 10^{16} Hz
(5) 10^{18} Hz

41. According to the diagram, which has the shortest wavelength?

(1) long radio waves
(2) AM radio waves
(3) microwaves
(4) visible light waves
(5) gamma rays

42. The illustration shows one molecule of the most common form of butane.

Which of the following is the chemical formula for butane?

(1) C_2H_5
(2) CH
(3) C_4H_4
(4) C_4H_{10}
(5) $C_{10}H_{10}$

43. The theory of evolution by natural selection states that individual plants or animals with characteristics that give them an advantage over other members of their species are most likely to survive and to reproduce. What does this theory imply?

(1) Dogs evolved from wolves, not from coyotes.
(2) Giraffes with the longest necks will be least likely to be shot by hunters.
(3) Birds with strong beaks are most likely to survive on an island whose trees produce very hard nuts.
(4) Elephants are likely to evolve smaller feet and larger brains within the next 50 years.
(5) Plants survive best in the absence of pollutants such as ozone and sulfur dioxide.

44. Newton's Third Law of Motion states that if Object 1 exerts a force against Object 2, Object 2 will exert that same amount of force against Object 1. Which of the following is a restatement of this law?

    (1) For every action, there is an equal reaction.
    (2) An object keeps moving until something stops it.
    (3) All objects fall at the same speed.
    (4) If nothing moves, no work is done.
    (5) Friction against an object does not affect its movement.

45. Scientists testing a new medication found that patients seemed to catch fewer colds while they were taking it. How would the scientists determine if the medicine was really working?

    (1) Compare the patients taking the medicine with a similar group of patients who were not taking it.
    (2) Compare the patients taking the medicine with a similar group of patients who were taking another medicine.
    (3) Give the patients a vaccine.
    (4) Try to make the patients catch colds.
    (5) Find out how many colds the patients caught after they stopped taking the medicine.

46. A fluid, such as air or water, that is forced to flow from a wide space into a narrow space will speed up. Which of the following is *not* an example of this property?

    (1) Water moves faster when it travels around an island in the middle of a stream.
    (2) Air moves faster when it passes over the rounded top of an airplane wing.
    (3) Soda pours faster when it reaches the narrowest part of a bottle's neck.
    (4) A glacier flows faster in a narrow valley.
    (5) Water expands faster when it freezes at very low temperatures.

47. A chemical change is a change in which a new substance is created. For example, burning a piece of wood causes the wood to break down into ashes, carbon dioxide gas, and water. The new substances that have been created cannot be changed back into wood. Which of the following is an example of a chemical change?

    (1) ice melts
    (2) leaves turn color
    (3) an iron pipe rusts
    (4) dirt turns to mud
    (5) rocks erode

Questions 48 and 49 refer to the following map and passage.

The scissor-tailed flycatcher is one of the earliest birds to arrive in Oklahoma each spring. Across most of the state, Oklahomans begin looking for these birds during the first week in April. Their limited nesting range is concentrated primarily in the southern Great Plains states, from New Mexico to Louisiana and Nebraska southward to southern Texas and adjoining areas of northern Mexico. However, the birds have wandered as far north as Hudson Bay, as far east as New Brunswick, and as far west as Colorado.

Scissor-tailed flycatchers winter in the southern half of Florida and the Florida Keys, in south Texas, Mexico, and Central America. The birds are common winter visitors to Guatemala at altitudes under 5000 feet.

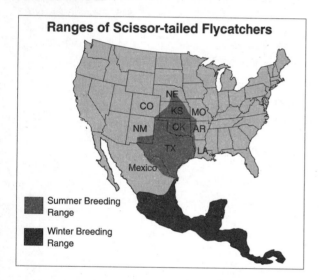

Ranges of Scissor-tailed Flycatchers

Summer Breeding Range

Winter Breeding Range

48. According to the map and the information given, what is the northernmost state in which scissor-tails usually nest?

(1) Kansas
(2) Nebraska
(3) Texas
(4) Arizona
(5) Louisiana

49. In what way does the information on the map differ from that given in the paragraphs?

(1) The map does not show that the birds' summer range extends into Oklahoma.
(2) The paragraphs do not state that the birds winter in Mexico.
(3) The paragraphs do not state that the birds' summer range extends into Texas.
(4) The map does not show that the birds winter in Florida.
(5) The map does not show that the birds winter in Mexico.

50. The Italian scientist Galileo first described the laws of motion for everyday objects. Sir Isaac Newton further refined these laws. Later, Albert Einstein restated the laws of motion for objects traveling closer to the speed of light. The laws of modern quantum mechanics supersede Newton's laws for the motion of subatomic particles.

Which of the following statements is supported by this paragraph?

(1) New observations require throwing out the old to develop replacement theories and laws.
(2) Scientific work continues to build on ideas and theories developed by earlier scientists.
(3) Scientists cannot use false data to prove their theories.
(4) Science is the art of using data to prove a point.
(5) Some scientific theories are developed before the world is ready for them.

Model Test 1 Answer Key

1. **(2)** The graph shows that, except for a short time, the percentage of adult smokers generally is highest among American Indians. (1) African Americans is not correct even though for a short time the percentage of African American smokers was about the same as that of American Indians. (3) Asian Americans have the lowest percentage of adult smokers. (4) Hispanics and (5) Caucasians are significantly lower than American Indians.

2. **(5)** Although it is not possible to determine exact percentages from the graph, 18% is obviously closer to the value shown on the graph than any of the other answer choices. (1) 40% is approximately the percentage for American Indians. (4) 22% is not correct because the line on the graph for Asian Americans is obviously below 20%.

3. **(4)** The graph shows that the percentage of American Indian smokers fell until 1985, then rose slightly, fell again after 1988, rose slightly again, and has remained steady since 1993. This is the only answer choice that describes the trend shown on the graph.

4. **(1)** The graph could be used by scientists to support the need for health information for specific groups. None of the other uses are supported by information in the graph—designing experiments, youthful smokers, geographic regions. The concept of "deserve" is not something that could be shown in one graph.

5. **(2)** Although the percentage of smokers in each ethnic group decreased over the entire period, only among Hispanics was the decline steady, with no level periods and no upswings.

6. **(3)** The formula CO stands for one atom of carbon (C) and one atom of oxygen (O). Answer choice (1) is not correct because carbon dioxide is a molecule, not an atom. Choice (2) is not correct because the chemical formula CO indicates one atom of carbon and one atom of oxygen. Answer choice (4) cannot be correct because carbon monoxide is not an ion, and thus has no charge. Choice (5) is not correct because the formula (CO) demonstrates that carbon and oxygen are present in equal amounts.

7. **(3)** When the switch turns the lamp off, the circuit is incomplete. Some circuits do create light waves (2) such as the one that powers a microwave, the output device. (4) If the switch closed the gap, the lamp would turn on. (1) The potential energy source is the household electricity and (5) the lamp is the output device.

8. **(5)** The block and tackle shown in the figure is a simple machine that has an output force that is greater than the input force. The distance the rope is pulled is greater than the weight is lifted. A block and tackle is a set of movable and fixed pulleys. The more pulleys that are included in a block and tackle, the more the input force is multiplied. However, the greater the input force is multiplied, the greater the distance the rope must be pulled to lift the weight.

9. **(2)** Mickey did not move the keyboard anywhere. Therefore, he did no work on the keyboard. What he typed (1), the speed he typed (3), or the force he applied to the keys (4) does not matter because he did not move the keyboard. Therefore, no work was done on the keyboard or (5) on the monitor.

10. **(2)** The map shows both the location and the severity (size of circles) of recent earthquakes in Alaska. The map does not show earthquakes in Europe (3) or in the entire U.S. (4). It also does not show how much damage was caused (5).

11. **(4)** The strongest earthquake shown has a magnitude of approximately 6, based on the size of the circle.

12. **(1)** The map shows that the area of greatest earthquake activity occurs near a plate boundary. Earthquakes tend to occur near plate boundaries, where plates are moving past each other or bumping into each other. There is no evidence from the map to suggest that earthquakes can occur anywhere, but are stronger near plate boundaries (2), or that earthquakes do the least damage when they occur near plate boundaries (3). The map very definitely shows a relationship between the location of earthquakes and plate boundaries (4). While the plate boundary on the map lies under the ocean (5), the location of earthquakes can be identified in the ocean.

13. **(2)** The graph shows that about 70 percent of all children (total) were vaccinated in 1994.

14. **(3)** The graph shows that approximately 70 percent of children below the poverty level were vaccinated in 1996.

15. **(5)** This conclusion is supported by the graph; the graph does not support option (2) or (4). Both (1) and (3) are the opposite of what is shown in the graph.

16. **(2)** The graph does not (1) identify clinics or (3) reflect the number of children living in poverty. The graph offers no explanation for (4), vaccination of wealthier children, and has nothing to do with (5), worldwide influenza rates.

17. **(3)** This is the only statement that is broad enough to be the main idea of the entire passage. All of the other statements are true, but each is only a detail from the study—not the main idea of the investigation.

18. **(4)** Asking a question always is the first step in scientific inquiry. Dr. Art's question is brought up in the first paragraph. Choices 1–3 are all things that Dr. Art did in his study, but they were all done to answer the question. Option (5) was not mentioned in the passage.

19. **(1)** The passage does not state this directly, but it does state that fields are "returned to wild land." Some of the fields could be used for scientific experiments (2), but certainly not most of them. Fields once used for farming could also be used for grazing (3) or farming (4), but this was not the focus of the passage. Option (5) is nonsensical.

20. **(5)** The maps showed Dr. Art which areas had never been used as farmland, thus had never been plowed. Dr. Art found which fields had the most wildflowers, the most trees, and the fewest ants by studying the land, not from a map. The passage does not state whether settlers had owned the woodlots that had never been plowed.

21. **(2)** The passage implies that wildflowers will return, but very slowly. There is no basis for predicting statements (1), (3), or (4) in the passage. (5) Ants spread seeds slowly in small areas.

22. **(2)** The race car speeding down the track is the only example of a moving object, thus it is the only example of kinetic energy. The other answer choices describe objects with potential energy.

23. **(4)** The Frisbee in its owner's hand is not moving, but it has the potential to move, so it is the only example of potential energy. The other examples given are examples of kinetic energy.

24. **(4)** The outer core is the only layer of Earth that is specifically mentioned as completely molten.

25. **(3)** The only thing that is not mentioned about the mantle in the diagram is whether it contains nickel, so this must be the incorrect statement. The diagram states that the outer core contains nickel.

26. **(1)** The diagram states that the crust is thinner under the oceans than under the continents.

27. **(4)** A seesaw is an example of a class 1 lever. Pulleys, hammers, screws, and swings are simple machines, but they are not levers.

28. **(1)** The sparks on the key demonstrated to Franklin that lightning was indeed a form of electricity. We now know that lightning is caused by static electrical charges that build up in thunderstorms. The other answer choices do not make sense with respect to Franklin's experiment.

29. **(1)** The passage states that inner solar system comets are the ones we can see. All of the other choices describe other phenomena related to the Oort cloud.

30. **(3)** The passage implies that the Oort cloud is a theory and that scientists have no direct knowledge of it. None of the other answers are supported by the passage.

31. **(1)** The passage states that encounters between the sun and nearby stars disturb the comets' orbits. The passage does not mention changes in the gravitational pull from the sun, nor does it mention the effects of the gravitational pull from other planets.

32. **(2)** Although this is not directly stated, gravitation is mentioned as the force that affects the movement of comets and planets. None of the other forces makes sense in the context of the passage.

33. **(4)** The map shows that the wolf's current range extends into parts of Montana, Minnesota, and Wisconsin.

34. **(1)** Although this is not stated directly, it is clear from the map and the accompanying text. Animals sometimes stray out of their ranges, and are sometimes killed within their ranges, but neither of these facts is part of the definition of a range. Most animals will protect their young, even outside their range.

35. **(3)** A wildlife biologist might be interested in finding new areas to support wolf populations. The map or the passage supports nothing else.

36. **(1)** This is the earliest date cited on the map.

37. **(1)** As used in the first paragraph, *uniform* means "the same as or similar to." *Evolving* means "changing," and the other terms listed are self-explanatory.

38. **(3)** The passage implies that uniformitarianism allows geologists to study Earth's past history by reading the record contained in rocks and sediments. (1), (2), and (4) are not mentioned, and (5) is more like catastrophism.

39. **(1)** The passage implies that Hutton's idea was based on his observations of the world around him. He concluded that small, everyday events act over long periods of time to shape Earth. Catastrophes do affect Earth, but not as much as the theory of catastrophism stated. Other planets are not mentioned, so (4) is not a valid response. The belief that few changes take place on Earth was held by the theory of catastrophism, not by Hutton.

40. **(3)** In the diagram, visible light has a frequency between 10^{14} Hz and 10^{15} Hz, so 10^{14} Hz is the best response.

41. **(5)** On the diagram, wavelength decreases as you go to the right on the scale. Gamma rays have wavelengths shorter than 10^{-10} meters. All of the other choices have wavelengths longer than gamma rays.

42. **(4)** The structural formula for butane shown in the diagram has four carbon atoms (C) and 10 hydrogen atoms (H), so the chemical formula for butane is C_4H_{10}.

43. (3) Option (3) is the best example of the theory of evolution. The birds' beaks give them a survival advantage in this specific environment, as the theory implies.

44. (1) Option (1) is the best example of Newton's Third Law of Motion, as described in the question. Option (2) is Newton's Second Law. Options (3) and (4) are true, but do not answer the question. Option (5) is false.

45. (1) The group not taking the medicine is called the control group. To determine if a new medication is effective, scientists perform clinical trials that compare people who are using the medication with people who are not.

46. (5) This is the only option that is not an example of a fluid flowing through a narrow opening but of a change of state from liquid to solid.

47. (3) The oxygen in water combines with the iron to form rust, a chemical change. All the other choices are examples of physical changes.

48. (2) Though the passage stated that the scissor-tail has wandered farther, the map shows that Nebraska usually is the northernmost state of the scissor-tail's range.

49. (4) By comparing the information given in the text with that shown on the map, you can see that the map does not show the winter range extending into Florida and the Florida Keys.

50. (2) This summarizes the ideas presented in the paragraph. None of the other statements can be derived from the passage.

Model Test 1 Evaluation Chart

Use the chart below to identify the science content areas and the skill areas you need to review before you take the 2002 GED Science Test. Circle the number of any question you answered incorrectly. Then look at the top of the column to find pages in each book that will help you review the material.

Content Level/ Subject Area	Earth Science (T*: pages 145–173; C: pages 375–398; E: pages 156–171)	Physical Science (T*: pages 175–252; C: pages 399–449; E: pages 172–198)	Life Science (T*: pages 81–144; C: pages 355–374; E: pages 141–155)
Fundamental Understandings	10, 11, 24, 25, 26, 29, 30, 32	6, 8, 22, 23, 27, 28, 40, 41, 42, 46, 47	1, 2, 3, 13, 14, 17, 18, 19, 33, 34, 36, 48
Unifying Concepts and Processes	12, 37	7	20
Science as Inquiry	31		15, 43, 49
Science and Technology		9	
Science in Personal and Social Perspectives		45	4, 5, 16, 21, 35
History and Nature of Science	38, 39	44, 50	

*T = Contemporary's GED Test 3: Science
C = Contemporary's Complete GED
E = Contemporary's Essential GED

2002 Science Model Test 2

Directions: This model test will help you identify the skills you will need to be successful on the new 2002 GED Science Test. This is a half-length test that consists of 25 multiple-choice questions. Some of the questions are based on short reading passages, and some require you to interpret a diagram or a table. Questions are based on information from the areas of earth science (including space science), physical science (including physics and chemistry), life science (including environmental and health science), and the National Science Education Standards guidelines.

You should take no longer than 40 minutes to complete this test. When you are finished, check your work with the answers and explanations at the end of the test. Use the evaluation chart on page 352 to determine the areas in which you will need more study before taking the 2002 GED Science Test.

MODEL TEST ANSWER GRID

1 ① ② ③ ④ ⑤	8 ① ② ③ ④ ⑤	14 ① ② ③ ④ ⑤	20 ① ② ③ ④ ⑤
2 ① ② ③ ④ ⑤	9 ① ② ③ ④ ⑤	15 ① ② ③ ④ ⑤	21 ① ② ③ ④ ⑤
3 ① ② ③ ④ ⑤	10 ① ② ③ ④ ⑤	16 ① ② ③ ④ ⑤	22 ① ② ③ ④ ⑤
4 ① ② ③ ④ ⑤	11 ① ② ③ ④ ⑤	17 ① ② ③ ④ ⑤	23 ① ② ③ ④ ⑤
5 ① ② ③ ④ ⑤	12 ① ② ③ ④ ⑤	18 ① ② ③ ④ ⑤	24 ① ② ③ ④ ⑤
6 ① ② ③ ④ ⑤	13 ① ② ③ ④ ⑤	19 ① ② ③ ④ ⑤	25 ① ② ③ ④ ⑤
7 ① ② ③ ④ ⑤			

1. When an astronaut throws a ball in outer space, the ball keeps moving until it hits something. This is an example of Newton's First Law of Motion.

Using this example, which of the following best restates Newton's First Law of Motion?

(1) There are no forces at work in outer space.
(2) All objects are exerting force at all times.
(3) For every action, there is an equal reaction.
(4) Objects keep moving until something stops them.
(5) Friction does not exist in outer space.

Questions 2 and 3 refer to the following paragraph.

Prairie plants have adapted to the stresses of their environments by growing extensive root systems and underground growing points. Thus, the common prairie fires, which typically occur in early spring, move swiftly by without harming the plants' roots or tender growing points. Similarly, growing points are protected from grazing animals and from seasonal temperature changes. In addition, the plants' deep, wide root system draws water from far underground, protecting the plants from frequent droughts.

2. According to the paragraph, which of the following is *not* a stress that prairie plants are subject to?

(1) flooding
(2) drought
(3) fires
(4) grazing
(5) temperature changes

3. According to the paragraph, what is one way that prairie plants have adapted to the stresses of their environment?

(1) growing irritating spines
(2) secreting poisonous fluid
(3) drawing extra water and storing it
(4) making additional layers of bark
(5) growing long underground roots

4. Organic chemistry can be said to have begun in 1828 when Friedrich Wohler discovered that an inorganic substance, ammonium nitrate, could be converted to urea, an organic chemical produced by many animals. Previously, scientists had thought that some kind of "life force" had to operate to produce an organic compound.

What was the most important result of Wohler's experiment?

(1) Urea contained carbon and nitrogen.
(2) Organic compounds and inorganic compounds obey similar chemical laws.
(3) Carbon is present in all organic compounds.
(4) Carbon is a unique element because of its ability to form long chains and rings.
(5) The life force operates in inorganic compounds as well as organic compounds.

Questions 5–7 refer to the following diagram, which shows distances both in light minutes (the distance that light travels in one minute) and in astronomical units (the average distance between the earth and the sun).

The Main Asteroid Belt
(Orbits drawn approximately to scale)

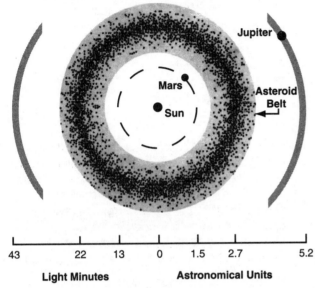

| 43 | 22 | 13 | 0 | 1.5 | 2.7 | 5.2 |

Light Minutes   **Astronomical Units**

5. What is the approximate distance between the sun and the thickest part of the asteroid belt?

(1) 13 light minutes
(2) 22 light minutes
(3) 43 light minutes
(4) 1.5 astronomical units
(5) 5.2 astronomical units

6. What is the approximate diameter of the orbit of Mars?

(1) 1.5 astronomical units
(2) 2.7 astronomical units
(3) 13 light minutes
(4) 26 light minutes
(5) 43 light minutes

7. Which statement about astronomical units and light minutes is correct?

(1) They represent the same distance.
(2) One astronomical unit represents a longer distance than one light minute.
(3) One light minute is a longer distance than one astronomical unit.
(4) One astronomical unit is equal to one light year.
(5) Earth is one light minute away from the sun.

8. Primitive green plants such as mosses and liverworts lack specialized organs for storing water in their tissues. Which of the following best describes the type of environment in which these plants must live?

(1) moist
(2) hot
(3) dark
(4) cold
(5) dry

9. A chemist wonders if she can find a way to change the formula for gasoline to improve gas mileage and reduce pollution. After studying the problem, she develops a new compound that she thinks will work. What is the next step in the scientific process for the scientist to carry out, in order to determine if her idea is correct?

(1) Define the problem.
(2) Collect information about the problem.
(3) Form a hypothesis.
(4) Test the hypothesis.
(5) Draw conclusions.

Question 10 refers to the following simple food web diagram.

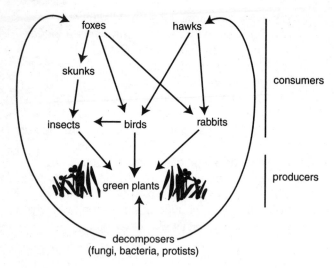

10. Which organisms in this food web produce their own food?

    (1) insects
    (2) green plants
    (3) decomposers
    (4) hawks
    (5) skunks

11. A physical change is a change that does not affect the kind of material something is made of. For example, cutting a piece of paper into small pieces is a physical change, because although the size and shape have changed, the material still is paper. Which of the following is *not* an example of a physical change?

    (1) melting butter
    (2) burning a piece of paper
    (3) freezing water into ice
    (4) chopping an onion
    (5) folding a piece of paper

12. Sound intensity (or loudness) is measured in units called decibels. Decibels are arranged on a logarithmic scale. This means that an increase of 10 decibels represents a sound that is now 10 times louder than before.

    The loudness of a shouted conversation is around 70 decibels, and the loudness of the music at a live concert is around 100 decibels. How much louder is the music than the conversation?

    (1) 10 times louder
    (2) 30 times louder
    (3) 100 times louder
    (4) 1,000 times louder
    (5) 10,000 times louder

13. Ozone (chemical formula O_3) is a colorless, odorless gas that is composed of molecules with three oxygen atoms. "Good" ozone occurs naturally in the upper atmosphere, where it shields us from the sun's harmful ultraviolet rays. "Bad" ozone is formed in the lower atmosphere where pollutants from vehicles, factories, and power plants react with sunlight.

    Based on the passage, which of the following statements about ozone is true?

    (1) Ozone is made of carbon and oxygen.
    (2) Ozone has different chemical formulas depending on where it is found.
    (3) Ozone is harmful in the lower atmosphere.
    (4) Ozone blocks ultraviolet rays in the lower atmosphere.
    (5) The ozone in the upper atmosphere is caused by a reaction from pollutants and sunlight.

Questions 14–16 refer to the following table showing the number of people worldwide who are infected with HIV (the human immunodeficiency virus) or who have AIDS.

Global Estimates of the HIV/AIDS Epidemic as of end 1999

People newly infected with HIV in 1999	**Total** Adults *Women* Children < 15 years	**5.4 million** 4.7 million *2.3 million* 620,000
Number of people living with HIV/AIDS	**Total** Adults *Women* Children < 15 years	**34.3 million** 33.0 million *15.7 million* 1.3 million
AIDS deaths in 1999	**Total** Adults *Women* Children < 15 years	**2.8 million** 2.3 million *1.2 million* 500,000
Total number of AIDS deaths since the beginning of the epidemic	**Total** Adults *Women* Children < 15 years	**18.8 million** 15.0 million *7.7 million* 3.8 million

Source: UNAIDS

14. According to the table, how many people were newly infected with HIV in 1999?

(1) 34.3 million
(2) 5.4 million
(3) 4.7 million
(4) 2.3 million
(5) 620,000

15. According to the table, what was the total number of people living with HIV/AIDS?

(1) 34.3 million
(2) 33.0 million
(3) 18.8 million
(4) 5.4 million
(5) 2.8 million

16. This table does *not* tell you which of the following?

(1) how many people have died of AIDS since the epidemic began
(2) number of people who died of AIDS in 1999
(3) how many women were living with AIDS in 1999
(4) number of people who were infected in 1998
(5) total adults who were infected in 1999

17. Atoms contain three kinds of particles: protons, neutrons, and electrons. Protons and neutrons make up the nucleus of the atom. Protons have a positive charge and neutrons have no charge. Electrons exist around the nucleus of the atom and have a negative charge. The force that holds protons and neutrons together is called "the strong force."

Based on the passage, which of the following statements is true?

(1) Electrons can leave the atom easily by simply floating away.
(2) Nothing can escape from the strong force.
(3) Electrons are much larger than protons.
(4) All atoms are exactly the same.
(5) Positive and negative charges have an effect on the atom.

18. The chemical formula for photosynthesis, the process by which plants produce simple sugar, is

$$6CO_2 + 6H_2O \rightarrow C_6H_{12}O_6 + 6O_2$$

What are the basic elements that plants use to produce sugar?

(1) water and carbon dioxide
(2) water and oxygen
(3) carbon dioxide and oxygen
(4) carbon, hydrogen, and oxygen
(5) oxygen and starch

Questions 19 and 20 refer to the following table and passage.

The U.S. Environmental Protection Agency uses the Air Quality Index to report levels of ozone in the air. Although the AQI scale extends to 500, levels above 300 rarely occur in the U.S. If ozone levels above 300 should occur, everyone should avoid physical exertion outdoors.

Air Quality Index Scale

Ozone Concentration (ppm) (8-hour average, unless noted)	Air Quality Index Values	Air Quality Descriptor
0.0 to 0.064	0 to 50	Good
0.065 to 0.084	51 to 100	Moderate
0.085 to 0.104	101 to 150	Unhealthy for Sensitive Groups
0.105 to 0.124	151 to 200	Unhealthy
0.125 (8-hr) to 0.404 (1-hr)	201 to 300	Very Unhealthy

Source: EPA

19. Based on the table, why is it important for people to know the ozone level in the air?

    (1) High levels of ozone are unhealthy.
    (2) Low levels of ozone make it hard to take in oxygen.
    (3) Ozone levels vary with temperature.
    (4) High levels of ozone are rare in the United States.
    (5) Ozone levels are reported as 8-hour averages.

20. Suppose you hear on the TV news that today's Air Quality Index is 76. What does this tell you about the ozone concentration?

    (1) It is between 0.0 and 0.64 ppm.
    (2) It is between 0.065 and 0.084 ppm.
    (3) It is between 0.085 and 0.104 ppm.
    (4) It is between 0.105 and 0.124 ppm.
    (5) It is above 0.125 ppm.

Questions 21 and 22 are based on the following paragraph.

Alfred Wegener first proposed the idea of continental drift in 1912. Wegener observed that many of the continents, particularly the east coast of South America and the west coast of Africa, could fit together like pieces of a jigsaw puzzle. His theory of continental drift explained the apparent movement of the continents, but his ideas were ignored for over 50 years. Not until the mid-ocean ridges were discovered in the 1960s did scientists understand the mechanism by which continents could "move" atop a layer of semi-solid rock. Soon after, however, additional evidence about earthquakes and volcanoes fell into place, and Wegener's theory was widely accepted.

21. Based on the paragraph, which of the following statements about advancements in scientific theory is true?

    (1) Theories do not have to be based on evidence.
    (2) Theories require laboratory experiments.
    (3) Theories may combine old ideas and new discoveries.
    (4) Theories are always proven correct.
    (5) Theories are always later proven incorrect.

22. According to the paragraph, what did Wegener observe?

    (1) Some of the continents could fit together.
    (2) There was a mid-ocean ridge.
    (3) Earthquakes and volcanoes were related.
    (4) South America was the same shape as Africa.
    (5) The continents floated on semi-solid rock.

23. Suppose scientists develop and extensively test a new technology that allows people in poor countries to grow more productive rice crops. As a result, human populations grow rapidly in countries that grow rice in the new way. The new technology requires large amounts of chemical fertilizers. After ten years, it is found that the fertilizers cause diseases in infants that result in health problems throughout their lives.

What conclusion can be drawn from this paragraph?

(1) Scientists should not test new technologies on human populations.
(2) Technology sometimes has unintended consequences.
(3) Human populations will soon run out of food supplies.
(4) Fertilizers are harmful to humans.
(5) Humans need to find sources of food other than rice.

24. Electric current flows only when it can complete a path, or circuit. The circuit begins with a starting point, which is a source of electric power. It includes wires that conduct electricity along its path. One or more output devices, such as lamps, radios, or other appliances, may be plugged into the circuit. Eventually, the electricity flows back to its source, completing the circuit.

According to the paragraph, what happens when you turn on a radio or lamp?

(1) You provide a power source.
(2) You increase the electric voltage.
(3) You produce resistance.
(4) You create static electricity.
(5) You complete a circuit.

25. A chemist has developed a new material that he believes will be a superior insulator. In order to test the new material, he has an engineer build a special kind of ice chest. He lines the chest with his new material, fills it with ice, and records the time it takes for the ice to melt.

What else must the chemist do to determine if the new material really is a superior kind of insulator?

(1) Test it in a larger ice chest.
(2) Test it with a smaller ice chest.
(3) Test it with the same chest, but with different amounts of ice.
(4) Test the chest with less ice.
(5) Test the chest with a different insulator.

Model Test 2 Answer Key

1. **(4)** If the ball keeps moving until something, such as friction or gravity, stops it, the First Law is implied. Although forces such as friction and gravity are at work in outer space just as they are on Earth, and all objects are exerting such forces at all times, those facts are not relevant to the question.

2. **(1)** The passage states that the stresses on prairie plants are drought, fire, grazing, and temperature changes.

3. **(5)** The paragraph states that the plants grow long roots as an adaptation to the stresses of their environment. The other options are not mentioned in the paragraph.

4. **(2)** Although options (1), (3), and (4) are true, you could not determine those facts from the paragraph. Option (2) follows logically from the information given. Option (5) is illogical in terms of what the paragraph states about the origins of organic chemistry.

5. **(2)** The distance is 22 light minutes or 2.7 astronomical units.

6. **(4)** The diameter of a circle is twice the radius, and the radius of the orbit is shown on the chart to be approximately 13 light minutes. The diameter is also 3.0 astronomical units.

7. **(2)** The chart shows that 43 light minutes equal 5.2 astronomical units. Therefore, an astronomical unit represents a greater distance than a light minute. Options (1) and (3) are incorrect according to the information on the illustration. You cannot determine whether options (4) and (5) are correct from the information given in the illustration.

8. **(1)** Because these plants lack specialized tissues for storing water, they must live in places that are always moist, such as swamps or stream beds.

9. **(4)** The scientist has carried out the first three steps of the scientific process already—she has defined the problem to be solved, collected information about the problem, and formed a hypothesis (that her new compound will increase mileage and reduce pollution). The next step is to test the hypothesis by conducting controlled experiments.

10. **(2)** Only green plants produce their own food, converting sunlight and carbon dioxide into sugars and oxygen through the process of photosynthesis. As the diagram shows, all other organisms depend on green plants for food.

11. **(2)** Burning is not a physical change, because burning, or combustion, is a chemical reaction. Before the reaction, the paper was composed of one substance. Ash has a different chemical composition than paper and it cannot be changed back into paper.

12. **(4)** A logarithmic scale increases by powers of 10. If an increase of 10 decibels is 10 times louder than before, an increase of 20 decibels would be 100 times louder (10×10), and an increase of 30 decibels would be 1,000 times louder ($10 \times 10 \times 10$).

13. **(3)** The paragraph implies that "bad" ozone in the lower atmosphere results from pollution and is harmful. Options (1) and (2) are incorrect because the paragraph states that all ozone has the formula O_3, which means that it contains no carbon. Options (4) and (5) are the reverse of the truth. Ozone blocks harmful ultraviolet rays in the upper atmosphere, and occurs in the lower atmosphere because of a reaction between pollutants and sunlight.

14. **(2)** The table shows that the total number of people newly infected in 1999 was 5.4 million.

15. **(1)** The table shows that the number of people living with HIV/AIDS in 1999 was 34.3 million.

16. **(4)** The table does not show how many people were infected in 1998. It gives cumulative totals for the entire epidemic and specific information for 1999 only.

17. **(5)** The paragraph mentions positive and negative charges because they are indeed very important to the makeup of the atom. The positively charged protons attract the negatively charged electrons, keeping them from floating away.

18. **(4)** C stands for carbon, H stands for hydrogen, and O stands for oxygen. These are the basic elements. Water, carbon dioxide, and starch are the raw materials formed by these elements.

19. **(1)** The table states that high levels of ozone are unhealthy. Options (2) and (3) are not mentioned and are irrelevant to the question. Option (4) does not make sense, because if high levels were rare, reporting them would not be important. Option (5) is true, but it has nothing to do with the question of why people need to know the ozone level.

20. **(2)** The table shows that 0.065 to 0.084 corresponds to an Air Quality Index of 76.

21. **(3)** Advances in scientific theories often combine old, unexplained observations with new information. Although theories often arise from laboratory experiments, they may also arise from observation, as in the case of continental drift. All theories, however, must eventually be based on empirical evidence. Because theories are not facts, they are not always proven correct or incorrect.

22. **(1)** The paragraph states that Wegener's initial observation was that South America and Africa could fit together.

23. (2) The paragraph implies that although the new technology benefited human populations, it also had unforeseen consequences. Option (1) is irrelevant because the paragraph is not about human testing. Option (3) is incorrect because, although the paragraph is about food supplies, it does not imply that supplies are running out. Options (4) and (5) are oversimplified statements. Not all fertilizers are harmful to humans. Also, there is nothing in the paragraph to imply that rice is not a good food for humans.

24. (5) According to the paragraph, electricity can power an output device only when it is part of a complete circuit. Therefore, when you turn on a lamp or radio, you are completing a circuit and allowing electricity to flow.

25. (5) In order to determine if the insulator works better than other kinds, the chemist must test the same chest using a different type of insulator and compare the results. This would comprise a controlled experiment, with the new material as the variable and a standard kind of insulator serving as a control.

Model Test 2 Evaluation Chart

Use the chart below to identify the science content areas and the skill areas you need to review before you take the 2002 GED Science Test. Circle the number of any question you answered incorrectly. Then look at the top of the column to find pages in each book that will help you review the material.

Content Level/ Subject Area	Earth Science (T*: pages 145–173; C: pages 375–398; E: pages 156–171)	Physical Science (T*: pages 175–252; C: pages 399–449; E: pages 172–198)	Life Science (T*: pages 81–144; C: pages 355–374; E: pages 141–155)
Fundamental Understandings	5, 6, 7	13, 17, 24	2, 3, 8, 10, 18, 20
Unifying Concepts and Processes		1	
Science as Inquiry	22	9, 11, 25	23
Science and Technology			
Science in Personal and Social Perspectives		12	14, 15, 16, 19
History and Nature of Science	21	4	

*T = Contemporary's GED Test 3: Science
C = Contemporary's Complete GED
E = Contemporary's Essential GED